NEUROFEEDBACK
And State Regulation In ADHD:
A Therapy Without Medication

Werner Van den Bergh, M.D.
Translation by Stephanie Clark

BMED Press
www.bmedpress.com

For information about this book:

BMED Press LLC
5656 South Staples
Suite 302
Corpus Christi, Texas 78411
Phone: (817) 400-1639
www.bmedpress.com

10-digit ISBN 0982749805
13-digit ISBN 9780982749807

CONTENTS

Introduction

Chapter 1

Attention, Self-Regulation, and State Regulation

Chapter 2

The Functional Anatomy of Attention and "Executive Functions"

Chapter 3

Self-Regulation, Executive Functions Embedded in Motivation

Chapter 4

EEG: Mechanisms of Attention and Self-Regulation

Chapter 5

Dynamic Organization of Vigilance in EEG

Chapter 6

Neurofeedback (EEG-Biofeedback)

Chapter 7

Tomographic (LORETA) 3D Neurofeedback

Chapter 8

Slow Cortical Potentials (SCP) Neurofeedback

Chapter 9

ADHD: A Clinical System Perspective

Afterword   225

References   231

LIST OF ILLUSTRATIONS

An Important Message To Our Readers

The information provided in this book is not a substitute for professional medical or psychological advice or treatment. Always seek the advice of your physician or other qualified health care provider with any questions you may have regarding a medical condition. Always seek the advice of your physician, psychologist, or other qualified healthcare provider with any questions you may have regarding a psychological condition. Never disregard medical or psychological advice or delay in seeking it because of something you have read in this book.

Introduction

ADHD (Attention Deficit Hyperactivity Disorder) is the most common psychiatric disorder in children (2% to 5%) (American Psychiatric Association, 1994). ADHD is caused by a disruption to the functioning of certain neural networks in the brain. ADHD is hereditary in more than half of the cases; 30% of those affected have a least one parent with ADHD; 30% to 50% of children with ADHD have significant difficulties that persist into adulthood and they also have an 80% chance of having at least one child with ADHD. It is necessary to note that ADHD has neurobiological origins, and is therefore neither caused by shortcomings in upbringing nor by the increased expectations and demands of modern society.

ADHD is frequently comorbid with other behavioral disorders (Barkley, 2006), including sleep disorders (30 to 56%), oppositional defiant disorder (40 to 80%), conduct disorder (20 to 56%) as a precursor of antisocial personality disorder (20%), anxiety disorders (10 to 40%), depression (30%), bipolar disorder (6 to10%), substance use disorder (15 to 50%), tic disorders (10 to 15% for simple tic, less than 2% for Tourette's disorder), specific learning disorders, such as dyslexia (20%), premenstrual dysphoric disorder, borderline personality disorder, autism spectrum disorders, and non-verbal learning disorders.

A number of studies have shown (Cumyn, Lucy, French, Lisa, Hechtman, & Lily, 2009) that more than 50% of adults with ADHD have a comorbid behavioral disorder.

As with the majority of psychiatric disorders, ADHD is diagnosed using subjective behavioral ratings. This subjectivity often leads to persistent doubts concerning the validity of the diagnosis and its neurobiological causes. Over the last ten years, independent research groups published a steady stream of articles on the value of using QEEG (quantitative electroencephalogram) in the diagnosis of ADHD. This prompted the American Academy of Paediatrics, in their guidelines on ADHD, to describe QEEG as a valuable diagnostic tool that can improve our understanding of the fundamental neurophysiological disruption. To the present day, this new and important tool for objective diagnosis has been underused in clinical practice.

Brain imaging studies (single photon emission computed tomography [SPECT], positron emission tomography [PET], and functional magnetic resonance imaging [fMRI]) of people with ADHD have provided growing evidence about the underlying neuroanatomical correspondences, especially at a functional anatomic level. A limitation of these imaging methods is that they provide no information on the temporal neurodynamics. EEG (electroencephalogram) analysis evaluates neuronal functional processes that last for just milliseconds, and is therefore more suited for this purpose. Although QEEG can confirm an ADHD diagnosis in the form of statistically distinct or deviant EEG patterns, fundamental EEG research can provide a greater insight into what is amiss in the regulation of brain function and can enable a better understanding of how dysfunctions in behavioral regulation arise.

A great deal of published literature describes only the behavioral characteristics of ADHD. While these are frequently sufficient to guide a diagnosis, there remains a strong need for more objective parameters rather than subjective behavioral descriptions alone. Insight into the underlying dynamics can help us understand the essential nature of ADHD. We shall discuss further how a deficiency in state regulation is the fundamental underlying problem in ADHD. All too often, the simplified formulas that arise from a purely descriptive viewpoint of ADHD lead to the prescription of simplified solutions: motley tips on how to best handle behavioral difficulties, such as instructions that enable children to remain seated longer to complete homework.

That attention is a complex, dynamic self-regulating system is often overlooked. In ADHD, problems exist at far deeper levels than the superficial behavioral problems. Inadequate self-regulation is fundamentally responsible for the problems with attention and the consequent behavioral difficulties. The principles of cognitive behavioral therapy (CBT), attention training, and cognitive self instruction methods frequently fall short because the basic underlying neurobiological difficulties are not taken into account. Behavior therapy has its foundations in simplified behavioral models, such as Pavlov's classical conditioning model, which forgets that Pavlov himself described how the degree of conditioning depends on individual variations in a dog's temperament. ADHD is a syndrome with a reduced susceptibility to behavioral conditioning. These fundamental aspects of ADHD should be kept in mind during diagnosis and treatment. We must first understand the causes of behavioral symptoms, and we must not allow ourselves to think that the symptoms are the problem. Symptoms are the expression of poor self-regulation, and it is self-regulation that is the key to guiding effective behavioral change.

To build a practical understanding of self-regulation, we will consider the organization of the electrical activity of the brain. These include not only the statistical differences expressed in the QEEG pattern, but also the recently uncovered dynamic changes in the electrophysiology of ADHD. These dynamic electrophysiological abnormalities provide increased insight into the system dysfunction that underlies ADHD and brings into focus a neuropsychological perspective of disturbed state regulation in ADHD.

In this book, we will examine deeply and systematically how these patterns of electrical activity arise as well as the nature of the neural dysfunction in ADHD. In this way, we will arrive at a better understanding of ADHD and of the way in which effective treatment can address problems with state regulation.

Effective treatment is built upon improvement in self-regulation with a substantial contribution of both neurofeedback therapy and medication. As a treatment, neurofeedback therapy trains individual to normalize the abnormal EEG pattern that reflects deviant brain activity specific to ADHD. Neurofeedback training not only modulates a particular EEG-pattern, but also encourages a broader reorganization of the EEG with consequent behavioral organization.

Neurofeedback originated in the late 1960s when Sterman described its accidental discovery as a treatment for epilepsy. In 1976, Joel Lubar reported its first application to the treatment of ADHD. Controlled studies were not available until 1995 and only in 2004 were the first randomized controlled studies published with follow up assessment for up to 2 years. Only since 2003 have neurofeedback studies been published in leading journals, such as Paediatrics and the Journal of Child Psychology and Psychiatry. In a recent meta-analysis which included research from 2009, Arns (2009) concluded that neurofeedback for ADHD is proven to be effective at a "Level 5" classi-fication (i.e., 'efficacious and specific'). The classification scheme is based on The Guidelines for Evaluation of Clinical Efficacy of Psychophysiological Interventions (LaVaque, 2002) which is jointly accepted by the International Society for Neurofeedback and Research (ISNR) and the Association for Ap-plied Psychophysiology and Biofeedback (APPB) and is similar to those for the American Psychological Association (APA). The guidelines specify five types of classification that range from 'not empirically supported' (level 1) to 'efficacious and specific' (level 5)." In the1980s, the first theoretical model emerged to explain how neurofeedback works. This was followed by a suc-cession of published studies that investigated the application of neurofeed-back to ADHD during the 1990s. As a result of these positive developments, neurofeedback became more connected to the objective and measurable QEEG instead of being based solely on clinical observations. Both neuro-feedback and QEEG remained almost purely empirical and without a solid theoretical base. In the sixties, a functional dynamic model was developed to offer a theoretical framework for empirical EEG research into psychiatric problems (Bente, 1964; Ulrich, 1994).

A parallel stream of research examined the influence of psycho-pharmaceu-ticals on the EEG. This provided a framework to study and understand how methylphenidate medication (brand names: Ritalin SR™, Ritalin™, Con-certa™) works.

There is a great need to advance our understanding of neurofeedback's mech-anism of action, and this book aims to integrate available data from different research areas. It is vital that the theoretical models, formed out of the still growing studies on neurofeedback mechanisms in ADHD, find their way into clinical application.

Thorough background knowledge of neurofeedback is not an optional ex-travagance for the neurofeedback therapist. The commercialization of this method leads too often to inadequate therapist training that provides 'sufficient' simplified background guidance but without proper training or supervision. These commercial neurofeedback training methods use exciting video games with simplified, standardized operating instructions, and they promote these games for the most divergent symptoms. Because of varying degrees of therapist incompetence, neurofeedback therapy was ineffective in many of these cases. These factors lead to the discrediting of neurofeedback in some scientific and clinical circles, and, moreover, the fact that knowledgeably applied neurofeedback can be a highly effective treatment failed to gain widespread public acceptance.

A number of important conditions should be fulfilled for the responsible and ethical use of neurofeedback in clinical practice:
- neurofeedback should be limited to proven applications;
- while knowledge of the treatment protocols used in group studies is an important starting point, an individualized approach to treatment is necessary to obtain an optimal result in a clinical case;
- the locations and frequency bands used in training should be individually tailored by QEEG measurements;
- the percentage of rewards available should be carefully selected and adjusted to the age, expectations, and motivation of the patient;
- the auditory and visual feedback rewards should also be carefully considered, balancing excitement, satisfaction, and motivation on the one hand and avoiding the possibility of distraction from what really matters on the other (training of the EEG pattern);
- the therapist should be aware of the types of EEG activity that are, in principle, trainable (e.g., should understand why they are trainable, and should be aware of the number of ways in which the learning process during neurofeedback differs from that of behavioral modification training;
- building on the previous point, the therapist should understand the connection between the anatomical organization of consciousness and the trainable EEG rhythms;
- the therapist should have insight into how the client's learning progresses on each EEG band during training, accounting for the band's characteristics and limitations;

- changes in the whole EEG spectrum, not just changes in the targeted EEG frequency bands, should be monitored during training;
- the therapist should have insight into the fundamental nature of ADHD, and its effect on state regulation and appearance at the behavioral and EEG levels;
- only when therapists have a sufficient understanding of these previous elements can they combine this knowledge with acquired clinical skills to motivate clients during the training process and to respond to the EEG dynamics of state regulation as well as the establishment of vigilance organization. The therapist should also recognize that in EEG biofeedback training, in which optimal state regulation is the intended goal, the complexity of his or her EEG reflects the complexity of the individual's disorder;
- insights into these complexities connotes insight into the reciprocal relations between top-down and bottom-up processes, which partially cloud our view of the individual as a self-willed, behaving agent;
- finally, a 'clinical system perspective' is inherent in this view at not only the brain state level, but also when the therapist forms a 'dyad' with the patient during successful treatment, becoming a part of a more spacious system. Thus, a skillful therapist participates in a cycle of feedback and makes appropriate personal interventions during a neurofeedback session. Likewise, the therapist becomes a part of that more spacious system within the broader therapeutic treatment of ADHD.

This book will not elaborate on other supplementary therapeutic measures beyond what is briefly mentioned here:

Psychoeducation as well as *neuroeducation* are important for helping someone with ADHD understand why things go wrong; however, understanding alone is not enough to advance much change in the problem areas. Medication and neurofeedback are the only treatments that can address the fundamental symptoms. Neuroeducation, in which individual QEEG study results are discussed with the patient and his or her family, offers the important advantage of individualized confirmation, insight, and explanation. QEEG interpretation and feedback supplies not only objective evidence of brain dysfunction, but also brings to life what that means in terms of a deeper understanding of the dynamic organization of the brain and in terms of providing a different view of problematic behaviors. This understanding can lead to increased treatment adherence, whether taking medication and/or following a course of neurofeedback therapy, to an increased ability to deal with the problems of ADHD, and possibly to a more adequate implementation of system dynamic behavioral therapy.

Behavioral therapy for children and *coaching* for adults can effectively improve behavioral structure, which could happen through the provision of a structured environment that would provide a complementary support for an individual's poor behavioral management strategies. Practical behavioral tips can sometimes prove useful; however, the person with ADHD often does not employ the learned tips at an appropriate time, which can be problematic. In fact, if the problem is so easily solved the problem is likely not ADHD. Behavioral therapy, which is based on learning principles, is of limited application to behaviors that are strongly anchored in biology.

Social skills training can be useful in children who lack development in this area, but will have no effect on the ADHD related problems.

Metacognitive skill training programs, such as the Meichenbaum method of "Stop, Think, and Act," can certainly be useful if the skills they target are underdeveloped. However, they often have essentially no effect on the ADHD itself, as the newly acquired skills seldom become daily habits. These cognitive training programs often consist of modular computer programs based on cognitive models of human cognition that are now obsolete. Furthermore, cognitive skills are not separable from global behavior, motivation, and emotion and precisely these cognitive executive functions are disrupted in ADHD. People who do not suffer from ADHD believe that executive functions coexist with the so called "self-controlled" and "self–willed" actions and do not realize that executive functions unfold in our brains while providing a feeling that everything is under control. Now, this is precisely what is amiss in ADHD. Many people find it difficult to grasp ADHD because the underlying problems contradict the prevailing commonsense view of humanity, and it is not easy to cast aside or change that view. It is not surprising that we encounter so much misunderstanding of ADHD.

Cognitive skill training can certainly be useful when cognitive skills are undeveloped, but the connection to problems of attention and self-regulation is far from clear.

Psychotherapeutic guidance can be useful to improve the negative self-image that often forms in those with ADHD, which helps the ADHD individual learn how to lead a healthier and more productive way of life. But this does not alleviate the ADHD itself. Psychotherapy certainly plays a role in the treatment when comorbid psychiatric problems exist alongside ADHD.

A New 'System Perspective'

A treatment approach that harnesses self-effort towards bringing the self-regulatory system under control is frequently experienced as more meaningful when compared to other behavioral approaches (e.g., individuals with ADHD are at their best when their individuality is recognized); therefore, good behavioral management should take into account the need for varied activities by persons with ADHD (Cherkes-Juwolski, 1997). Such an approach is best suited to tackle the underlying self-regulation problems in ADHD as described in this book. Parents, teachers, and psychotherapists find it challenging to interact with the ADHD mode of functioning and to facilitate efforts at optimal self-regulation and adaptability. The final chapter of this book will discuss this new "system perspective' of ADHD.

Further, the positive talents that often go hand-in-hand with ADHD (i.e., passion, creativity, spontaneity, fair-mindedness) merit recognition of this approach.

Basic Structure of this Book

	Behavioral Level	**EEG Level**	**Neurofeedback Level**
Static	ADHD symptoms	Static QEEG (4.2)	QEEG based training
Dynamic	State regulation deficits	Dynamic EEG • EEG stabilization (4.3) • ERD/ERS (4.5)	Dynamic training • Global normalization • Mechanism training

A common theme throughout this book is that we need to deepen our understanding of the brain's dynamics at systems' level to improve assessment and treatment. In that vein, the figure on the cover of this book is not an image of a static QEEG, but illustrates the dynamics of an EEG following a motor response (event related desynchronization [ERD]/event-related synchronization [ERS]) during an attention task (unpublished figure from Kropotov).

1.

Attention, Self-Regulation, and State Regulation

The term ADHD (attention deficit disorder with or without hyperactivity) officially came into use only with its official introduction to the handbook of the American Psychiatric Association, the DSM-III in 1980. Previously, the terms 'hyperkinetic syndrome' or 'minimal brain dysfunction' (MBD) were used.

Consequently, the emphasis shifted decisively to the presence of attentional disturbances in ADHD. Canadian psychologist Virginia Douglas (1972) was the leading source of inspiration for this change, which emphasized problematic self-regulation of attention as the fundamental problem. Disturbed self-regulation expresses itself in difficulties of planning, organization, self-control, and the maintenance of a measured, adaptive level of alertness. Within this schema, sleep regulation problems were also described which, incidentally, were adopted in 1980 as one of the diagnostic criteria (hyperactivity during sleep). In later sanctioned guidelines, this last element would be dropped, not because it did not occur frequently, but because it was regarded as insufficiently specific. Douglas also emphasized that children with ADHD are guided to a much greater degree by the immediate results of their behavior rather than by the likely long-term consequences.

Since the introduction of the ADHD concept, a variant form without hyperactivity, which describes ADHD individuals as rather passive dreamers, has also been acknowledged. Even now, this form is still frequently overlooked because people with this variant are less disruptive (within their environment) and often only encounter learning and self-image difficulties at a later age (9 to 14) compared to those with hyperactivity. It has long been recognized that hyperactivity in adulthood often decreases or becomes expressed as inner unrest. This lies at the root of the old idea that hyperkinetic syndrome disappears in adulthood. Difficulties with attention and organization are stressed more often now. Increasingly, we have come to realize that for at least half of the children these problems with attention and organization will survive into adulthood.

Only after Douglas emphasized attention difficulties as the fundamental problem was it understood that the root cause of the disorder lies in the brain and not in the character of the child with ADHD. Moreover, after Douglas highlighted the role of attention, the interest in the disorder among psychiatrists and scientists has greatly increased. Later, Virginia Douglas commented that she personally would have preferred to call the disorder a "disturbance of self-regulation." Since the 1970s, she demonstrated in a number of studies that the nature of the attention deficits in ADHD is tied to task complexity. For example, in simple, stimulus-poor tasks, reaction times are too slow, but in complex, or stimulus-rich tasks, reaction times are too quick. This can be measured clearly with computerized attention tasks. Both reaction time anomalies improve after administration of Ritalin. These observations led Douglas to characterize ADHD as inadequate 'self-regulation', which negatively affects the appropriate investment, apportioning, organization, and maintenance of attention. Moreover, inadequate 'self-regulation' contributes to the development of impulsive behavior and a strong tendency to seek immediate gratification. Her studies reveal that Ritalin works not just to improve attention, but also self-regulation. For example, 'working memory' improves alongside 'divergent thinking ability' (i.e., creative 'fan-like' associations along lines of thought) and mental flexibility.

The American psychologist Russell Barkley (1994) further developed the self-regulation model in 1990. He defined self-regulation or, alternately, self-control to be any self-directed action that adjusts the individual's response to an event and produces a net change in the long-term consequences of that behavior to the long-term advantage of the individual. An adjustable level of self-control allows for the flexible adaptation of behavior to the changing demands of daily tasks. If self-control is insufficient, immediate external factors rather than foreseeable long-term consequences determine the behavior.

Together with other factors, this contributes to impairments in working memory and problems with self-control of motivation, working memory, attention, and emotion. Impaired self-control explains the development of problems in ADHD, especially the lack of perseverance towards long-term goals and the deficits in internal supervision. The definition of ADHD developed by Barkley implicates inadequate "executive functions" that are associated with the frontal cerebral cortex and contribute to the disruption of self-regulation. The term "executive functions" generally encompasses working memory (including, among other things, the sense of time, behavioral anticipation from previous experience that forms a base for planning and execution), self-talk (including self instruction), self-regulation of emotion, motivation, alertness, and the ability to analyze and recombine a problem to create a novel solution (reconstitution).

Because of this disturbance in self-regulation, ADHD behavior lacks sufficient internal guidance and others often judge it as chaotic, reactive, and ill considered. Thought and action, knowledge and performance, past, future, and the moment are all divided from one another. ADHD does not disrupt knowledge of a correct action but instead, affects the actual behavioral performance and optimal timing of that knowledge at the appropriate moments. These factors convey the impression that ADHD is a disorder of "will power" or motivation, which contributes greatly to misunderstanding and irritation from others. Normally, adaptive self-controlled behavior is governed less by immediate demands and more by long-term consequences (predicted based on experience). People with ADHD have a sort of "time blindness," so that the individual functions, for the most part, from moment to moment. This clouded time perception is linked to a diminished ability to hold the order of events in working memory. We have the impression that free will is curtailed; although, in a way, it could be argued that someone with ADHD is freer and less enslaved by time. We all think back nostalgically to the innocence of childhood when our behavior was free from time's dictates. However, as adults, we must let time co-rule our behavior if we are to adapt and survive in society. This impoverished sense of time explains why someone with ADHD cannot tolerate delay and is frequently impatient. This also partly explains the procrastination behaviors and the unsuccessful attempts to teach time management to someone with ADHD: no matter how well someone with ADHD learns these techniques, it often does not lead to behavioral changes (i.e., improved time awareness).

The executive functions associated with frontal brain areas start to develop clearly only at around 6 years of age. This explains why it is very difficult to diagnose ADHD before age six. Moreover, it can explain why executive functions that remain problematic after hyperactivity as well as situationally linked attentional difficulties diminish in adulthood. Considering that the prevailing diagnostic criteria were developed with children and adolescents between the ages of 6 to 18, they often offer little support for diagnostic decisions in adulthood. It is, therefore, useful in the assessment of adults, but also of children, to investigate working memory's (planning and strategy use) perception, organization of time, internal speech (following instructions), self control of emotions and motivation, goal directed creativity, and perseverance.

Virginia Douglas and Russell Barkley receive great merit for shaping the understanding of ADHD as a disorder of self-regulation. However, their approach does not sufficiently account for the neurodynamics as they do not question the origins of the "self" that self-regulates, instead, seem to assume unduly that "self" corresponds to our "I" that controls everything.

More recently, studies have highlighted the importance of *"state regulation"* in ADHD because attention problems are certainly partly attributable *to an erratic capacity to maintain an optimal and stable state of alertness; state regulation is too little internally steered and too strongly dependent on external factors* (Van der Meere, 2001).

Weak state regulation has been studied in many young children, and these studies shed light on possible later life malfunctions in attentional self-regulation. Small children with lax self-regulation demonstrate difficulty in stabilizing their alertness (in attentional terms: a fluctuating and frequently suboptimal alertness level) and an unregulated sleep wake cycle. State regulation can therefore be described as a task adaptive behavior, and is related to biologically-based (versus psychologically-based) motivation. State regulation is considered an important product of prefrontal and mesolimbic functions.

Caregivers who observed their child's own behavioral rhythms and efforts to self-regulate in order to change their own behavior positively promoted self-regulation in small children. Whenever vulnerable/impressionable children received this form of flexible caregiver feedback in which the initiative to succeed was transferred to the child, and in which feedback took cognizance of the child's own rhythms and needs, the children attained improved self-regulation and task focus. Behavioral regulation supported by the environment in this way can help develop an improved brain regulation rhythm. This environmental support best succeeds when the child does not perceive it as external because external regulation is responsive to the needs and rhythms of the child without taking a directive approach (Cherkes-Julkowski, Sharp, & Stolzenberg, 1997).

In this way, the caregiver can deliver a control parameter that can stabilize the functioning. This approach facilitates a positive influence on the child's ability to continue to self-regulate, to strengthen frustration tolerance, and to maintain full motivation to meet a challenge.

Weak internal state regulation leads to weak self-regulation with consequential attentional difficulties. In ADHD, the need for an external support that assists in state regulation through environmental structure is lifelong. Unlike adults with full neurobehavioral development, children are more unstable, unpredictable, and spontaneous. Children can concentrate powerfully on a task, and yet that attention can be waylaid by small internal or external factors. It is for this reason that children are only held partially responsible for their acts. In children and adults with ADHD, self-control is even less pronounced. During normal development, a greater variation in adaptive behavior allows for regulation that is more refined. Weak self-regulation can be expressed through unstable sleep, especially irregularity while falling to and awakening from the sleep.

Sleep deprivation in people without ADHD could be used as a model for ADHD. One night or more of insufficient sleep weakens attention and thus the complex organization of behavior. In this case, momentary stimuli in the outside world rather than internal planning reflexively determine the behavior. An analogy that comes to mind is a pile of unorganized paper on a desk that needs attention; people who are sleep deprived or with ADHD will muddle through without making clear decisions and will address the paperwork with equal urgency instead of employing classification and prioritization schemes.

Summary

The symptoms of ADHD are mere expressions of an underlying disturbance in self-regulation. Self-regulation is necessary for adaptive anticipation of changing circumstances whilst keeping the individual's best long term interests in view. Weak self-regulation is itself an expression of weak-state regulation, which indicates a weakened task-adaptive capacity.

Lax self-regulation is strongly associated with poorly operating "executive functions" in the prefrontal lobe regions that include working memory, time perception, planning, and organization.

2.

The Functional Anatomy of Attention and "Executive Functions"

Very broadly speaking, attention consists of three phases:
- first, overall *alertness* increases;
- second, attention becomes focused on meaningful stimuli; and
- third, responsive actions are performed in which complex processes, such as inhibition of inappropriate reactions, planning, and motivation, play an important role.

This is an oversimplification because we know that brain contains more inner control loops than channels carrying information to the brain. In effect, this implies that, for the most part, newly processed information barely reaches much of the total brain before it is selected and dispatched to a control loop where it must compete with other useful information for behavioral control.

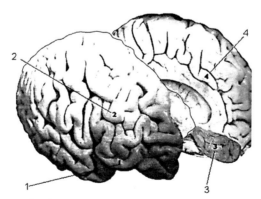

Figure 1. The cerebral cortex showing the prefrontal cortex: the dorsolateral (DLPFC) (outer side) (2), ventromedial (lower inside) (3) and orbital (situated above and behind the eye sockets) (1) areas, and the anterior cingulate (interior belt shaped zone) (4).

2.1 Alertness

The phases of attention are initiated with the action of the *alertness mechanism* in which the right frontal cortex plays a key role. Noradrenaline (a chemical that transmits stimulus information from the terminal of one neuron to the next neuron in the circuit) is an important neurotransmitter in this process.

2.2 The Orienting of Attention

The second link in this chain is the orienting of attention that plays a role in fluid attention and is anatomically placed in the right posterior parietal cortex. The major neurotransmitters involved are acetylcholine and noradrenalin (the posterior attention system).

Directed, selective auditory attention arises in the primary and secondary auditory areas of the temporal cortex and is measurable as a negative electrode potential occurring about 100 ms after the stimulus (N1 or N100). The prefrontal cortex modulates this early selective attention via the thalamus (the 'relay station' deep within the brain through which all sensory information passes en route to the cerebral cortex). This signal is frequently weaker in ADHD.

2.3 Executive Functions

Subsequent conscious processing of directed, selective attention takes place in the prefrontal cortex (measurable in the EEG as "late frontal negativity" or LFN) and is often found to be somewhat weaker in ADHD. Additional conscious processing, in which the neurotransmitter dopamine plays an important part, enables the "executive functions" of the anterior prefrontal cortex. Executive functions are located primarily in the anterior attention system: the anterior cingulate. This is a belt shaped zone, which borders the inner base of the frontal cortex. We can distinguish between the different executive functions, which are described in the next five sections.

2.3.1 Response Inhibition

Response inhibition is part of broader monitoring and evaluation mechanisms This function resides in the base of the frontal cortex along the midline (the most posterior, upper part of the anterior cingulate) in the frontal cortex above the eye sockets (orbitofrontal cortex) with connections to the caudate nucleus deep in the brain. The electrical activity of the brain during response inhibition is measurable using a 'go/no-go' stimulus incentive condition in which a specific stimulus is quickly followed by repetition of the same stimulus, whereupon the participant must push a button. This is the 'go' response (response execution) and can be recorded in the EEG. If the same initial stimulus is followed by a different distinct stimulus, the participant must inhibit the button-press response to which a 'no-go' response (response inhibition) is processed in the EEG. The maximum processed brain activity occurs at the front of the middle line of the scalp in the 'go' reaction and consists of an electrical negative component N2 (235 - 256 milliseconds [ms] after the stimulus) followed by an electrical positive component P3 (350 - 450 ms after the stimulus). A classic EEG recording uses surface electrodes that can accurately measure the electrical potentials at the scalp but does not allow inferring the source of the electrical activity in the deeper layers of the cortex.

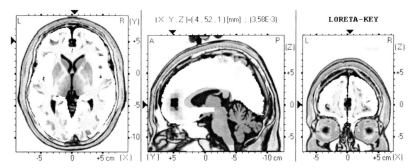

Figure 2. Source localization of the no-go P3 ERP (LORETA method): maximal (dark shading) in the anterior cingulate in the frontal cortex. **Left:** *Transverse section of the brain showing the anterior cingulate.* **Middle:** *A side view of the same level.* **Right:** *A frontal section of the brain through the same area. In this way a three dimensional reconstruction of brain activity is possible (see chapter 7).*

One method to locate the source of processed brain potentials (see figure 2) is LORETA (low resolution brain electromagnetic tomography) (Pasqui-Marqui, 1994). LORETA identifies the source generator of the electrical activity deep in the brain using mathematical computations of the strength of the processed brain potentials taken from the different scalp measurement points.

The source of the N2 signal lies in the right lower frontal cortex and plays a role in response inhibition. Research has also shown that the processed N2 activity strongly correlates with activity in the lower and dorsolateral prefrontal cortex, which indicates strong interconnections (Lavric, 2004). The N2 has a second source generator in the anterior cingulate that is known to play a role in conflict resolution between two concurrent response tendencies and is, therefore, related to recent extended studies of error related negativity (ERN). The P3 has its source in the anterior cingulate and probably plays a role in the monitoring of stimuli, in addition to its traditionally assumed function in response inhibition. The N2, ERN, and P3 are found to be weaker in amplitude (i.e., microvolts) in ADHD (Pliszka, 2000; Falgätter, 2003; Liotti, 2005; Kropotov, 2004).

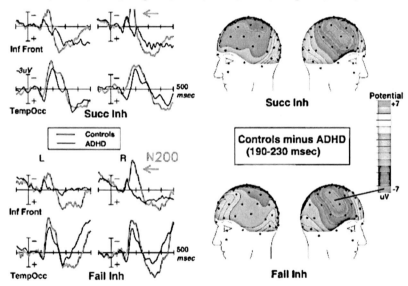

Figure 3. Error Related Negativity in a group of children with ADHD and in typically developing children: note that in the curves on the left, both the N200 and the P300 are weaker in ADHD, both for the instances when the children were successful and the instances when they failed to inhibit a response to the stop signal. On the right, the differences in the N200 between the two groups are presented with a brain mapping. The maximum difference is in the right inferior frontal area: in ADHD the N200 is weakest in this area. Reprinted from Biological Psychiatry, 48(3), Pliszka, Liotti, & Woldorff, Inhibitory control in children with attention deficit/hyperactivity disorder: Event-related potentials identify the processing component and timing of an impaired right-frontal response-inhibition mechanism, Copyright (2000), with permission from Elsevier.

Kropotov (2004) showed that the 'no-go' response is often weaker in children with ADHD and that neurofeedback therapy can normalize this response. A weak response is an expression of impulsivity and of more limited monitoring of the stimulus. In an fMRI (functional magnetic resonance imaging) study, which measures oxygen levels in the brain as an indicator of brain activity during a task, the brain was imaged during a 'go/no-go' task. Children with ADHD showed lower activity in the caudate nucleus (caudate meaning "tail like" located deep in the brain) during this task compared to children with typical development. This factor itself notably establishes that there is indeed a difference in functional brain activity between children with and without ADHD. Moreover, the effect of Ritalin on brain activity differs between the two groups.

Comparative studies using fMRI of normal children and adults have shown that during response inhibition in a 'go/no-go' task, activity in the nucleus caudate (in the striatum) is stronger in children (Booth, 2003). The researchers interpreted this to be an expression of the insufficient maturation of the frontostriatal circuit in children, such that these children must put forth more effort to compensate. This suggests that the lower activity found by Vaidya, Austin, Krikorian, Ridlehuber, Desmond, Glover, & Gabrieli (1998) (figure 4) in children with ADHD can be interpreted as a lack of compensatory effort in comparison to typically developing children. Ritalin can improve the normal compensatory over-activity during response inhibition in the caudate nucleus and the putamen in children with ADHD. In normal, typically developing children, administration of Ritalin does not impact this activity.

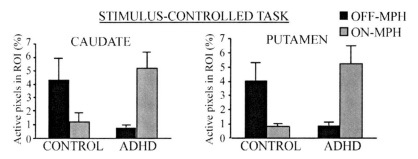

Figure 4. In ADHD during the go/no-go task, there is less activity in the caudate nucleus and the putamen. After the administration of Ritalin, activity clearly increases (contrary to the result in the control group) (Vaidya et al., 1998). Copyright (1998) National Academy of Sciences, U.S.A.

Most children with ADHD who receive neurofeedback training will experience an increase in brain activity and a normalization of the caudate nucleus during the go/no-go task (Beauregard, 2006). It is interesting to note that a decreased caudate nucleus size is one of the most consistent findings in structural MRI ADHD research.

Patients with Parkinson's disease have long been known to exhibit higher beta-1-activity (frequency range from 12-20 Hertz [Hz]) in the central motor region recorded in the EEG, and limited ERD (event related desynchronization: a weakening of the EEG activity) during hand movements. It is assumed that this results from reduced sensitivity of the motor cortex due to a dopamine shortage in the basal ganglia (a grey nucleus deep in the brain which includes the caudate nucleus). Recently, researchers examined the beta-1 activity in the basal ganglia of patients with Parkinson's during therapeutic deep brain stimulating electrodes (Dostrovsky, 2004). This demonstrated higher than normal beta-1 activity in the globus pallidus and subthalamic nucleus (also parts of the basal ganglia) and that this activity weakened after administration of dopaminergic medication. Moreover, beta activity in the basal ganglia decreased during voluntary movement. In a 'go/no-go' task, weaker beta activity in the subthalamic nucleus after a go-stimulus was followed by adjustment of the beta waves after the movement stopped. The high frequency therapeutic electrostimulation of the subthalamic nucleus also reduced beta activity. This is in good agreement with research from the sixties, when Sterman demonstrated correlations between activity in the caudate nucleus and other basal ganglia nuclei on the one hand and rhythmic beta waves in the transitional area of the sensory and motor cortex ("SMR" or sensorimotor rhythm) on the other hand.

2.3.2   Automatic Stimulus Categorization

In a predominately automatic attention task, a choice must be made between a series of identical stimuli and an intermittent unusual incentive stimulus whereby attention is mobilized in the anterior cingulate. After 200ms, the N200 or N2b electronegative component, which originates from the anterior cingulate *(automatic stimulus categorization)*, appears in the EEG. The N2 reflects a process of stimulus-response conversion that precedes the preparation of a motor response. In ADHD, the N2b is often weaker.

2.3.3 Response Selection and Implementation

Response selection and implementation is mirrored in the EEG by an electro-positive wave at around 300ms after the stimulus, giving a maximum scalp measurement at the center and the back (parietal) midline of the scalp (P300 or P3b). The P3b arises in the temporoparietal transitional areas of the cerebral cortex, and is modulated by noradrenaline produced by the locus coreleus in the brain stem. In ADHD, this response is often weaker or slower. Ritalin or neurofeedback training can normalize this response. The latter was demonstrated in Egner and Gruzelier's (2001) study.

2.3.4 Working Memory and Reconstitution

Working memory (verbal and non-verbal) and reconstitution (analysis and synthesis of a problem) are located in the lateral prefrontal cortex (dorso-lateral prefrontal cortex). The sense of time, organization, and planning are intertwined with working memory. Further processing of stimuli to which attention is focused is seen as "late frontal negativity" (LFN) in the EEG.

2.3.5 Regulation of Emotion, Motivation (the Will), and Activation State

The regulation of emotion, motivation (the will), and activation state (with regard to preparation for an action) are located in the foremost part of the anterior cingulate. This area is active during "voluntary" actions as opposed to actions triggered by an external stimulus. The anterior cingulate is thus involved in internal selection processes. In the performance of an action that feels consciously willed, negative potentials, maximally expressed along the middle of the scalp, start to be detected in the EEG 500 to 1000 ms before conscious awareness of the intention to act (the readiness potential or 'Bereitschafts potenzial').

Researchers have found that this neural activity has its origin in the most posterior part of the anterior cingulate and in the supplementary motor area of the cerebral cortex. The fact that the subjective feeling of a conscious intention to perform an action occurs barely 200ms before an action demonstrates that the notion of "free will" is in reality an illusion, albeit a crucial and useful one. This contradicts the subjective impression that we make a voluntary decision to prepare an action. This may occur because the underlying complexity of behavior is in reality too intricate to be entrusted to the limitations of individual consciousness. However, the illusion of free will gives the individual a sense of personal conscious responsibility for behavioral actions. The emergence of this early brain wave suggests that we may need this feeling of freely willed actions. Before a tic, for example, no negative brainwave precedes the tic movement. On the other hand, if someone with tics is asked to deliberately produce the tic movement, then the readiness potential is also produced. In ADHD, and in people with frontal brain injuries, the readiness potential is weaker. This could explain why in people with ADHD, while actions are associated with a feeling of free will, the degree of freedom is limited. Indeed, actions are generally more responsive to momentary stimuli in the environment rather than to long-term goals.

Overall, people with ADHD understand that work will be accomplished better if a goal is established, but beneath the surface lays a strange feeling that their motivation level, and thus free will, cannot be changed. In a normal individual, a voluntary action will take place with different brain areas working together in such a manner that the action is optimal for the individual and best adapted to the environment, while taking into account long-term consequences. It should be added that behavioral planning and the feeling of free will occurs in the dorsolateral prefrontal cortex (DLPFC), and that the practical execution of action occurs in the anterior cingulate and the supplementary motor area (where the readiness potential originates). The DLPFC is part of a higher level of integration, and this area is also less functional in ADHD.

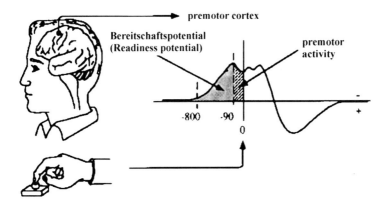

Figure 5. The readiness potential that precedes a movement

These various components of the executive function form a network that consistently interacts together to self-regulate (in a manner that is only partly conscious). The executive functions produce insufficient internalized representations of behavior in ADHD that makes self-regulation very difficult.

We previously discussed how sleep deprivation produces behavioral characteristics of ADHD. Moreover, functional imaging of the brain after sleep deprivation via PET (positron emission spectroscopy) shows diminished activity in the thalamus, the caudate nucleus, the prefrontal areas (including the dorsolateral prefrontal cerebral cortex [DLPFC], orbitofrontal cortex, and the anterior cingulate), and the posterior parietal association cortex during an attention task (addition and subtraction). This seems to imply that sleep is necessary to maintain optimal daytime attentional and behavioral functions (Thomas, 2000). The behavioral changes that follow sleep deprivation are similar in nature to those seen after injuries to the anterior cingulate, the orbitofrontal cortex, or to the DLPFC. Injury to the anterior cingulate and the orbitofrontal cortex regions lead to impulsive and uninhibited behavior, distractibility, and heightened emotional reactivity. DLPFC injuries lead to problems with decision making. The decision making process requires the integration of many facts, experiences, and estimates of future consequences to produce the optimal solution adjusted to the individual's interest. The strong interactions between the DLPFC and the anterior cingulate also contribute as the DLPFC plays an important role in selecting the most adaptive behavioral response while the anterior cingulate facilitates the implementation of the selected response. The DLPFC enables the anterior cingulate to take part in greater differentiation, particularly concerning time structure (needed for the control of prospective behavior), and thus plays a role in environmental interactions. The lateral premotor cortex plays a major role in spontaneous (not consciously willed) actions triggered by external stimuli. This area has many links to the parietal association cortex, which contributes to the perception of localization of objects in the environment. The performance of responsive actions to external visual or auditory stimuli activates the lateral prefontal motor cortex. For example, the mere sight of an apple can provoke a movement to grasp the apple. Children with ADHD often display such behaviors with frequent, seemingly reflexive motions, such as reaching for anything that comes within their field of view.

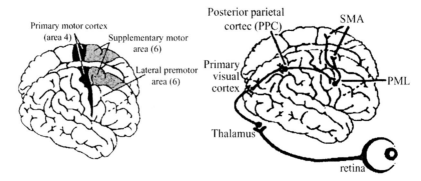

Figure 6. The supplementary motor area (SMA) plays a part in initiating freely willed actions. Left: the motor cortex is shaded black, lying immediately behind the sensory motor cortex. The lateral premotor cortex plays a role in reflexive actions.

3.

Self-Regulation, Executive Functions
Embedded in Motivation

Research into 'error related negativity' (ERN) provides a clearer understanding of how frontal executive functions are intertwined with emotional and motivational processes in the limbic system. Although it has long been known that important pathways exist between the frontal regions and the limbic structures (Nauta, 1971), research that is more recent delivers fresh insight into the mechanisms of self-regulation of executive functions, such as monitoring and planning.

An exhilarating development in contemporary EEG research is its illumination on how motivational and emotional processes are interwoven with the executive functions and its revelation of the self-regulatory processes. This research provides answers to a quintessential question: what underlies the adaptive, motivational control of cognition? While emotion and self-regulation are now popular research topics in cognitive neuroscience, concepts of motivational control are poorly developed within the theoretical framework of cognitive science. Behavioral theories of learning hit their peak in the years 1940 to 1950. Subsequently, cognitive psychology rejected this behavioral dogma and, based on a model of computers, described cognitive processes, such as observation, attention, and memory, as objective, definable information processing tasks. Consequently, behavioral fields of study, such as motivation, rewards, and learning, lost in popularity.

Remarkably, cognitive models of self-regulation and feedback control developed out of computer science inspired by Wiener's (1948) cybernetics (literally meaning: the science of control) research. All the more remarkable that Wiener was inspired directly by Canon's studies (1915) of physiological homeostasis that investigated changes in physiological standard (or baseline) values ("set points," such as body temperature, acid base balance, and oxygen concentration), which lead to adaptive regulation mechanisms. The word "homeostasis" means "the same state" and describes stabilization of internal states. Pribram (1960) was the first to apply cybernetic ideas of homeostasis to human planning and self-regulation, shortly followed by Nauta (1971). In Pribram's model, various motivational conditions replace homeostatic set points.

The concepts of behavioral control and executive functions are described in classical cognitive psychology without clear distinctions so that the two constructs are entwined. In this tradition, executive functions are described as high-level processes that exercise cognitive control over more elementary mental operations. A supervisory attentional system was introduced to bind behavior in situations where routine responses are inadequate (Norman, 1986). The cognitive psychological model of executive functions runs the risk of being confused with an external agent rather than being understood as an integral part of bodily, self-regulatory functions. Moreover, these cognitive models of executive functions are inappropriately invoked to explain how dysfunctions of executive control can cause psychopathologies of mood, motivation, and attention (such as ADHD). Rather, these pathologies suggest fundamental changes in the internal goals and regulatory set points that guide self-control rather than a problem with a remote supervisory source.

The study of ERN allows for the monitoring of actions as an elementary component of executive functions to be examined in the wider context of action regulation. Behavior is evaluated in the context of expectations (proposed to be a context for actions). Electrophysiological responses are frequently observed at moments when the execution of actions fall short of expectations: an ERN emerges when actual actions are discrepant with planned action goals. McEwen (2000) argued that because the ERN and related mediofrontal negative brain potentials seem to reflect various regulatory points, they may be important set points in frontal and limbic mechanisms for various homeostatic and allostatic processes.

Action monitoring is a crucial executive function that by definition monitors the divergence between expectations and outcomes. The measurement of the ERN provides a window into this process of "fault detection." Everyone makes mistakes, especially if we work quickly - we push the wrong button or almost knock something flying. How astonishing it is that this 'D'oh!' reaction has a distinctive pattern of brain activity: the ERN. The most popular research paradigm employs the following methodology:

> The participant sits at a computer screen and must respond using one of two buttons: one on the left, and one on the right. On the screen appears a series of five letters like HHHHH, SSHSS, SSSSS, or HHSHH.The participant must react as quickly as possible to the middle letter in each five-letter group with a left push for an H and a right push for an S. This is known as the "flanker task" in which the outlying letters are both identical to the middle letter and helpful to the task or not. The 'incongruent' flanker letters more often lead to a wrong button push. The averaged EEG potentials from correct and incorrect responses are calculated separately. The resulting difference curve gives the best image of the ERN.

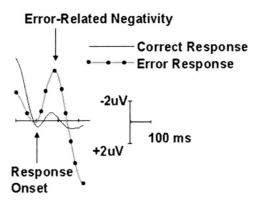

Figure 7. Error- Related Negativity

The error related brain activity appears 50ms - 100ms after the button push ("response onset"). That is quite notably fast. We "know" that just before the erroneous response movement is made (the brain has already registered: it is a preconscious response) that we are making a mistake. The error related brain activity is evoked in the anterior cingulate, which forms part of a control network that includes the prefrontal cortex, the basal ganglia, and the limbic areas. The anterior cingulate has been described as an "interface" and relay station between cognition, motor control, motivation, and arousal of activation state (Paus, 2001). Using alcohol or sedatives, such as lorazepam (brand name Temesta™), leads to a smaller ERN, whereas dextroamphetamine creates a larger ERN. In people with ADHD, a decreased ERN is observed, while those with obsessive compulsive disorder (OCD) exhibit an increased ERN, mirroring overactive action evaluations (Hehring, 2000; Johannes, 2001; Hajcak, 2002; Fitzgerald; 2005). OCD is not only a disorder of action monitoring, but also one of "affective evaluation." Although the affective evaluation of the ERN is a relatively new development (Luu, 2004), it can be a useful alternative to the error detection and conflict monitoring. In Luu's model, functional affective control via the anterior cingulate is central to self-regulation.

ERN research techniques allow examination of conscious 'executive attention' (Posner, 1994) that develops out of elementary and frequently conscious corticolimbic processes and is associated with activity in the dorsal region of the anterior cingulate. Recently, fMRI research found that the anterior cingulate is linked to certain limbic areas and has a role in evaluation (or more precisely detecting when cognitive control is required) while the dorsolateral prefrontal cortex (DLPFC) is involved in the strategic control of task performance (MacDonald, 2000). The anterior cingulate plays a part in the representation of adaptive goals, such as motivationally or emotionally important "set points." In fact, Luu's model (2004) treats motivational processes as an integral part of every behavior, from controlling simple actions to the most complex forms of executive self-regulation. The anterior cingulate's ability to identify appropriate actions in a given motivational context is emphasized as it monitors the action outcome and switches to another series of actions when that outcome falls short of the desired goal. In this theoretical framework, the anterior cingulate is part of a circuit with the amygdala. This circuit reflects the encephalization of the homeostatic motivation system from the mesencephalon (midbrain) in the brain stem and the hypothalamus in the diencephalon (the brain between mesencephalon and telencephalon). Encephalization permits greater behavioral complexity in the form of complex representations of motivational goals that can be consolidated in memory and used to guide action planning.

This discovery of higher levels of integration allows us to form global concepts about the integration of mental levels (Ey, 1952). Section 4.6 will explore and bring into perspective their reflection in the global EEG pattern (Bente, 1964). This perspective allows us to understand that sleep deprivation leads to an erratic EEG due to a lower degree of integration of mental processing and lowered activity in the frontal cortex. In this way, ADHD can be better understood by linking an unstable EEG, a lowered ERN, problems with executive functions and with motivational processes, and fMRI data that shows lowered activity in frontal areas, such as the anterior cingulate, during certain neuropsychological tasks. Also in this way, it helps to understand how successful neurofeedback training can normalize this lowered frontal activity in the EEG (Beauregard, 2006).

According to Luu (2004), fault detector and conflict monitoring theories are too narrow because they do not take into account the ways in which motivation, goals, and context contribute to adaptive adjustment of behavior. Set points can form motivational expectations. Human brains, and those of higher vertebrates, are not simply passive generators of reflexes but continuous predictors that guide interactions with their environment. Luu argues that cognitive neurosciences can do more than chart isolated mental operations because they can address the self-regulation of the whole organism.

Summary

Internal control circuits in the brain determine what information is processed, taking into account intention, motivation, and past experiences. Following an orientation response, the executive functions of the frontal cerebral cortex direct selective attention and suppress certain responses in the context of wider evaluative functions. At the same time, meaningful stimuli are automatically evaluated and, as a consequence, the behavioral response is further refined by the executive functions (i.e., working memory plus planning and sense of time), regulation of emotion, and activation state.

After sleep deprivation, all of these cognitive functions are poorly regulated in typical individuals and show some similarities to the regulation of these functions in ADHD.

More recent theoretical concepts emphasize the role of self-regulation in the context of variable homeostasis in which motivational factors determine the degree of variability of regulatory set points. The frontal executive functions in this approach are thought to be entwined with emotional and motivational processes, and higher executive functions can be seen in terms of a complex development of motivational processes in action regulation that produce adaptive behavior, all of which is constrained to a certain degree in ADHD.

4.

EEG: Mechanisms of Attention and Self-Regulation

4.1 *EEG and Underlying Brain Activity*

EEG (electroencephalogram) refers to the electrical brain activity that is measurable at the scalp. It was first described in 1929 by the German psychiatrist Hans Berger who investigated EEG correlations with mental states and with the influence of substances, such as caffeine. After some years, psychiatry found no useful application for EEG and from the 1960s onward, only neurologists utilized this technology as an applied research method within a clinical neurological context, but with little guiding theoretical framework. Gross abnormalities were described in patients with neurological injuries or in the brains of people with metabolic disorders, and some exceptionally useful research were undertaken, especially with reference to epilepsy. The emergence of other brain imaging methods significantly reduced the practical importance of EEG to neurology, although, EEG remained a useful research method that continued to shed light on the nature of epilepsy. Meanwhile, a stream of psychophysiological studies that emerged in 1964 adopted different ways to evaluate the EEG, more accurately re-evaluating deviant brainwave patterns, which according to neurological norms lay within normal variance, as manifestations of varying degrees of vigilance.

The Berlin psychiatrist Bente (1964) offered a compact definition of the concept of vigilance (i.e., wakefulness) that built on the clinical understanding advanced by the London neurologist Head in 1923 (i.e., the quality and degree of organization in an individual's adaptive interaction with the environment). It is noteworthy that this description contains recognizable ingredients from the later understanding of the executive functions of the frontal lobe regions.

In Bente's definition, vigilance is conceptualized as a function of a dynamic brain state that is mirrored by the global, organized EEG pattern.

During the 1970s, EEG enjoyed a revival in research laboratories using pharmaco-EEGs that allow one to characterize psycho-pharmaceuticals based on changes in the EEG spectrum. Since 1985, the wide scale availability of computers made possible to use QEEG (quantitative EEG) in clinical practice. As QEEG technology developed, the establishment of age-normed databases significantly increased its usefulness, and researchers and clinicians can now verify statistically significant differences between data obtained from various patient groups or between individual patient data and the distribution of normal age appropriate values (i.e., lifetime normative databases). Nevertheless, a major drawback to these exciting developments of the EEG becoming a practical, empirical examination method was the loss of impetus for the further development of theoretical models to better understand the internal dynamics of EEG. One such model that continues to retain its value, although mostly forgotten, is Bente's vigilance model based on sleep deprivation studies and the influence of pharmaceuticals on the EEG.

Further, EEG was not a priority for physiological research in the 1970's, and the research impetus shifted toward the study of neuron electrophysiology. Nevertheless, since the nineties, there has been a strong revival of scientific interest in EEG research, accompanied by the emergence of a whole series of new statistical analyses methods, such as joint time frequency analysis (JTFA), independent component analysis (ICA), entropy analysis, non-linear analysis methods, and more.

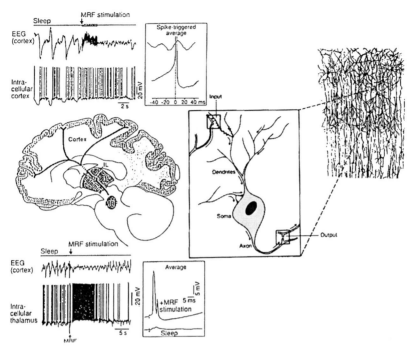

Figure 8. Slow waves are seen at the start of the uppermost EEG segment as observed during sleep. The curve directly underneath displays the action potential measured with microelectrodes at the cell membrane of the cortical neurons. During sleep, action potentials occur in 'bursts' and their duration determines the period of the EEG wave.

If the center for consciousness in the reticular formation of the mesencephalon (MRF) in the brain stem is stimulated, fast low voltage EEG activity is generated, paired with tonic action potentials.

The lowermost EEG segment is identical, but with the action potential of thalamic neurons displayed underneath.

The middle figure illustrates axons rising from the brain stem to the thalamus at the base of the cerebrum via the mesencephalon, forming synapses with the cell bodies of thalamocortical neurons, axons of which connect to various areas of the cerebral cortex (shaded). In these brain areas, axonal fibers make synaptic contact with apical (that is to say, running perpendicular to the

*scalp) dendrites. The electrical fields near these cortical neurons are measur-
able in the EEG at the scalp.*

*On the right, we can see a schematic cross section of a portion of cerebral
cortex and a network of neurons. In the box above, we see an enlarged drawing showing an axon forming a synapse at a dendrite of the depicted neuron,
allowing information transmission (in the direction indicated by the arrows)
through the soma (the cell body) along the axon which in turn synapses with
the dendrites of a neighboring neuron.*

The EEG is measurable at the surface of the scalp, normally taken at 19
points, and reflects the continuous electrical activity of the brain. The electrical rhythmic brain waves measured at the scalp reflect the massed activity of
the neuronal dendrites in the underlying cerebral cortex. The EEG is therefore
not the sum of the action potentials of the neurons as was once thought.

Around one hundred billion neurons form the cerebral cortex, and these neurons possess essentially a tree-like structure with many extensions growing
out of the cell body. Numerous dendrites, further split into smaller branches,
carry electrical signals from underlying neurons (part of neuronal networks)
into the cell bodies. From each cell body, electrical signals travel down along
axon in a process comparable to transmission along a telephone wire before
reaching yet even more divergent structures - the root-like axon terminals
that connect to the next neuron within the circuit. The synapse is the "contact
zone" between one neuron and the next formed between the axon terminal of
one neuron and the cell body, or the dendrites, of the recipient neuron in the
circuit. Electrical information that arrives at the axon terminal triggers release
of a chemical substance, a neurotransmitter (e.g., dopamine). Neurotransmitters carry information to the postsynaptic neuron by binding to receptors at
the cell body or on the dendrites. The binding process triggers ion channels to
open in the cell membrane of the postsynaptic neuron, altering that neuron's
electrical membrane potential. Every neuron has a resting membrane potential based on differences in ion concentration inside and outside of the cell
membrane. The membrane potentials vary continuously with the electrical
activity of the synaptic receptors determined by occupation of receptors by
neurotransmitters, such as dopamine, carrying information from the previous
cell in the neuronal circuits. The electrical potential difference changes along

both sides of the cell membrane and is carried from the dendrites to the cell body and finally along the axon. When electrical excitation is sufficiently great, an action potential is generated at the base of the axon that produces a reversal of the membrane potential lasting a few milliseconds. Sufficient excitation occurs from the summation of excitations from thousands of neighboring neurons that synapse with the target neuron. The average discharge frequency of an action potential is 50Hz. Strong excitation can raise the frequency to 90 Hz or more while inhibition reverses the electric potential and reduces the discharge frequency to 30 Hz or less. The discharge frequency is the most important parameter from an information-processing standpoint. Ionic fluxes around the neurons form a field potential outside of them. An EEG electrode registers a negative field potential when excitation of an apical dendrite or inhibition of the cell body occurs. Apical dendrites branch back from the next neuron in the circuit to synapse with the axon. They lay closest to the surface of the cerebral cortex, and run perpendicular down to deeper layers of the cerebral cortex.

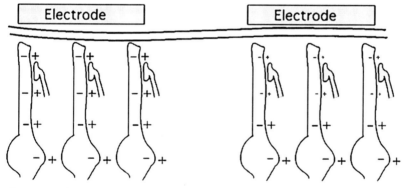

Figure 9. The drawing on the left depicts how neuronal axons synapse with apical neuronal dendrites at the surface of the cerebral cortex. There is no excitation at this moment and the extracellular electropositive charge is maximal. Axonal excitation (depolarization) is depicted on the right. The two EEG electrodes at the surface measure a potential difference, on the right the extracellular field potential around the active neuronal region is less electropositive than the inactive area depicted on the left. A short time later, the situation reverses.

The measured EEG activity is thus induced by a functional dipole: long vertical parallel target dendrites with numerous predominately excitable synapses
lie at the surface of the cerebral cortex, while the cell bodies that lie deeper
in the cerebral cortex form inhibitory synapses, albeit much fewer in number
than the excitatory ones. The EEG displays the typical wave pattern from
repetitive discharge of surface postsynaptic potentials.

4.2 EEG Frequency Spectrum and Attention

Each of the 19 electrodes measures the summed activity from about a million
neurons. The resultant waves have been classified in a purely descriptive
fashion according to their frequency band: delta for the slowest (1-4 Hz), then
theta (4-8 Hz), alpha (8-13 Hz), beta-1 (13-21 Hz), beta-2 (21-30 Hz) and
gamma (35-45 Hz). Initially, little was known about the functional significance of these waves, and they were often regarded as noise that was generated by the underlying brain activity. This frequency band classification arose
based on specific properties and consciousness states and, in recent years, its
validity has been supported through statistical calculations that estimate the
degree of variation of the underlying information (e.g., PCA, "principal component analysis;" ICA, "independent component analysis").

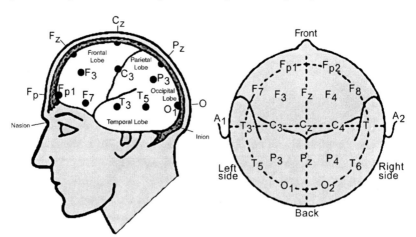

*Figure 10. The 19 measuring points employed by the classical "10-20" EEG
measuring system (Frontal, Central, Temporal, Parietal, and Occipital locations). Image created by WinEEG, Mitsar Co. Ltd.*

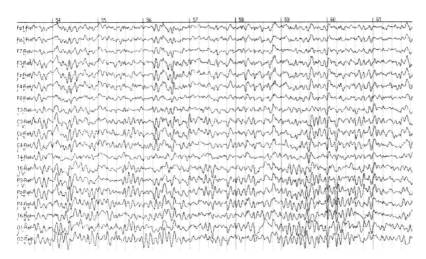

Figure 11. EEG readings from 19 measuring points on the scalp (each labeled on the left with a letter and number). Normally, as here, alpha rhythm is expressed maximally in the posterior brain areas (lowest two curves) mixed with faster (beta) and slower (theta) waves. This fragment lasts 9 seconds, indicated by the time scale along the top line. Image created by WinEEG, Mitsar Co. Ltd.

Quantitative electroencephalography, or QEEG, (and the graphical representation of the QEEG as a 'brain mapping,' which looks somewhat like a colored weather map) has remained in use since its introduction around 1985. The most frequent use of QEEG, even in the present day, remains restricted to the calculation of frequency spectra, which are then compared with averaged values from a database to calculate the coherency. A particular asset of QEEG is the capacity to calculate the strength of each frequency band between two measurement points, thus elucidating the degree to which each EEG wave type demonstrates more or less fixed phase relationships in comparison with each other. The phase relationship indicates differences in timing between wave patterns at two measurement points. Naked eye inspection of the EEG cannot reveal this information. Moreover, the processed values are only interpretable in comparison to values from a normative data bank.

The first chapter of this book, "Attention, Self-Regulation, and State Regulation" discussed how sleep deprivation in a normal person could produce characteristics akin to ADHD, including insufficient attention, poor organization and planning, more reflexive reactions to random environmental stimuli, and irritability. In 1952, the French psychiatrist Ey used sleep deprivation-related behavioral changes to build a model of state disintegration for many different psychiatric disorders. This inspired Bente (1964) to use changes in the EEG after sleep deprivation as a model for the neuropsychological correlations of consciousness disintegration (i.e., less organization [integration] of con-sciousness).

In a healthy sleep-deprived person, global theta and beta-2 waves increase and alpha and beta-1 waves decrease (Brunner, Dijk, & Borbély, 1993). These changes, visible to the naked eye, are most clearly measured along the middle of the head; the same location used to monitor different sleep stages in EEG research. As far back as the 1960s, Bente (1964) described three types of labile EEG dynamics after sleep deprivation: 1) decreased beta-2 (20-30 Hz) activity; 2) excess theta activity, with a reduction in alpha and beta-1 (13-21 Hz) activity; 3) discontinuous alpha activity interspersed with heightened theta and beta-2 activity. These 3 patterns compare remarkably well with dif-ferent EEG-types observed in people with ADHD without prior sleep depri-vation.

Quantitative analysis of the EEG (QEEG), in which the frequency spectrum of the EEG is calculated, allows for precise measurement and comparison of these changes with the spread of normal values across the life span.

In addition, it has been found that in an EEG taken the night following sleep deprivation, increased slow waves occur along with a reduced quantity of the 12-15 Hz waves that typically occur in series during sleep (sleep spindles) and are maximally measurable at the central point of the scalp (Cz) (Brunner, Dijk, & Borbély, 1993).

Sleep spindles are normally weak during sleep stage *transitions* (I, II, III, IV, and REM sleep) and are consequently thought to play a role in sleep state *stabilization*, somewhat akin to shock absorbers (Evans, 1993). Such a func-tion corresponds with Pavlov's concept of 'internal inhibition' (a process in which a conditioned reflex is extinguished through negative reinforcement). Sleep spindles are less numerous during the sleep of people with epilepsy and people with ADHD (Kahn, 1978).

The American researcher Barry Sterman, a founder of neurofeedback since his early research with cats in the late 1960s, demonstrated that a 12-15 Hz (or more broadly 12-20 Hz) daytime rhythm plays a similar role in stabilization of daytime vigilance levels. He called this the "sensorimotor rhythm" because it reached maximal levels over the sensorimotor cortex. Its anatomical origin was found to be primarily in the somatosensory cortex (where the sense of touch is processed) and in the VPL nucleus (ventral posterolateral nucleus) of the thalamus. Sterman argued that the somatosensory cortex is involved in the inhibition of movements alongside the motor cortex so that from a functional point of view the sensorimotor rhythm is aptly named. However, the broader EEG community did not employ this term; instead, it labeled these rhythms as 'central cortical beta rhythms.' Inhibition of movement is a necessary but not the only condition for the creation of this rhythm. If inhibition of movement were the only condition, it would be very simple to alleviate hyperactivity and its attendant low quantity of SMR rhythm through traditional behavioral training. A number of researchers, including Sterman and Lubar, demonstrated a link with attention such that focused attention increases the SMR rhythm. Canu and Rougeul (1982, 1992) showed that the beta rhythm in the somatosensory cortex and the thalamic VPL nucleus plays a role in focused attention in cats. On the other hand, they found that sleep spindles, measured over the whole surface of the scalp during sleep, originate essentially in the motor cortex and the thalamic reticular nucleus. More recently, a further differentiation of sleep spindles has been described based on localization and rhythm: a slow centroparietal rhythm peaking at about 14 Hz and a slower rhythm (peeking around 12 Hz) measurable in frontal areas. The frontal rhythm usually disappears in adulthood.

The motor cortex, the originator of some sleep spindles, is anterior to the somatosensory cortex with a large groove separating the two areas. The origin of thalamic sleep spindles is found to be in the thalamic nucleus and VLA (ventrolateral nucleus) in the brain stem. The reticular nucleus of the thalamus plays an important role in the mechanisms of selective attention. Although the origins of SMR rhythms lie primarily in different regions of the cerebral cortex and the thalamus, there is some slight overlap with other regions, and there are many indications that these areas functionally relate to or mutually influence each other. There are also hints that sleep spindles and selective attention employ the same neural networks.

Over long time scales, a certain minimum quantity of sleep spindles (and of the corresponding 12-20 Hz rhythm in the waking state) maintains the stability of the vigilance level, while over shorter time scales the 12-20 Hz SMR rhythm plays a role in focused attention. If after sleep deprivation a person without ADHD takes an attention test in which he or she must push a key after every stimulus except after one specific stimulus, then the fastest, most accurate responses occur at moments of minimal theta and maximum alpha and beta activity in the EEG (Townsend, 1979). The slowest reactions or omission errors occur moments after a change in the EEG pattern or after a short period in which the characteristic features of sleep deprivation in the global EEG pattern are exaggerated.

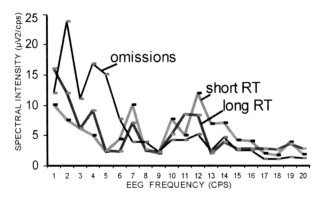

Figure 12. EEG frequency spectrum (C3 -right ear) over 1 second period corresponding to a reaction in a continuous performance test by a normal adult following sleep deprivation. Reprinted from Electroencephalography and Clinical Neurophysiology, 47(3), Townsend & Johnson, Relation of frequency-analyzed EEG to monitoring behavior, Copyright (1979), with permission from Elsevier.

In children with ADHD, their daytime EEG pattern often shows the same characteristics as found in normal people after sleep deprivation: increased theta, less beta-1, decreased alpha, and more beta-2. On top of this general pattern, attention is weaker in children with ADHD at moments during which these characteristics are more pronounced (Achim, 2004). Townsend (1979) described a similar phenomenon in normal adults after sleep deprivation.

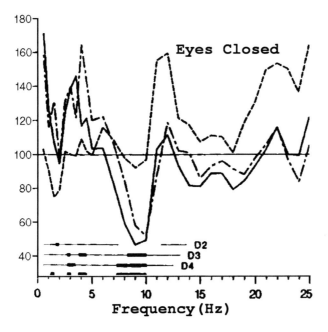

Figure 13. Percentage of EEG frequency spectrum values (C3-right ear) following partial sleep deprivation on day 2 (D2), 3 (D3), and 4 (D4) in comparison with day 1 in normal adults. A dotted line represents D2, alternating dots and dashes D3, and an unbroken line D4. The central horizontal midline marks 100 % (that is, day one values). The black bands in the left bottom corner emphasize the area of the EEG frequency that shows significant changes from day one. Reprinted from Sleep, 16, Brunner, Dijk, & Borbély, Repeated partial sleep deprivation progressively changes the EEG during sleep and wakefulness, Copyright (1993), with permission from American Academy of Sleep Medicine.

This phenomenon brings to mind an anecdote that the mathematician Mandelbrot (1982) told about the development of fractal theory. One day he received a call from a company that suffered interference on the lines connecting their computers and needed his help. Human error or technical fault did not seem to cause the interference. Mandelbrot noticed that certain storage 'densities' occurred in groups over a period of a day. That was nothing special, but as the duration shortened to half a day, this interference-grouping pattern *stayed the same*, whether the period was a few hours or less. The percentage of disturbance in different episodes was identical: a self-repeating pattern was accumulating. Every time scale repeated the same figures (groups, fractals). In other words, the pattern of phone interference continuously repeated itself across different time scales.

The EEG pattern in people with sleep deprivation is similar to that; therefore, in people with ADHD, measurements in the middle of the head (Cz) frequently show an increase in theta waves and a decrease in beta-1 waves, as well as a variant form that expresses low voltage EEG with predominately beta-2 activity. The American researcher Monastra (1999, 2001) used the central theta/beta-1 ratio as a measure of distraction; this ratio is greater in 94% of people with ADHD compared to barely 2% of control subjects. The average distractibility index is higher in ADHD than even in ADD (attention deficit disorder) and is frequently accompanied by increased frontal coherence of alpha and/or theta waves.

$$V = P([Theta]) / P([Beta1])$$

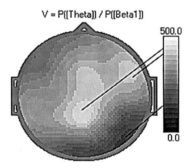

Figure 14. This example illustrates an increased theta/beta-1 ratio in central scalp regions: 21.9/5.2 (normal ratio <3.31 for a comparable age range).

In recent years, consecutive studies from Clarke's Australian research group (2001) confirmed Monastra's results, supporting an increased theta/beta-1 ratio in central and frequently frontal areas in ADHD children with and without hyperactivity. In the group with hyperactivity, this anomaly is more marked than in the group without hyperactivity. Clarke also showed that, on average, the hyperactive subgroup evidenced this increased activity maximally at the frontal midline while the subgroup without hyperactivity expressed maximal activity in the centroparietal area along the midline. As the children matured, the ratio also became more similar in both subgroups. Both Lubar and Kropotov found that in 6 year old children or younger, the maximal deviation is found along the parietal or centroparietal midline, at 7-8 years this occurs maximally along the central midline, and by 15 years, this pattern maximizes along the frontocentral midline.

Clarke observed that in a group of 298 ADHD children aged 8 to 12 years, 15% showed increased beta activity (12.5-25 Hz) over the whole scalp that was maximal in frontal areas and a diminished theta/beta-1 ratio (rather than increased). Principally, this was predominately measured in boys with the hyperactive form of ADHD. Typically, more tantrums and moodiness were described in this group. Initially, Clarke considered that the excess beta activity was a marker for hyperarousal. However, he later showed that Ritalin has an equally good therapeutic effect in the heightened beta subgroup as in the theta group (Clarke, 2003). Consequently, he no longer thought that this increased beta activity could be considered a sign of hyperarousal. Clarke went on to propose that this likely represents a problem with frontal behavioral regulation, independent of arousal strength, because children with this

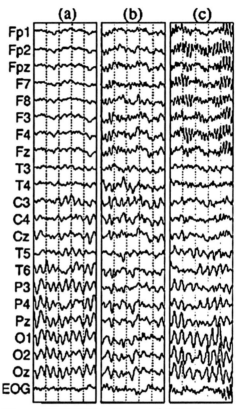

Figure 15. QEEG subtypes of ADHD as expressed by increased frontal beta activity (12.5-25 Hz): a) normal; b) increased frontal beta activity; c) frontal beta spindles. Reprinted from Psychiatry Research, 103(2-3), Clarke, Barry, McCarthy, & Selikowitz, Excess beta activity in children with attention-deficit/hyperactivity disorder: an atypical electrophysiological group, Copyright (2001), with permission from Elsevier.

subtype display mostly hyperactive and impulsive behavior. This subtype frequently shows greater frontal alpha coherence.

Increased beta-2 activity is also seen in people without ADHD after sleep deprivation. In adults with ADHD, 10% show increased beta activity, reaching a maximum frontally at the center (i.e., Fz) of the scalp (Gurnee, 2000). EEG source localization frequently indicates that this beta activity originates in the anterior cingulate. This increased beta-2 activity subgroup often shows additional difficulties: sleep disorders, anxiety disorders, alcoholism, bipolar disorder (manic-depressive disorder), irritability, impatience, compulsion disorders, and a hyperactive stream of thought.

In agreement with Monastra and Clarke's research, Thompson & Thompson (2005) described a group of 154 adults with ADHD of whom 80% showed increased theta/beta-1 ratio measurable at the Cz position. In 40% of the 80% (thus 32% of the complete group), he also observed an increased 26-34 Hz/13-15 Hz ratio at Cz, and this often appeared to correlate with an overactive thought stream.

In another subgroup of adults with ADHD, and sometimes in children with ADHD, an excess of slow alpha activity is found, especially in the frontal areas (often on the right more than the left). The most likely explanation for this phenomenon is that theta waves evolve into slow alpha waves by a small frequency increase (Gurnee, 2000) often accompanied by reduced frontal delta activity (Chabot, 1996). This is a striking discovery because in neurology, delta activity is normally associated with pathology. Repeated QEEG studies of normal adults have shown that delta activity uses 20% to 30% of total energy in frontal and central areas. In typical adults, this delta activity is associated with higher mental functions and covaries with P300 amplitude (Basar, 1984; Intriligator, 1994). Delta activity in typical adults increases during calculation, reaction time tasks, and abstract thinking. A functional role of delta waves reflects an 'internal concentration' in which external cortical inputs are inhibited in order to maintain maximum available attention during tasks in which internal representations are concerned (Fernandez, 1995). A lowered frontal delta quantity can correlate with decreased frontal regulation or blockage of inadequate behavioral impulses or external stimuli. Research exists to suggest a significant functional relationship between the delta rhythm and the mesotelencephalic dopamine projection system that also plays a role in ADHD. Studies with dipole models (Michel, 1992, 1993) and correlations of PET research with EEG (Alper, 1994, 1998) have estimated the location of the main delta generator site to be on the midline of the anterior part of the frontal cortex, which corresponds to the location of the most important terminal field of the mesotelencephalic dopamine projection system. Delta electrical activity of individual neurons has been directly measured in the nucleus accumbens (Leung, 1993), frontal cortex (Steriade, 1993), and the ventral tegmental area in the brain stem (Grace, 1995). Negative shifts of the slow frontal (DC, direct current) potentials occur in humans in situations of expectation; the analogous states in animals are associated with heightened VTA activity (Caspers, 1993; Haschke, 1993; Kivatkin, 1995). This corresponds to the well-known finding of a diminished contingent negative variation (CNV) in ADHD, which an appropriate treatment can normalize. Moreover, behaviors related to dopamine increase selectively through stimulation of dopamine cell axons at 2-3 Hz (Grace, 1995), which is consistent with the resonance of delta frequency bands in the mesotelencephalic dopamine projection system.

Gurnee (2000) noted that in the subgroup of adults with ADHD with excess frontal alpha activity, as well as in the subgroup of adults with ADHD without EEG abnormalities, at least half of cases showed an abnormal rise in theta and alpha activity during an attention task. Lubar (1999) described the same phenomenon. Further, this is in agreement with Amen (1998), who conducted research using functional neuroimaging, expressly SPECT (single proton emission computerized tomography), and found that many people with ADHD have less frontal activity during mental effort that requires attention. In the hyperactive form of ADHD, frontal activity decreased on both the outside (dorsolateral) and the underside (orbitofrontal) of the cerebral cortex, while in the variant without hyperactivity, there was only a diminution in dorsolateral frontal activity.

Whenever participants from these subgroups are instructed to intensify mental effort in a task that does not interest them, paradoxically, the quality of their attention decreases further. This means that attention in children with ADHD might even exhibit poorer performance when they are asked to pay more attention.

Chabot (1996) distinguished two types of EEG profiles in children with ADHD: 1) 46% show an increase of theta and/of alpha activity, maximal in frontal and/or central regions, associated with a normal peak alpha frequency and a decreased quantity of frontal delta waves. This pattern has also been observed in cocaine users and subjects with depression. Increased alpha activity in ADHD, in Chabot's view, is predictive of a favorable response to treatment with Zyban™ (bupropion) and, according to Suffin (1995), to antidepressives. Increased theta activity seems to respond better to Ritalin. 2) 30% demonstrate an increase in alpha and /or theta together with a slower alpha peak frequency.

In both EEG profiles, there is also an increased coherence of alpha and theta waves, especially between left and right frontal areas. According to Suffin, increased alpha or theta activity that is paired with increased coherency responds best to treatment with anti-epileptics.

In 2000, the official guidelines of the American Academy of Pediatrics argued that the diagnosis of ADHD can be made only on the basis of behavioral observations and behavioral rating scales (i.e., symptom check lists) for ADHD. In 2004, the American Academy of Pediatrics came to a different view in the monograph, "ADHD: A Complete and Authoritative Guide." They argued that brain scans, such as quantitative electroencephalography (QEEG) will provide more distinctive classification of the neurological and behavioral features of ADHD, which may help further the knowledge base and treatment of ADHD. This re-evaluation was reached based on 13 studies published after 1997 covering 2,642 children with ADHD and conducted by five independent research groups. It is remarkable that this objective diagnostic assessment (QEEG) receives so little use in daily clinical practice.

In earlier sections, we have briefly discussed how sleep deprivation leads to behavioral changes similar to those that occur in ADHD, and that this can be described as a lessening of activity in the anterior cingulate, the orbitofrontal cortex, and the dorsolateral prefrontal cortex (DLPFC). Functional imaging studies (PET) of the brain during an attentional task following a night of sleep deprivation further confirm decreased activity in these areas as well as the thalamus, caudate nucleus, and the posterior association cortex (Thomas, 2000). Evidently, these areas are most sensitive to sleep deprivation and have a greater need of restoration processes during sleep.

We shall examine how lowered activity in the DLPFC, the nucleus caudate, and the orbitofrontal cortex leads to fewer sleep spindles in the sleep EEG and lesser quantity of beta-1 waves in the waking state.

The majority of EEG waves measurable at the scalp are generated in the neuronal circuits between the cerebral cortex and the thalamus. Deep in the brain, lying at the top of the brain stem, the thalamus is the central 'relay station,' through which most sensory information passes before it is diverted toward posterior areas of the cerebral cortex (where sensory perception is processed). The continuous cyclic flow of information between the thalamus and the cerebral cortex establishes the awareness of sensory information. We know that the wave properties of the thalamocortical circuits are important for normal functioning of the cerebral cortex. Theta waves in the EEG indicate slower rhythms. Abnormal amounts of theta are seen in multiple psychological and neurological disease states. States with excess theta waves are often coupled with 'burst' discharges in the thalamus, resulting in excessive inhibition. Burst discharges are action potential firings that constitute a complex periodic eruption of activity in thalamocortical neurons (these neurons originate in the thalamus with dendrites connecting to the cerebral cortex). Normally, they occur only during sleep, as neurons in waking states normally fire in tonic bursts (continuous discharges of action potentials with a sustained voltage). Source localization methods can uncover the brain areas responsible for the dysfunction in theta activity. These dysfunctional regions are responsible for the inhibition of thalamic areas whereby the thalamic neurons show a slower rhythm in thalamocortical circuits.

In 1999, Llinas and Jeanmond defined a number of disorders as thalamocortical dysrhythms that included movement disorders (Parkinson's disease, for example), depression, neurological pain, tinnitus (the perception of phantom sound), and epilepsy. In these cases, increased coherence between theta, alpha, and beta rhythms is frequently observed: the simultaneous deployment of these various wave types point to increased cooperation but at the same time to decreased differentiation between different neural operations. In ADHD, the increased theta activity is often maximally measurable in the middle of the head and source localization frequently identifies the source of this theta activity in the cingulate (Lubar, personal communication; Lubar, 1997). This suggests a disturbance in the circuit linking the thalamus and cingulate. Moreover, increased coherence between theta activities in the two cerebral hemispheres is often observed in ADHD, which is probably an indication of poor differentiation between the functions of these brain areas.

On the other hand, there is another important circuit that connects the prefrontal cerebral cortex to the caudate nucleus, and hence to the middle dorsal area of the thalamus and on to the prefrontal cortex. We know that a substantial portion of people with ADHD show lessened activity in a region of the caudate nucleus. This could contribute to a specific thalamocortical dysrhythm that causes increased theta activity in the prefrontal cortex. Ritalin increases the amount of dopamine between the synapses of local neurons in the caudate nucleus and in neurons linking the caudate to the thalamus. Thus, Ritalin can temporarily correct weak activity in the caudate nucleus, effectively repair the thalamocortical dysrhythm, and normalize theta activity.

In this way, the neurotransmitter dopamine can normalize thalamocortical bursts discharges in ADHD, also decreasing theta activity. Neurotransmitters can act as 'neuromodulators,' able to modify synaptic excitability by adjusting membrane receptivity at the cell terminals through which ions pass into the neuron. The neurotransmitters acetylcholine and noradrenaline both close the slow potassium channels in thalamic relay neurons and the thalamic reticular nucleus, causing cell membrane potentials to increase and burst discharges to disappear in favor of tonic activity which improves information transmission by electrical conductivity. A clinical application is in the treatment of Alzheimer's disease symptoms, where medication is used to block acetylcholine degradation, increasing the availability of this neurotransmitter. Experimental trials showed that such medications could increase attention in ADHD. The use of antidepressants with a noradrenergic effect is known to have a therapeutic effect in ADHD. Strattera™ also has a noradrenergic effect, as well as a localized effect on prefrontal dopamine.

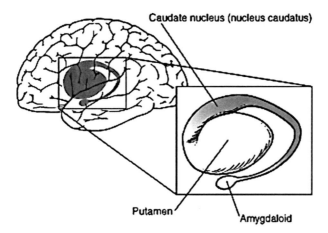

Figure 16. The caudate nucleus ('tail nucleus') is a grey nucleus that together with the putamen forms part of the basal ganglia (grey nuclei deep in the brain). The putamen and caudate nucleus together form the striatum. Certain areas of the caudate nucleus play a part in higher cognitive functions such as attention regulation. In ADHD, dopamine reuptake receptors in the caudate nucleus are overrepresented because of insufficient dopamine available over time at the synapse to modulate the transmission of electrical stimulus information to the next neuron in the circuit.

Summary

The *electroencephalogram* (EEG) consists of different frequency brain waves (in order of increasing frequency: delta, theta, alpha, beta, and gamma). The quantitative EEG (QEEG) demonstrates distinctive patterns in 94% of people with ADHD, making it both a useful objective diagnostic support tool and a means to further insight. Insufficient beta-1 waves (plays a role in guiding attention) and excessive slow theta waves (normally only present in elevated levels during sleep) characterize the most common pattern. During sleep, there are less stabilizing sleep spindles (rhythmic series of 12-15 Hz waves). Last, the excess of theta waves originates in the cingulate or in the thalamus (possibly because of nucleus caudate dysfunction).

4.3 The Stabilizing Role of Sleep Spindles and SMR

We have already discussed the role of sleep spindles and the sensorimotor rhythm in differentiated flexibility during the waking state. The consistency of this rhythm indicates the stability of both sleep and wakefulness phases and these states determine the flexible stability of the individual's power to adapt to changing circumstances. In people with ADHD who have insufficient sleep spindles and lessened beta-1 rhythms, their consequently disrupted system is manifested in broken sleep and a deficit in flexible attention and behavioral modulation. A phase transition in wakefulness level occurs whenever the density of the rhythm decreases periodically around the onset and completion of each sleep cycle (about 90 minutes). This also happens during sleep state transition periods within each sleep cycle. This sequence of cause and effect is circular: the diminishing cyclic action of the rhythm near a phase change is the result of the interaction of different system components within defined waking or sleep states while the cyclic action in turn influences the composition of component systems. Briefly, the cyclic variability of the sleep or wake cycles determines the variability of the cycle at any particular moment. The sleep-wake cycles, the sleep cycles, and the vigilance cycles are necessary to provide adequate behavioral flexibility during wakefulness by enabling fluctuations at smaller time scale. The need for a sleep wake cycle arises because a living being must maintain integrity against the forces of its environment and never achieve a stable balance, as evidenced by the work of Belgian Nobel Prize winner Ilya Prigogine (1984). On the contrary, permanent imbalance is a necessary condition for a living system that must maintain itself while adapting to internal and external disturbances and environmental changes.

To understand the concept of circular causality, think of toy boats on a pond. Each boat generates its own wave. Individual waves combine to form a big wave to which all the boats are subject. We can therefore argue that although weakening of the sleep spindles (or the beta-1 rhythm) arises from interaction between the subsystems, self-organization reconfigures the component systems (see figure 59).

A small-scale study (Khan, 1978) demonstrated a lesser quantity of sleep spindles in people with ADHD (12-15Hz) and their normalization after the administration of Ritalin. Additionally, a more recent larger-scale study

(Miano, 2006) showed fewer alternating sleep stabilization cycles in ADHD. These discoveries provide an explanation for the ample evidence linking broken sleep to ADHD as well as an increased movement (hyperactivity) that it is probably linked to less stable sleep accompanied by more sleep phase transitions. Other research links broken sleep with fewer sleep spindles. Lastly, it has been demonstrated that a much greater variability in sleep duration and waking and falling asleep time occurs in people with ADHD over the course of a week (Gruber, 2000).

Developmental psychology emphasizes the role of stability and instability in the development of neurological behavioral systems (Thelen, 1993). Generally speaking, a high level of variability points to an unstable system. Normally, a reliable stability develops in which the organization of a stable sleep wake cycle reflects the maturation of the nervous system and the development of systems of inhibition and feedback control (Halpen, 1995; Parmalee, 1972). A greater variability in this system can affect other systems. The prefrontal cerebral cortex, which acts as an interface between the sleep/wake system, the emotion system, the higher cognitive functions, and behavioral system, appears to modulate the relationship between higher cognitive functions and the regulation of sleep and emotions (Dahl, 1996). The influence of unstable sleep patterns on daily functioning can be compared to that of sleep deprivation.

Various research studies have shown that broken sleep is associated with the weakening of many mental functions including selective and sustained attention (Sadeh, 2003; Van Dongen, 2003), memory consolidation (Naylor, 2000; Macquet, 2003), executive control (Fluck, 1998), consolidation of motor skills (Fischer, 2002), and P300 amplitude (Kingshott, 2000).

Additionally, studies have shown that fewer sleep spindles correlate with decreased reaction time. It has been known for a long time, as previously noted, that sleep spindles play a role as stabilizers of ongoing sleep states during sleep. A gating mechanism allows this by diminishing or blocking sensorimotor information via the inactivation of thalamocortical circuits. As a result, the information interferes less with the processing of endogenous neural information during sleep. In the daytime, decreased capacity in this system can lead to failure of the thalomocortical circuit (required for the automatic sensorimotor processing requisite for sensory attention). This supports the hypothesis that selective attention and sleep spindles use the same neural network. In this regard, sleep spindles can reflect a sleep specific process that focuses on the maintenance or repair of some aspects of sensorimotor performance. A diminished quantity of sleep spindles can thus reflect a disturbance in the capacity of the thalamocortical circuit to contribute to the filtering of incoming sensory information.

Sterman showed that sleep spindles, as well as the beta-1 rhythm in waking states, can be seen as a mark of 'internal inhibition' as Pavlov described. Pavlov argued that conditioned reflexes fade if no reward or punishment follows the expression of the conditioned reflex after stimulus onset. A generalized internal inhibition leads, according to Pavlov, to the transition from sleep to waking states. Based on his experiments with dogs, Pavlov proposed individual differences in the tendency to internal inhibition, which are linked to differences in individual temperament. Sterman noted that after establishing a state of internal inhibition in cats using the conditioning methods described by Pavlov, a rhythm of 12-15 Hz (or more broadly 12-20 Hz) was measurable in the sensorimotor cortex, which he named the SMR rhythm (sensorimotor rhythm). He also observed that the rhythm arose in the cats' ventrobasal complex in the thalamus, which relays sensorimotor information to the cerebral cortex. Rougeul-Buser and Bouyer confirmed these findings in 1983.

Inhibition of cortically induced movement and an increase in attentive focused awareness accompany the appearance of the SMR rhythm. Activity in multiple brain areas contribute to this rhythm: sensory information about spatial movements of the limbs from the ventrobasal thalamus, information from the orbitofrontal cerebral cortex, the cerebellum, the orbitofrontal cortex, and information from front and central positions at the head of the caudate nucleus. Electrostimulation at points in these latter areas triggers slow waves in the EEG in the sensorimotor cortex. Since the nucleus caudate is underactive in ADHD, this may partly explain diminishing SMR rhythm and increased theta activity measurable at the midline of the skull in people with ADHD. Other research has shown that electrostimulation of the basal ganglia or the non-specific thalamus (thalamic reticular nucleus) in a cat generates an SMR rhythm that leads to motoric inhibition.

The orbitofrontal cortex modulates the areas of the thalamus that play a role in consciousness (reticular nuclei), which in turn modulates the sleep spindles that originate in the ventrolateral nucleus of the thalamus. It is likely that the nucleus caudate also participates in this process.

The generators of the SMR rhythm and the sleep spindles are located in the thalamus. Although their thalamocortical projections and the associated behavioral states differ slightly, it seems the functional origin of both is a mechanism specifically involved in suppression of movement (phasic motor activity) and in sensitivity to stimuli. The neural mechanisms responsible for the establishment of these rhythms over the somatosensory thalamocortical projections are essentially identical. This would explain why behavioral modification (in the form of neurofeedback) that increases the SMR rhythm also increases quantity of sleep spindles.

The reticular nucleus is a thin layer around the thalamus and has an inhibitory effect on sensory information passing from specific thalamic areas to the posterior cerebral cortex for perceptual processing. The reticular nucleus has a major modulatory influence on the generation of both sleep spindles and the sensorimotor rhythm, although, regarding the sensorimotor rhythm of the cat, investigation with deep electrodes could not confirm this effect (Canu, 1992). The prefrontal cerebral cortex and the caudate nucleus modulate the reticular nucleus such that higher behavioral strategies (executive functions), including goal directed attention, modulate the passing of selective information to the cerebral cortex. Thus, the 'executive functions,' including behavioral strategies and goal focused attention, can select which information is likely to reach the stimulus bound posterior cerebral cortex. Scheibel (1984) later extended this model to include Sterman's suggestion that the sensorimotor information which arrives in the cortex itself can also inhibit the reticular nucleus by a feedback loop.

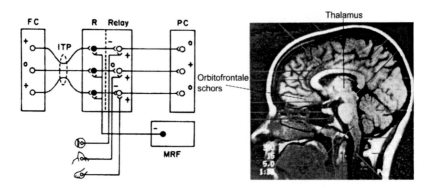

Figure 17. Skinner and Yingling's (1977) thalamic gating model of sensory cerebral cortex activity. Gates in the thalamic relay areas that allow the flow of sensory information to the posterior cerebral cortex (PC) are closed (inhibited) by the reticular nucleus (R). The orbitofrontal cortex (FC) stimulates the inhibiting neurons in the reticular nucleus (R) of the thalamus via the inferior thalamic peduncle (ITP). These inhibiting neurons are themselves inhibited by neurons arising from the brain stem (MRF: mesenecephalic reticular formation). In addition to the orbitofrontal cerebral cortex, the cerebellum and the caudate nucleus can also stimulate this system.

Sterman (1979) also examined the wakefulness cycle (basic rest-activity cycle, BRAC) and sleep spindles during the first few weeks after birth. Based on this research, he came to some conclusions on the fundamental role of sleep and the alternation of dream sleep and non-dream sleep in the "biological economy."

Sterman showed that the BRAC cycle lasts 60 minutes in one month old infants (compared with 90 minutes later in life). The rest phases are associated with increased EEG slow-wave activity (delta waves between 0-3 Hz) and decreased quantity of movements, heart and breathing rhythms. Such periodicity can be discerned as early as 24 weeks gestation in the movement of the fetus. These cycles originate in the pons in the brain stem.

From just 10 weeks after birth, the sleep-wake cycle gradually superimposes over the rest of the activity cycle, and the sleep-wake cycle's progressive development, together with that of the sleep spindles, is associated with a periodicity that coincides with the slow EEG waves. At 19 weeks old, the periodicity of the sleep spindles is still 60 minutes while the periodicity of the delta waves reaches 120 minutes. The development of these slower cycles appears to reflect a more mature sleep-wake cycle. The BRAC cycle length extends to 90 minutes by the age of 24 months.

During sleep, five to six 90-minute cycles occur, each consisting of a sequence of four stages of NREM sleep and an REM stage (rapid eye movement sleep). These NREM-REM 90-minute cycles coincide with a cyclic weakening in the density of sleep spindles and no longer primarily with cyclically changing quantity of slow waves in the EEG.

Sleep spindles originate in the thalamus (in the mid brain) and continue to develop until full maturity. This leads to ripened awareness accompanied by the alertness necessary for adapting to the environment beyond reflexive brain stem mechanisms such as breathing, sucking, and swallowing. The orbitofrontal cortex, the cerebellum, and the caudate nucleus modulate sleep spindles later in development, allowing for more differentiated behavior adaptations.

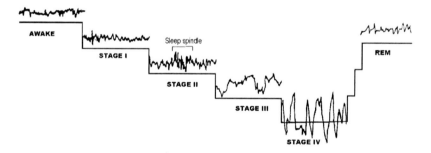

Figure 18. Course of a NREM-REM 90 minute sleep cycle preceded by a waking state: The 4 REM stages and the NREM stage. A representative sleep fragment from each stage is illustrated.

It is stimulating to note that the increase in the quantity of sleep spindles in the first 6 months of life is associated with a decrease in quantity of movement and variability of the heart and breathing rhythm. Possibly, if the frontothalamic system that modulates sleep spindles is insufficiently developed, the flexible state regulation described in the first chapter will also be insufficiently developed; thereby, weakening the internal control mechanism's ability to adapt, leaving a deficient and somewhat more primitive, reactive external regulatory system.

These EEG findings can also be linked to the development of neuronal organization. The apical dendrites of the cortical pyramid cells are first to mature. They provide the medium for receptive interaction between the cortical cells and the synchronous activity of diffuse delta waves in the EEG. This early delta activity can be seen as the beginning of intracortical communication that precedes other connections in this early developmental state. In time, this leads to maturation of dendritic projections that receive efferent sensory information and are involved in the patterns of thalamocortical interactions that create the 12-15 Hz sleep spindles and, somewhat later, the alpha and theta rhythms.

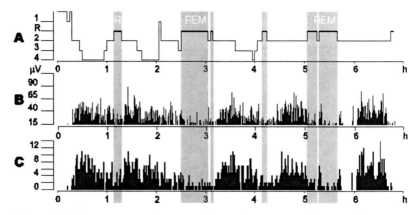

Figure 19. The uppermost diagram (A) is a hypnogram depicting the course of the NREM stages and the REM stage. An NREM-REM cycle lasts an average of 90 minutes. Deep sleep (III-IV) occurs early in the night and REM sleep dominates in the later part of the night. The middle diagram (B) illustrates the density of sleep spindles per minute. Bottom diagram (C) shows the amplitude of the sleep spindles. Note that during the REM stage, there are almost no sleep spindles; indeed the sleep spindles mark the beginning and the end of the NREM stage. During the NREM stage, the sleep spindles are strongest in stage I-II and weakest in III-1V (deep sleep with slow waves). The vertical grey lines indicate the REM states, showing the least sleep spindles.

There are indications that the 90-minute cycle occurs not just in sleep but also during wakefulness throughout the day. The quality of performance of many tasks, measurable during task performance by physiological measures (such as the EEG), varies with a cycle of about 90 minutes. Kleitman (1963) who was first to describe REM in sleep in 1953, advanced the basic rest-activity cycle (BRAC) hypothesis that the rhythmic action of REM sleep is just a fragment of broader biological rhythms that are continually expressed during sleep as in the waking state. REM sleep is associated with desynchronization of the EEG (as in the waking state). For that reason, REM is called paradoxical sleep, representing the active part of the cycle while NREM sleep is associated with synchronization of the EEG and represents the restful section of the cycle. Indeed, multiple researchers have demonstrated that these 90-minute cycles occur in the daytime. Superimposed on these are even slower rhythms that possibly may arise from interaction with the 90-minute cycles. Sleep spindles increase in density around the time of transition of one sleep phase into another, lasting about 90 minutes. Slower 90-minute cycles are expressed within daytime wakefulness cycle. Most people reach peak alertness about six hours after waking. Afterwards, wakefulness clearly declines in the early afternoon in adults, which is considered a remnant of the child's need for an afternoon nap. The next period of wakefulness occurs at around 5 p.m. for most people. Body temperature also reaches its maximum.

Kripke (1978) discovered that daydreams follow a 90-minute cycle, accompanied by continuous alpha waves and fewer rapid eye movements. Although this has been measured in people in a natural, social environment, it is more pronounced in sensorimotor isolation. Lavie (1982) suggested the hypothesis that alertness rhythms reflect the degree of difficulty experienced in falling asleep at different times in the course of the day. To test this hypothesis, nine adult participants were asked to close their eyes three times an hour and to try to sleep for five-minute periods of darkness over twelve daytime hours. Sleep and wakefulness were measured using EEG. Significant fluctuations within 90 minutes were measured in sleep stage 2. Theta waves increased and alpha waves decreased in the EEG during the sleep stage 2 episodes. This seems to correspond well with cyclical alpha waves and their correspondence to daydreaming observed in Kripke's study. In the latter case, alpha waves correlated negatively with wakefulness, that is, increased alpha waves related to decreased wakefulness, while in Lavie's research, the darkness condition reinforced the increase in theta waves. Lavie showed that the ability to fall asleep showed a periodic increase over a ninety-minute cycle. Moreover, the slower cycles that we have already mentioned modulate these cycles as well. Increased wakefulness occurs around 1:30 p.m., 3 p.m., and in the late afternoon (5:30 to 6:00), with an increased susceptibility to sleep stage 2 around midday (12:30 to 1:30) and afternoon (around 3:30 to 5:00). After a night of sleep deprivation, the 90-minute cycles disappear. This may possibly suggest that no clear daily cycle exists in people with ADHD, which would explain the dysfunctional behavioral regulation.

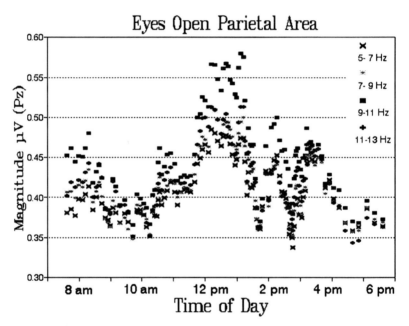

Figure 20. The valleys occur between 10:00 a.m. - 12:00 p.m. and 4:00 - 6:00 p.m. and the peak is just before 2:00 p.m. (lowest alertness). Less pronounced cycles of 90-120 minutes are visible (Kaiser & Sterman, 1994). Figure appears courtesy of David Kaiser.

Another study investigated fluctuations in EEG parietal activity in healthy volunteers through the course of a day. The study measured EEG activity for 2-3 minutes with eyes open (staring at a blank screen) at various times between 8:00 a.m. and 8:00 p.m. (Kaiser & Sterman, 1994). The absolute quantity of EEG activity from frequency bands lower than 15 Hz showed increasingly slower rhythms with a trough between 10:00 a.m. and 12:00 p.m. and again between 4:00 p.m. and 6:00 p.m., and a peak around 2:00 p.m. A visual inspection of figures published by Kaiser (not shown) shows a weaker cycle modulating every 90 to 120 minutes (Kaiser & Sterman, 1994).

Whenever the percentage of alpha and theta activity is examined over the course of a day for the same group of participants, a 90-120 minute alpha activity cycle (BRAC) is found. There is no clear daily cycle for slower waves.

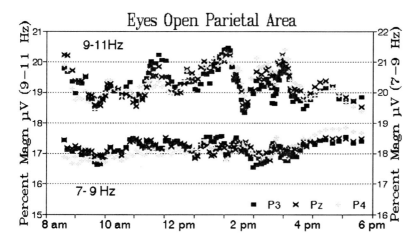

Figure 21. The percentage of alpha activity (9-11Hz) cycles every 90-120 minutes, but that is not the case for the percentage of theta activity (7-9Hz). Figure appears courtesy of David Kaiser (Kaiser & Sterman, 1994).

The Belgian sleep researcher Quadens (2003) has suggested that periodic attention is the daytime equivalent of REM sleep. Both play a role in learning new information. A prominent characteristic of attention is the orientation reaction, which directs the movement of the eyes to the source of information. The daytime EEG characteristics, including desynchronization (the action of low voltage beta activity), systematic eye movements, and the inhibition of motor activity, all show similarities with the physiology of REM sleep. Decreased EEG desynchronization, random eye movements, and overall less inhibition of motor activity are all observed in ADHD. Attention is to wakefulness as REM sleep is to sleep. As in sleep, periods of attention are interspersed with periods of rest in the daytime (BRAC, basic rest-activity cycle)

Sleep and wakefulness both contribute to optimal adaptation to the environment, especially the social environment. Attention employs the very same neural connections as REM sleep.

Sleep is now considered a prime example of the emergence of self-organization in neuronal circuits and systems, without the intervention of a supervisor or instructions (i.e., does not require a specific localized supervising system). Disturbances in sleep structure in psychiatric disorders, such as in ADHD, are often seen as consequences of daytime difficulties. However, contemporary insights strongly suggest the contrary, showing that changes in normal sleep structure can cause altered brain functioning during wakefulness. Deciphering the dynamics of self-organization in neuronal circuits involved with sleep structure may be the key to understanding the brain's response to environmental processes. EEG rhythms in sleep offer a striking example of 'reciprocal causality,' i.e., emergent rhythms at the macrosystem level in the EEG may be considered as 'order parameters' that force certain limits on the timing of neuronal action potentials (see also figure. 59) (Haken, 1986; Kelso, 1995).

Furthermore, evidence suggests that the relationship between sleep and wakefulness can be extended to the relationship between sensorimotor coordination and dynamic attention, giving greater insight into the functional relationships between sleep spindles and sensory motor beta rhythms (SMR: sensory motor rhythms in the EEG). Therefore, it seems no coincidence that the rhythms involved in the dynamics of attention also play a role in sensorimotor coordination. Sleep spindles and sensory motor rhythms both occur spontaneously without movements; they are self-generating. That does not mean that an absence of movement is sufficient for their generation. Nevertheless, movements can certainly disturb the central generating mechanism by introducing external triggers via sensory feedback to the brain.

In general, we can think of sleep as the uncoupling of the brain from the environment and, to a great extent, from the body. In infants, movement via sensory feedback triggers sensorimotor EEG rhythms. Over the course of development, from childhood to adulthood, sensorimotor coordination matures and the thalamocortical circuits come under control of subcortical modulating systems that can hinder triggering of these sensorimotor rhythms. Early development can be viewed as the process of the brain's 'awakening' from an overwhelming drowsiness. Adults still display sporadic sensorimotor rhythms triggered by the sensory feedback that follows movement but for the most part, causation is reversed since the absence of movement triggers these rhythms. Crucially, these rhythms arise constantly out of self-organization processes and play a part in the creation of a 'default state' in the brain responsible for adapting to changing circumstances. This is in agreement with Head (1923) and Bente's (1964) concept of vigilance being not merely an activation state but a modulated activation state, in which an inhibition mechanism operating from the frontal cortex plays a modulatory role.

Therefore, we can infer that sleep stabilizes the dynamics of sensory motor coordination and hence the 'situated' nature of the brain within the world and within environmental processes (Varela, 1991). Moreover, this leads to stabilization of waking states and to 'situated wakefulness' or vigilance. Adequate vigilance corresponds to adequate behavioral organization and implies interaction between exploratory motor output and the flow of sensory perception. Sleep shares many characteristics with autonomous early brain development in which EEG rhythms temporarily stabilize brain dynamics.

Quadens (2003) has shown that decreased amounts of sleep spindles are almost always associated with a lower quantity of rapid eye movements in REM sleep (rapid eye movement sleep) and that the sleep phase is associated with dreams and is indistinguishable in the EEG from attentive wakefulness (low voltage fast beta activity). In people with low intelligence, rapid eye movements are less, or sometimes more, regularly spaced. Learning capacity (necessary for the ability to adapt to environmental changes) seems to be related to sleep spindle patterns and patterns of eye movements in REM sleep. Both sleep spindles and rapid eye movements are endogenous neuronal activities and signalize redundancy of the thalamic network, which contributes to a fluent adaptation to environmental changes. Quadens' opinion is that, in terms of neuronal activity, sleep spindles play a part in temporal correlation between different parts of the brain responsible for information processing and represent a link between different parallel processing systems. Acquiring new information activates these links to mobilize different strategies and continue to modulate potential communications between different brain parts. The pattern of these brain signals is a code that forms the language of the brain. Such complex signal patterns can represent the meaning of a situation in reality that goes beyond pure pragmatic detection of anomalies that correlate with learning. This reality is "intelligence," probably innate but modulated by specific learning. After extensive research, Winson (1986) has suggested a plausible hypothesis that during REM sleep, also known as paradoxical sleep because of the similarities with attentive wakefulness, information stored during the daytime is processed so that it is "learnt" or 'integrated" at night. REM sleep, just like daytime wakefulness, is in the hippocampus associated with theta rhythms generated from the brain stem. These theta rhythms play a role in working memory and are determined by previous behavior. Winson's hypothesis is that the experiences stored daily are integrated 'off line' during REM sleep, thus contributing to the development of future behavioral strategies. In fact, the presence of the hippocampus, the limbic system, and the neocortex in mammals allows the development of more appropriate behavior (by playing a role in learning in new situations) in contrast with the more rigid instinctive behavior of reptiles whose brains contain only the cerebellum, brain stem, and basal ganglia.

In the thalamus, redundancy is linked to the parallel structure of its cell fibers and to the recruiting activity of some of its nuclei. If the thalamic system is functioning optimally, its redundancy but also its reliability decreases as a consequence of the system's reactivity to random environmental stimuli. The system will then, at least for some time, adjust and function with increased variety, which is the consequence of a decreased redundancy. The brain adapts to its environment strategically. This occurs in the context of a continuous control of incoming information and with the addition of information that circulates in parallel loops between the sensory fibers of the thalamus and the cerebral cortex. Interneurons, which form links between the parallel fiber systems, modulate this information. In their turn, these interneurons are connected via feedback loops to the eye movement system in the prefrontal cortex. In people with low intelligence, and possibly also in people with ADHD who also have a weaker adaptive capacity, the time structure of the brain wave patterns (sleep spindles, rapid eye movements during REM sleep) is altered such that the order normally arising from an increased level of complexity in the system is in fact weakened. Perhaps an analogy exists with the well-known fact that people with ADHD exhibit more 'random' eye movements during wakefulness, and this reflects a difficulty with focusing.

Redundancy of the sleep spindles and of the bursts of rapid eye movements in REM sleep advances stepwise during a child's psychomotor development, bringing higher planning levels into play. The dynamics of the brain activity during sleep is a way to integrate the information from the surroundings for evaluation, which is needed for normal social adjustment.

In addition, research has shown that EEG rhythms of 6-7 Hz to 20 Hz activate, in relevant neuronal circuits, the long-term potentiation (LTP) process responsible for learning processes via mechanisms of neural plasticity. These EEG rhythms initiate a fast influx of calcium ions into neurons, launching a chain reaction of biochemical processes inside cell nuclei at the genetic level and culminating in the manufacture of new postsynaptic receptors, thus strengthening neurotransmission. In sleep, these processes continue so that sleep strengthens the learning processes. It has been demonstrated that following procedural learning, the number of sleep spindles during sleep increases, enhancing the performance of a learned task the following day (Schabus, 2004).

Thalamocortical EEG rhythms therefore reflect the evolution of the human brain, as the brain becomes more and more alert throughout adulthood, reflecting more task-adaptive behavior. This can provide the foundations for higher learning, which in turn forms basis for further brain development.

Summary

The 12-20 Hz (or 12-15 Hz) EEG rhythms over the border areas between the sensory and motor cerebral cortex (thus the name SMR rhythm) and the sleep spindles (12-15 Hz series during sleep) play a stabilizing part in attention and in sleep levels. They originate in the thalamus (a central relay station deep in the brain) being modulated by the frontal cerebral cortex and the caudate nucleus (a tail shaped structure near the center of the brain). They have a functional relation with the dynamics of sensorimotor coordination that ensures, during early development, that behavior and wakefulness are 'situated' as they develop in the real world environment.

There are indications that EEG rhythms play a modulating role in the "basic rest activity cycle" that lasts ninety minutes and expresses itself not only in sleep, but also in wakefulness. Slower cycles are superimposed on them.

Lastly, both the sleep spindles and the sensorimotor rhythms play a role in leaning through the promotion of neural plasticity.

4.4 Gamma Rhythms (35-45 Hz) EEG Activity: Conscious-ness and "Focused Arousal"

Measuring 40 Hz ("gamma rhythms" from 35-40 Hz) EEG activity at the scalp is technically very difficult due to the difficulty in separating the many small low voltage waves of around (5-15 µV) arising from noise and from the electrical activity of the muscles that circle the scalp. Only in the last few years has it been possible to measure these rhythms without interference, with the development of technologically advanced techniques.

When electrodes are placed directly in the brain, the signal varies strongly from 20 µV in passive states up to 100 µV in focused attention (Rougeul, 1994). Signal strength at the scalp is only 5-15 µV because of volume con-duction by the skull and surrounding tissue. Several decades of published studies point to a role of these rhythms in focused attention. More specifi-cally, they could play a role in the conscious experience of perception. Llinas (1991) has demonstrated that the thalamocortical and the thalamic reticular nucleus can both, just like the cerebral cortex, generate 40 Hz rhythms, mak-ing it likely that an intrinsic network resonance exists at about 40 Hz. This is observed during wakefulness and during dreaming. This resonance begins in the brainstem, receiving sensory input during wakefulness and input from in-trinsic activity during dream sleep. The dream state can be considered a state of hyperattention in which sensory information is blocked from reaching the mechanism that generates conscious perception, that is, we cannot perceive the external world because the intrinsic activity of the nervous system does not locate the sensual information in the context of the functional state, which serves to generate awareness.

Both the specific and non-specific thalamus nuclei generate the 40 Hz rhythms. The 'specific' system provides the sensory information for cogni-tion; the 'non specific' system is responsible for the simultaneous "binding" of these different "specific" aspects, as is necessary for the unity of cognitive experience. Focusing attention on a specific perceived stimuli leads to an in-crease in 40 Hz activity. Desmedt and Tomberg (1994) performed an intriguing experiment that revealed the neurophysiological nature of consciousness. Recognizing that gamma activity is measurable in all of the thalamocortical and cortical areas and that it increases with increased wakefulness, they wanted to know if this rhythm plays a role in specific cognitive functions. A brief electrical stimulus was delivered to the fingers of both hands during the experiment. Whenever the stimulus was delivered to the right hand, subjects were asked to make a foot press insuring that attention was focused selectively on the right hand because that stimulus was allocated a special significance. Then, 130 ms after the stimulus appeared on the right side, increased gamma activity over a 125 ms period was observed in the left parietal and prefrontal areas. It was possible to reliably measure this induced rhythm by calculating the average value of the 35-45 Hz filtered EEG segments, which appeared after a complete series of these stimuli as phase coupled cognitive induced 40 Hz activity. Calculating the average curve erased other 40 Hz rhythms unrelated to the task. The processed 40 Hz activity had amplitude of 0.5-2 µV. The researchers concluded that increased vigilance increased gamma activity over the whole cerebral cortex via the thalamocortical circuits, which forms the basis for specific cortico-cortical connections that further increase gamma activity. This last increase starts 130 ms after the stimulus, when representations of objects and events, stored in the prefrontal cortex, are activated. A functional 'binding' of processes in the prefrontal and parietal cortex is necessary for their functional integration in the conscious perception of an object. The transient selective frontoparietal increase in 40 Hz rhythms is responsible for this integration. Selective attention is therefore associated with awareness, both of which play a critical role in integration of the relevant cortical processes in object identification; thus, enabling informed behavioral decisions.

As far back as 1956, Morrell and Jasper had already examined the effects of classical sensory-sensory conditioning of apes on EEG 'desynchronization,' which is always low voltage and refers to flattening of classical alpha and beta waves. This is interpreted as a manifestation of general cerebral activation consisting of 40 Hz activity. Pavlov's reflex is the archetypal example of classical conditioning as dogs previously conditioned to the ringing of a bell immediately before feeding begin to salivate on the ringing of a bell. This differs from operant conditioning in which a reward reinforces desirable voluntary behavior. Morrel and Jaspers experiment was not EEG biofeedback but was similar to Sterman's early experiments with cats in which the cats' EEG activity was recorded after behavior had brought them to a state of internal inhibition. Morrel and Jaspers found that generalized desynchronization spread throughout the cerebral cortex only during the first stage of behavioral conditioning. Stable localized desynchronized activity was demonstrably limited to the relevant area of the cerebral cortex once conditioning was completed. The first stage of conditioning, diffuse cortical desynchronization, gives rise to the initial response to the new stimuli within the complex matrix of irrelevant environmental stimuli. Whenever neuronal connections form because of pattern formation in space and time, as is the case for classical conditioning, groups of neurons show synchronous 40 Hz activity limited to the relevant circuit. EEG desynchronization is not more diffuse but can often seem more desynchronized because the synchronized neurons are limited to certain selective brain areas hidden within the total EEG activity. Sheer (1975) labeled these localized 40 Hz activities that reflect a definitive cortical activity optimized for conditioning as 'focused arousal.' During a visual discrimination task, Sheer (1970) demonstrated the existence of a consistent link between 40 Hz activity in the visual and motor cerebral cortex and the acquisition phase of learning in a cat. During a period of 10 seconds in which a 7 Hz flickering light acts as a warning signal, a discharge of 40 Hz activity in the visual and motor cortex appears 0.5 second before a correct lever response and during this response and lasts 1.5 seconds after the correct response. In 1970, he demonstrated that significant coherence and phase synchrony of 40 Hz activity occurred in reticular areas in the mesencephalon (lower brain stem) and in cortical and visual areas whenever a cat began to satisfy the learning criteria in a consecutive visual discrimination task. The method of phase coupled with induced cognitive 40 Hz activity was also used in this experiment.

Galambos (1958) induced 40 Hz activity in both the nucleus caudate and globus pallidus of cats who learnt that the last in a series of 11 loud clicks led inevitably to an electric shock. Rowland (1958) induced 40 Hz activity in the lateral cerebral cortex and the medial geniculate body of cats by pairing an auditory conditioned stimulus paired with an electric shock as the unconditioned stimulus. Freeman (1963) showed that neutral stimuli could condition 40 Hz activity in the prepiriform cortex (concerned with the sense of smell) in cats. Smell is a vital sense in animals, allowing perception of remote stimuli, thus triggering important orientation reactions. Killam (1967) demonstrated

40 Hz activity in the lateral geniculate body in the thalamus in cats once they were fully trained to distinguish the correct visual pattern from three different patterns offered. Pribram (1967) discovered 40 Hz activity in the striate area of the occipital lobe in apes just after making an erroneous response to a difficult visual discrimination task. Dumenko (1961) induced 40 Hz activity in the auditory, somatosensory, and motor cortex of dogs whenever they made, with one limb, a response to a tone as the conditioned stimulus and an electric shock as the unconditioned stimulus. Sakhuilina (1961) also demonstrated this 40 Hz activity in the sensorimotor cortex of dogs when various conditioned stimuli accompanied the bending of opposite hind paws. Subdural metal electrodes were used in all animal subjects. It is very well known that these extremely low voltage gamma frequencies are barely measurable at the scalp due to volume conduction phenomena in which transmission by the scalp and tissue underlying the electrodes weaken the signal.

Normally, generalized desynchronization of brain activity occurs during phases of exploration and focused attention on the surroundings. However, Bouyer (1981, 1987) and Rougeul-Buser (1994) demonstrated that 40 Hz activity is measurable in cats and apes with subdural electrodes placed in motor (areas 4 and 6a) cortex and posterior associative parietal cortex (area 5), and that this activity increased whenever a cat focused unmoving attention on its surroundings. Moreover, coherency of the 40 Hz activity increased in the thalamic areas linked to these cortical areas; however, there was no relationship with the thalamic reticular nucleus. Rougeul-Buser's opinion was that the 40 Hz activity that he had measured in cats indexed a more general focusing of attention. Area 5 of the cerebral cortex thus takes a strategic place, allocating attention between areas of sensory cerebral cortex and acting as a kind of supramodal structure (Rougeul, 1994). It is important to recognize that 40 Hz rhythms in frontoparietal cerebral cortex accompany every modality of focused attention (visual, aural, and smell). In a sense, Rougeul's hypothesis concurs with Crick's proposition (1984) that attention is required to bind different sensory domains.

Area 5 also functions as an interface in the transformation of a sensory response into a signal in a motor command chain. The 40 Hz activity in this area signals that a kind of inhibition process is developing in the named motor and parietal areas that will interact with neurons responsible for the organization of movement orders during focused attention, thus provoking immobility. Bouyer (1981), however, considered that the 40 Hz frontoparietal rhythm in cats and apes is homologous with a weaker 16-20 Hz rhythm in humans during freely willed movement, which rhythm in turn is functionally homologous with the central mu rhythm (9-13Hz) (Pfurtscheller, 1980). Sheer (1975) found only a low correlation of 40 Hz with 21-30 Hz activity; therefore, he proposed that the 40 Hz activity is a manifestation of focused arousal and the 21-30 Hz activity is a expression of diffuse arousal. Increased 40 Hz activity is experienced as concentrated attention associated with effort while 21-30 Hz is experienced as active, energetic, and restless (Sheer, 1977).

It was also shown that the ventral tegmental area (VTA) in the brain stem, which releases dopamine to modulate many brain areas, could modulate the sensorimotor 40 Hz rhythm. In 1994, Rougeul-Buser was able to demonstrate that dopamine strongly modulates certain thalamic areas (the posterior medial complex) and the corresponding cortical area 5. An increase in 40 Hz coherency in these two areas occurs during attentive stillness. In 1980, Simon showed that rats with injuries to the VTA showed hyperactivity and an inability to focus attention. Rougeul-Buser demonstrated the same result in cats and further noted that the 40 Hz rhythm completely disappears after such injuries. Administration of DOPA, a precursor of dopamine also used to treat Parkinsons patients, produced an increase in 35-40 Hz activity in healthy cats but had no effect after injury to the VTA. On the other hand, apomorphine, an agonist of postsynaptic dopamine receptors, produced an increase in 40 Hz activity and normalized the components of the thalamocortical system. Dopamine has probably no direct effect on thalamocortical circuits but an indirect effect via the amygdala and nucleus accumbens.

Giannitrapani (1969) measured 40 Hz activity along the middle of the scalp in children of normal or high intelligence just before production of an answer during a multiplication task. This 40 Hz activity was not present in passive states.

Sheer found no difference between the 40 Hz activity in children with learning difficulties and normal children. However, in problem solving tasks, children with learning difficulties had significant increase in 40 Hz activity in contrast to normal children. Giannitrapani (1969) had already come to this

conclusion. Sheer (1976) described his group of children with learning difficulties in the following way: the primary deficit was in 'focused arousal,' followed by problems with higher order processing, sustained attention, weak
modulation of activation, hyperactivity or hypoactivity, and to varying degrees with motor clumsiness and reading problems. Sheer suggested that the
central problem for these children was that they cannot learn as they cannot
assimilate new material and cannot solve problems at the level of their peers.
Therefore, it seems likely that Sheer was primarily thinking about children
with ADHD. ADHD as a diagnosis did not exist then as it was officially introduced only in 1980. In his experimental group, Sheer did not observe an
increase in 40 Hz activity during problem solving tasks in contrast to healthy
children. This 40 Hz activity plays a role in the storage of sequential information in short term memory necessary for problem solving and for transferring
information into long-term memory.

Sheer's study compared 20 typically developing children with two groups,
each comprising of 30 children with learning difficulties. The second group
with learning difficulties had poorer school results compared to the other
group with learning problems. The average age was 10 years and the average
IQ was 100 with the learning difficulty group showing a greater variation.
The investigation covered three sets of problem solving tasks, each set comprising of three tasks:

> • Verbal-visual: calculation problems using pictures; visual classificati-
> ons; visual rhymes;
> • Verbal-auditory: calculation problems with words; auditory classifica-
> tions; auditory rhymes;
> • Tactile-kinesthetic: form board; comparison of section outlines; com-
> parison of different threads.

The two groups with learning difficulties made significantly more errors
compared to the group with typical development. EEG activity was measured
at the left and right parietal and occipital electrode, with the central Cz point
providing the reference electrode. The detection criteria for a 40 Hz discharge
were a minimum of three cycles of 40 Hz activity above 3.1 µV (corresponding to a duration of 75 ms), and no measurable electrical muscular activity
(65-75 Hz) within a 100 ms (the same criteria that he employed for adult

participants.) The research established that in the typically developing children, 40 Hz activity increased in both parietal areas during problem solving tasks, but this was not the case for children with learning problems. Sheer suggested that this group of children failed to activate the temporo-parieto-occipital junction (corresponding to the angular gyrus and supramarginal language areas) in the cerebral cortex and that their difficulties in solving the problem tasks support this interpretation. Sheer argued that 40 Hz activity is optimal for consolidating the processed contents of short-term memory because repetitive synchronous excitation of these neurons maximizes the efficiency of synaptic transmission and transfer of information over this limited circuit. In all, 40 Hz activity does not simply correlate with diffuse cortical activation level; it also mirrors interaction between cortical facilitation and the processing of specific sensory input located in specific areas of the cerebral cortex. Inhibition of synaptic activity in surrounding areas accompanies this localized processing, leading to a sharpening of attention and curbing of gratuitous movement together with greater precision of relevant movements. Cholergenic input from the reticular formation of the mesencephalon (at the top of the brain stem) facilitates this 40 Hz activity. Others have demonstrated that direct electrical stimulation of the reticular formation facilitates learning if the stimulation immediately precedes the registration of information (Block, 1970). Amphetamine administration increases the activation level through its affect on the reticular formation. Sheer, however, believed that the behavioral data indicates no deficit in general arousal in most children with learning difficulties/ADHD; however, a deficit in focused arousal in the cerebral cortex is indicated. Acetylcholine also plays a central role in these processes. As early as 1982, Spydell and Sheer had demonstrated an increase in 40 Hz activity during verbal tasks in the left cerebral hemisphere and during spatial tasks in the right hemisphere.

Lutzenberger (1994) demonstrated that reading meaningful information rather than reading pseudo words was associated with greater 25-35 Hz activity over the left cortical language areas.

Tallon (1995) demonstrated that visual perception of meaningful figures rather than pseudo figures was associated with more 40 Hz activity over the visual cerebral cortex. Mattson and Sheer (1992) showed less 40 Hz activity measurable over the left hemisphere during a verbal task in dyslexic children than in typically developing children, while in children with mathematical learning problems, less 40 Hz activity was measured over the right hemisphere during a visual face recognition task. In 1989, Sheer found that 40 Hz activity was lower in patients with Alzheimer's dementia compared to the healthy elderly, and more saliently, that 40 Hz activity did not increase during problem solving tasks. This was already established in the early stages of the disease, when only subtle behavioral symptoms are expressed. In 1989, Sheer used new gamma oscillations phase-coupled to a cognitive event that delivered greater accuracy compared to previous methods that filter raw EEG to derive the 40 Hz activity.

A recent study from the Finnish research group under Ahveninen (2000) observed a dopamine-2 receptor antagonist (that hinders the neuronal action of dopamine) and a transient increase of 40 Hz activity (normally inhibited in this task due to the focus of attention on a series of tones from headphones) after ingestion of 2 mg Haldol by healthy participants.

Summary

The 40 Hz gamma rhythm is very low voltage, occurs in the cerebral cortex whenever a specific functional area is active, and is therefore more active under specific perceptual conditions. Both the thalamus and certain parts of the brainstem play decisive roles in generating this rhythm. The simultaneous action of this rhythm in different areas of the cerebral cortex contributes to the 'binding process' necessary in producing a unitary conscious experience of action. Dopamine and acetylcholine promote this synchrony. The 40 Hz rhythm decreases in people with ADHD. A localized 40 Hz rhythm can be measured following behavioral conditioning.

Only with the use of advanced EEG technology is it possible to filter out interference from EEG 40 Hz rhythms reliably.

4.5 Event Related Desynchronization (ERD) and Synchronization (ERS)

In recent years, the reflection of different levels of task performance in the EEG has been studied. Immediately after presenting distinctive auditory or visual stimuli that require a specific reaction from the experimental participant, the EEG shows a weakening of certain rhythms (event related desynchronization, ERD). Desynchronization denotes that more neuron groups are active independently from each other, making a more differentiated response possible. After the fading of the ERD, event related synchronization (ERS) occurs or, in other words, a temporary strengthening of the rhythm. Synchronization describes the simultaneous action of varied neuronal groupings and is associated with a less differentiated response. This is thought to represent an inactivation (or active self-inhibition).

4.5.1 Alpha ERD and ERS

In an attention task (CPT, Continuous Performance Test) in which the participant presses a button on hearing a tone or viewing a certain letter (or geometric shape), a fast ERD normally appears in posterior brain areas, followed by a quick recovery. Conversely, paradoxical ERSs, followed by late ERDs and a slow recovery can reflect inefficient cognitive processing.

Possibly, the complex nature of human cognitive function throughout alert waking behaviors produces continued ERD-ERS sequences, expressed by the instability of the EEG. In these sequences, restoration follows the expression of cognitive responses, allowing recovery of the system in preparation for the next challenge. In a well functioning system, the ERD alternates with the ERS.

4.5.2 Beta, Theta, and Gamma ERD and ERS

Whenever an individual performs a motor activity (for example a button push with the forefinger), beta wave strength decreases in the preceding time frame (lasting an average of 1.7 seconds) by an average 34% in the contralateral motor cortex and along the midline in frontal areas. This last area probably corresponds with the supplementary motor area (SMA), known to play a part in movement initiation. From the moment that movement begins, beta activity weakens in the motor cortex across both cerebral hemispheres. This weakening, or event related desynchronization, occurs even if the individual merely imagines the movement. Immediately following the index finger button press, desynchronization of alpha and beta activity in the contralateral cerebral cortex persists and then fades. After the ERD fades, an event related synchronization (ERS) is observed, that is, a temporary intensification of beta rhythm in the motor and frontal cerebral cortex. This probably reflects an inactivation (or active self-inhibition) of the motor and frontal cerebral cortex. This seems to indicate that motor planning is initiated in the frontal cerebral cortex, and this is synchronized with the expression of attention over the same area. During beta synchronization, coherency of activity in both areas increases, reflecting increased cooperation between them.

The ERS reveals the preparation of active self-inhibition of involved motor and premotor cerebral cortex and neuronal circuits. It is believed that sleep spindles are also a form of beta ERS during sleep, which involves the circuit that includes the thalamic reticular nucleus, the frontal cerebral cortex, and the brainstem. As previously described, the sleep spindles play a gating role, weakening the transmission of certain information.

The Russian scientist Kropotov (2004b) has studied these dynamics during a go/no-go task. In this task, shortly after an initial stimulus, a second identical stimulus follows, whereupon the participant is required to push a button with the index finger (go condition). However, if the initial stimulus is followed by a different stimulus, the button push must be withheld (no-go condition). Kropotov found that a fast pronounced ERS would follow a fast pronounced ERD after adequately executed cognitive aspects of the motor task. This ERD-ERS cycle runs continuously during wakefulness and reflects the sequential current of internal and external stimuli and the restoration of a state of preparedness following these responses.

A wave analyses offers a rather more elegant manner to demonstrate the different frequencies of the EEG. The average EEG is calculated from a hundred small sections of the EEG (each of one second duration) that followed the key press in the go condition (identical stimuli presented), and the resulting spectrum displays the changes in the course of the frequency spectrum over the

period of one second after stimulus presentation. Using this method, the calculation of averaged values such as the case with ERP research does not smooth
the background EEG. Instead, what is found here is the energy of different frequency bands present after the stimulus. The evoked desynchronized and synchronized activity always appears at the same moment (sequentially) after the
stimulus and is, therefore, more clearly visible using a time window method.

Kropotov (2004b) showed that in participants with ADHD, alpha synchronization in the left motor and frontal cerebral cortex is weaker following a button press; moreover, theta, gamma, and beta synchronization are also weaker.
Evoked theta activity has a different significance to the theta activity occurring during rest. The latter originates in the thalamocortical circuit and points
to a dysfunction, but cognitively evoked theta activity originates in the hippocampus and participates in working memory. The evoked gamma activity
is an expression of the intensity of attention associated with a task such as go/
no-go. There are indications that the increased attentional demands in a task
such as the go/no-go contribute to a more pronounced ERD prior to movement. The extent to which attentional difficulties in voluntary movement can
hamper evaluation of ongoing movement progress is unclear.

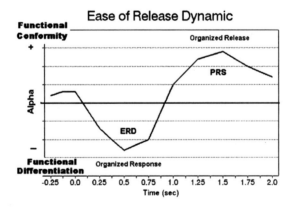

*Figure 22. ERD (event related desynchronization) and PRS (post response
synchronization) in a model of adaptive functioning of the brain, a theoretical
framework for neurofeedback therapy (Kaiser, 2001). Figure appears courtesy of David Kaiser.*

Kaiser (2001), a collaborator of Sterman, proposed a functional model based on event related desynchronization phenomena in order to introduce a more functional framework into neurofeedback training. He argued that a healthy system adaptively responds to a stimulus. Global neural networks can proceed with information processing either with functional conformity or with functional differentiation. How quickly and fluently these two extremes can be achieved is an objective measure of adaptive functionality. Differentiation refers to the dissimilarity of reactions in different neuronal groups (desynchronization) while conformity reflects similarity of response from various different neuronal groupings (synchronization). Ideally, the system is able to move freely from one extreme to the other. This can be assessed by the form of ease of release dynamic, which shows how fluidly the brain can adapt itself to processing requirements (ERD: event related desynchronization), followed by how quickly it releases from activation and returns to base state (PRS: post response synchronization).

The combination of both a less pronounced ERD and ERS would suggest that in ADHD, actions are more poorly adapted to processing requirements and that the functional activity of the underlying neuronal circuits after action execution is less likely to return to the resting state that is necessary in preparation for the next action. Increased motor reactivity in the cerebral cortex and the motor activity associated with it can obstruct attentional processes. Moreover, weakened attentional mechanisms can themselves weaken these processes.

In a normally developing 10-12 Hz ERD in the right motor cerebral cortex (C4) following a left finger movement, a transient increase in coherency (a measure of functional cooperation) is simultaneously observed in EEG activity between C3 and C4 (probably the left finger moves but the right finger is held still) and between C4 and F4 (probably because the frontal area is concerned with motor planning) (Rappelsberger, 1994). This argues for a globally unregulated system in ADHD, an interpretation supported by the observation that a certain mechanism that is successfully trained in neurofeedback can contribute to global changes in the EEG.

In normal states, little or no theta waves appear in the EEG. Certainly, they occur, for a fixed time, after the storage of information in memory. That can be seen at the bottom of each window in figure 23, showing a theta synchronization which always occurs in connection with the task and in the go/no-go task when the button is pressed on presentation of the correct stimuli. This may be the expression of the storage of new information in the hippocampal circuit. In a normal EEG, theta is rarely measurable because it is not distinguishable from the EEG background rhythm. However, on occasion, it is measurable as a rhythmic theta activity of 6-7 Hz of some 50 μV, maximal at the frontal mid line. Source localization shows this theta activity originates in the anterior cingulate and has strong connections with the hippocampus. This 'healthy' theta activity is thus a reflection of new information in the thalamocortical circuits. Pathological theta activity, as can be measured in rest states in ADHD, originates in the poorer functioning of the thalamocortical circuits. Llinas (Llinas & Ribary, 1999) described this activity as "thalamocortical dysrhythm." There are indications that the 'healthy' rhythm in ADHD is less synchronized, offering a partial explanation for the evoked P300 potential (that follows 300 ms after a stimulus associated with a cognitive task) often having a weaker voltage in ADHD (taking into account that the P300 is at least partly formed by evoked 'healthy' theta waves).

At the same time, the alpha rhythm, normally dominant in rest states as a base rhythm, is weakened (desynchronized) in connection with task execution. This would indicate recall of stored information from long-term memory. In passive situations with eyes closed, a clear alpha rhythm is seen in the EEG. This indicates that alpha synchronization of large-scale information processing takes place as large neuronal populations fluctuate at the same phase and frequency. In cognitive processing, mutually different alpha rhythms are uncoupled at different phases of these rhythms and different neuronal networks fluctuate with different frequencies and different phases. This gives an impression of global desynchronization, but it is in reality the progression of a complex pattern of microsynchronizations.

In the normal comparison group, there are weaker intensities than those observed for beta and theta voltages; a strengthening occurs about 6 times a second at higher wave frequencies (gamma 30-50 Hz). These gamma waves are grouped, nested within the rhythm of theta waves. This phase-coupled gamma activity is attributed to the binding process as multiple areas of the cerebral cortex demonstrate such gamma synchronization, which corresponds to specific contents of consciousness. In ADHD, especially the most symptomatic forms, this gamma activity is weakened, which can be interpreted as the presence of less intensive conscious attention. One wonders how all these different gamma activities, responsible for awareness of a great range of different processes, are synchronized in the same brain area without becoming entangled with each other.

Lisman (1995) has demonstrated that during a memory task, the gamma waves nest in packets within theta waves (the theta waves of the hippocampal circuit that are responsible for storing information in memory), which would mean that some six to seven packets are processed per second. This principle plays a role in attention, perceptual, as well as memory processes and explains why people can hold, on an average, a series of about seven figures in short term memory (the average is somewhat lower in ADHD). Theta waves act as an internal clock, determining which gamma activity is responsible for any particular perception or memory characteristic. This could explain why only a short time is needed in the Sternberg test in which the participant must decide, for example, if the letter B is present in a series of three letters. If, however, the series consists of four letters, then participant needs another 30ms corresponding to the duration of a gamma wave. Apparently, various letters pass through memory with a speed that corresponds to that of gamma waves.

Research has shown that gamma waves are necessary for consciousness. In 1989, Sheer employed a specific technique to find which bands of gamma synchronization are linked with specific cognitive functions. Many others followed, including Desmedt and Tomberg (1994) already mentioned in connection with this technique. Sheer assumed that the spontaneous gamma activity measurable in EEG is actually a summation of multiple gamma rhythms, each of which is itself the expression of different functional mechanisms. In a typical EEG, these different gamma rhythms are not separable from each other. However, whenever a specific task is linked to the start of an EEG segment lasting one second, phase-coupled induced gamma activity is obtained. This can be demonstrated, for example, using the go/no-go task in which the participant must press a button only on perception of a definitive stimulus and not the other stimulus. The filtered gamma activity is calculated when it occurs, immediately upon pressing the button. From

50 one-second segments, the averaged curve is calculated, from which all the gamma activity that is not directly connected to the button pressing is smoothed, resulting in greater visibility of the phase-coupled gamma activity. Gamma synchrony that occurs after the perception of a stimulus, as in the go/no-go task, is a measure of the cortical binding process necessary for conscious perception. Dopamine and acetylcholine are important modulators in this process. In the go/no-go task, an early (0 to 150 ms) and a late (200 to 550 ms) gamma synchrony occur after a stimulus in which the pressing of a button is required. Early gamma synchrony reflects the integrative aspects of preparatory attention. In ADHD, this early gamma synchrony is weaker in global, frontal, centrotemporal, and centroparietal areas in both hemispheres (unpublished data from the Brain Resource Company, Australia). This could indicate a functional disconnect brought about by an inadequate alignment and integration of the network. Late gamma synchrony indicates the preparation of a motor response.

Summary

During the execution of certain tasks, a phase weakening (desynchronization: less coordination between neuronal areas) or increase in certain brain wave types (synchronization: more coordination between certain neuronal areas) can be viewed in the EEG.

In ADHD, a weaker alpha desynchronization and a weaker beta-1, theta, and gamma synchronization are recorded:

• The weaker theta synchronization is an expression of weaker working memory.
• The weaker gamma synchronization is an expression of weaker conscious processing (therefore weaker attention);
• The weaker alpha synchronization is actually a weakening of multiple localized micro scale alpha synchronizations, reflecting the weakening of cognitive processing in ADHD;
• The weaker beta synchronization in motor and frontal cerebral cortex indicates weakened motor planning.

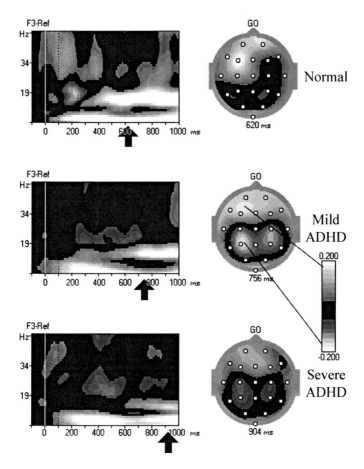

Figure 23. Wavelet analysis of the evoked EEG - the uppermost window shows the processed left frontal (F3) brain waves of a subject without ADHD following the Go stimulus in a Go/No-Go task. The middle window shows the same conditions for a participant with moderate ADHD, and in the bottommost window for someone with severe ADHD. Time is on the x-axis, the y-axis represents the EEG frequency spectrum (1-40 Hz). The mappings on the right show the spread of beta activity at the moment indicated by the arrows at each window: notice that for the uppermost subject, early intense beta activity is observed in left central and left frontal areas while in ADHD, beta activity appears later and is less intense. Notice the 'nested' gamma activity in the normal participant, which is less clear in the ADHD windows. The same images are featured on the cover of this book in color. (Image provided courtesy of Kropotov, unpublished)

4.6 Post Reinforcement Synchronization (PRS)

Whenever cats learn by operant conditioning to press a handle to receive foodstuff, a parietal alpha rhythm, the post reinforcement synchronization rhythm, occurs after receipt of the reward (Maczynski, 1981). This is associated with 'drive reduction' and the subjective experience of satisfaction. The percentage of PRS in the EEG increases when the reward is greater and thus when the performance of the learned task improves.

According to some hypotheses, a link exists between the rhythm of brain activity in the preoptic area of the basal forebrain and areas that have an inhibitory influence on thalamocortical circuits and this link plays a role in the process of falling asleep. When this area is stimulated electrically in laboratory animals during goal directed behavior, the animals lose interest in pursuing this behavior. Synchronized EEG rhythms can be observed before the thalamocortical rhythms are inhibited. An injury to the preoptic area causes loss of interest in rewards in experimental animals, resulting in the loss of the rewarded behavior, and a decrease in the EEG PRS rhythm.

Alpha synchronization becomes more pronounced after an adequate behavioral response (namely when the reaction time is faster) during an attentional task (continuous performance test). Sterman interpreted this result as an expression of a reward experience, that is, the execution of a motivated response. Sterman also opted to use the acronym PRS, but defined it as post response synchronization. After a better quality performance, alpha synchronization is thus more pronounced. A less adequate performance is observed in people with ADHD and, therefore, less PRS activity would be visible during such a task. This can be interpreted as a reflection of insufficient base dynamics resulting in a less appropriate response to external stimuli accompanied by a less pronounced phase transition to the ERD/ERS phase. Sterman further assumed that unstable EEG during alert wakefulness could be interpreted as a sequence of ERD-ERS phases, as a reflection of the sequential flow of cognitive response, and the recovery of the system from these responses. Fast ERD-PRS sequences signal an accurate recognition of cognitive associations. Thus, excitation–inhibition sequences in thalamocortical circuits can reflect efficient coding and integration of information and the reorganization of the system in preparation for the next challenge.

4.7 Phase and Coherence in the EEG

Measuring the coherency of certain frequency bands between different points on the scalp allows us to assess the degree of cooperation between different regions of the brain. Coherence is a measure of the extent of cooperation between two different areas of the cerebral cortex over certain frequency bands (delta, theta, alpha, and beta). The degree of coupling of specific frequency bands in certain phase relationships in the EEG signal can be precisely calculated over the measurement period. Coherence is maximal if two signals hold a constant phase angle in a distinct frequency band over the course of time.

Coherence can also be defined in terms of spectral coherence: the measurement of spectral similarity of a defined frequency band between two EEG signals over the course of time.

A very low coherence indicates functional independence of the two areas. Coherency between two areas that is lower than measured normally indicates insufficient integrative cooperation between these areas. Increased coherence indicates an inadequate degree of differentiation, often observed in people with low intelligence. In adulthood, coherence normally decreases. Thatcher (1998) demonstrated that coherence is typically higher in frontal rather than posterior areas, as might be expected from evidence that more local processing occurs in posterior areas, together with more focal differentiation and short-range interaction.

Thatcher reasoned that the frontal cerebral cortex regulates the posterior cortex. He developed his suggestion further with an ecological model or a 'predator-prey' model of human cerebral development. Considering that in ADHD, increased coherence in frontal areas is frequently observed, it is plausible that such frontal control of posterior areas (where higher integration of sensory information is processed) is less efficient.

Chabot (1996) found a hypercoherence of alpha and theta activity between the left and right frontal areas during rest states (such as is the case after a concussion) and between the frontal and temporal areas within each cerebral hemisphere in children with ADHD. This reflects a lack of differentiation in the processing performed in these brain areas, which may lead to attention difficulties. Barry's (2002) findings are slightly different, indicating increased coherence of delta and theta activity between left and right frontal areas but decreased alpha coherence. However, it can be said that increased global coherence is often seen in people with ADHD. Increased coherence goes hand in hand with phase angle constancy between different frequency bands (each at a different location). In high coherency, the phase difference is usually low because functional connections are flatter. In these cases, and probably also in ADHD, there is likely to be a decreased number of phase updates: normally the phase relationship suddenly switches to another phase relationship at least once a second. These phase updates play another role in working memory (Rizutto, 2003), thus, a diminished number of phase up dates in ADHD might explain poorer working memory functioning in people with ADHD.

Summary

Coherence is a measure that indicates how two different brain areas cooperate in certain EEG frequency bands. Increased coherence is frequently observed in ADHD, which suggests insufficient differentiation between the brain areas concerned. If coherence is high, the phase angle between two frequency bands (each measured from a point on the scalp) remains constant longer, probably accompanied by less phase updates, which may explain the existence of poor working memory, as in ADHD.

4.8 Cognitive Evoked Brain Potential

Whenever a stimulus such as a sound or light flash is presented to an experimental subject, evoked brain activity in the form of a wave pattern (potential) appears in the EEG within fractions of a second. Evoked brain potentials are not often visible to the naked eye against the background of the present EEG waveforms. However, if a hundred stimuli are presented one after the other, and the resulting short coupled EEG fragment following each stimulus is measured, then the average EEG pattern can be calculated from all these fragments. The background EEG activity is smoothed, rendering the evoked potential (formed at exactly the same time after the stimulus) clearly visible. Potentials that are triggered purely by auditory, visual, or tactile stimuli are termed exogenous potentials, and they can reveal neurological injuries in the affected brain areas. If a cognitive task is coupled with a stimulus, these potentials can allow the investigation of cognitive processes. All these potentials reveal different aspects of attentional processes and all of them can be disturbed in people with ADHD.

4.8.1 The Odd Ball Test: Processing of Incoming Information

The best-known EEG cognitive test is the 'odd ball paradigm.' This test is used to obtain insight into processing of *incoming* information. Four stages have been distinguished in the central processing of incoming sensory information, each revealed by characteristic electrical activity maximally measurable along the midline of the crown of the skull: N100, N200, P300, and LFN.

In the most used auditory variant of the odd ball, therefore, the most standardized, a series of tones are presented, some with a higher ('odd') tone than the others. The evoked brain potentials give information about cognitive capacities such as various attention mechanisms important to the processing of incoming information. In the first trial, 150 tones are presented (120 low, 30 high tones) while the participants' attention is focused on a simple calculation task. The brain activity that follows for half a second after each tone is measured. In the second trial, the same 150 tones are presented, but this time, the participants must actively listen to the tones having the additional task of pressing a button after identifying an infrequent (high) tone.

4.8.1.1 Selective Attention: N100 (Electrically Negative Brain Wave After 100 ms)

The extent to which the amplitude of this wave (N100) increases (both after the frequent and infrequent tone) whenever an individual actively focuses attention on the series of tones is a measure of how well the individual selectively focuses on the listening task without being distracted by irrelevant stimuli. In passive states, these waves originate from the primary auditory temporal cerebral cortex; in active listening tasks, the auditory cortex is prepared for the stimuli. The frontal integrative association cortex also contributes to the amplitude of the N100 wave. Normally, the increase is greater than 20%.

4.8.1.2 Automatic Discrimination: N200 (Electrically Negative Wave After 200 ms)

This wave (N200) appears only after the onset of the infrequent tone in the active listening trial or during the first trial when the individual is not focused on the tones. This wave indicates how well an individual automatically notices an unexpected stimulus (therefore possibly important) outside the field of focused attention. Most events that occur outside the laboratory are unexpected and the N200 provides a constant spur to explore the outside world. This wave originates in the auditory temporal association cortex and in part of the frontal integrative association cortex. Normally, this wave will be at least 20% higher after infrequently rather than frequently presented tone.

4.8.1.3 Controlled Assignment of Meaning: P300 (Electro-Positive Wave After 300 ms)

When an individual is asked to listen selectively for infrequent tones (or sometimes to count them), typically, a higher positive wave appears after the infrequent tones than after the more frequent low tones. This wave (P300) originates in the integrative temperoparietal and frontal integrative associative cortex. The wave's amplitude is an indication of the extent to which an individual succeeds in assigning a particular significance to meaningful stimuli in a controlled manner. Normally, this wave should increase by 50% whenever attention is actively focused on the task.

4.8.1.4 Further Controlled Processing: LFN (Late Frontal Negativity)

When the individual selectively attends to the listening task, a frontal increase of the late frontal negativity (at least 5 µV more negative) appears after presentation of both the frequent and infrequent tone. The LFN is an indication of the extent to which additional controlled processing of information occurs after stimulus recognition.

The presence of the LFN indicates the predominance of an internal control system that is able to inhibit the inflow of distracting or irrelevant information. This system is especially active in task situations when attention is controlled from "inside out" (for example, search processes in short-term memory in which consciousness knowingly directs attention to certain aspects of the environment). It is associated with intentional, controlled focusing of attention. A low LFN points to domination of an external control or orientation system, facilitating the influx of stimuli to the cerebral cortex. The external control system is especially activated during situations of "attentional demand" or in association with orientation reactions. If there are weaknesses in divided attention, which may be clearly demonstrated by an increase in intrusive errors during the Stroop task, for example, the LFN will decrease (there is less controlled processing and therefore attention is more reactive to external control processes).

4.8.2 The Go/No-Go Test: A Window on Behavioral Control

In recent years, research interest in ADHD has shifted from the processing of incoming information (for example as elucidated by the oddball test) to the study of the executive functions that control behavior (from attention deficit towards intention deficit). The latter can be investigated using, for example, the "go/no-go" test in which action monitoring and inhibition of inadequate responses can be observed. In the "go/no-go" test, a series of visual or auditory stimulus pairs are presented. The stimuli can have two different values presented consecutively at a fixed interval. The second stimulus can have either value. A series of a hundred stimuli are presented with a fixed rhythm. Pairs of identical or different stimuli are presented in a random order, with half of the stimuli pairs being identical. In the go condition, participants must push a button only after a pair of identical stimuli; the other condition is termed no-go. Following the last stimulus in each pair, the evoked brain potentials are measured over half second periods.

A negative potential (N2), followed by a positive potential (P3) maximally measured in frontal regions appears initially after not pushing the button. The negative potential N2 originates in the right lower part of the frontal cortex and in the anterior cingulate (see also figure 3 on page 10). The N2 is associated with response inhibition. The positive P3 potential originates in the anterior cingulate (see also figure 2 on page 9) and is implicated in evaluation and the monitoring of conflict between stimuli and in response inhibition. In ADHD, the positive potential that follows on the no-go condition is maximal not at the frontal midline but at the central midline, indicating weaker inhibition (Kropotov, 2004).

4.8.3 CNV (Contingent Negative Variation)

Another important cognitive brain potential is the "contingent negative variation" (CNV), a slow, electrically negative wave maximally measurable at the vertex (Cz) that follows a stimulus warning. Then, in 2 to 5 seconds, a second command stimulus will occur at which point participants must press a button. The CNV in ADHD is lower and will be further discussed in chapter 8. We will examine how biological insights into these slow wave potentials in the cerebral cortex throw a new light on to the cognitive potentials of the oddball paradigm and give rise to the abandonment of classical cognitive psychology concepts. In this new theoretical framework, the significance of evoked brain potentials is reinterpreted as an expression of biological processes in the brain that play a fundamental role in the adaptation of an organism to the environment.

4.9 More Detail in EEG (Induced EEG Oscillations)

The evoked cognitive brain potentials were traditionally considered as a separate research area. Because of the methodology employed, evoked cognitive brain potentials seemed to be separate phenomena from EEG waves. The aperiodic fluctuations in EEG were long considered a noise from the activity of neuronal dendrites and were therefore averaged and smoothed out from measurements of evoked cognitive brain potentials. The evoked smoothed EEG activity corresponds to the activity recorded during the second that follows an auditory or visual stimulus. In reality, the EEG contains much information that can no longer be thought of as neuronal noise.

The core concept of these research paradigms is that cognitive brain potentials are a valid means towards the localization of the specific processes in the depths of the brain. The Low Resolution Electromagnetic Tomography (LORETA) technique (Pascual-Marqui, Michel, & Lehmann, 1994) can reconstruct and locate the source generator within the brain based on the application of an inverse biophysical model of EEG activity. On the other hand, research has shown that the evoked activity in the EEG represents a phase update that induces classical EEG waves (Makeig, 2004). Furthermore, in recent years, research has explored the evoked potentials using the method of joint time frequency analysis (JTFA) (Blanco, D'Attellis, Isaacson, Rosso, & Sirne, 1996) and has evaluated the role of these potentials in classical EEG rhythms. The traditional Fourier Spectrum Analyses cannot be used in such cases; they can only be applied to longer EEG fragments in the time domain. A Fourier spectrum analysis assumes that a periodic signal (a superposition of sinusoidal waves) is an infinitely long signal. Applied to finite sequences, artifacts are obtained, more so at the lowest frequencies. A JTFA or wavelet analysis allows analyses of EEG frequencies at each moment (time-frequency-domain). This method allowed studying how the go/no-go task induces changes in the EEG rhythm during the second that follows the go stimulus. In people with ADHD, these changes are not as developed (see the front cover and figure 23 on page 71).

Another, new method for the analyses of these induced EEG rhythmic components of cognitive potentials is the ICA method (independent component analysis) (Bartlett, Makeig, Bell, Jung, & Sejnowski, 1995). This method originated in information theory. In ICA, the extent to which different components can be distinguished is calculated based on calculated 'mutual information.' This information is determined according to a specific time course and specific dispersion patterns at the scalp created by different components.

This method has been applied to the classic EEG itself, and it has demonstrated the classic classification of EEG waves as delta, theta, and alpha. It is also valid on the grounds of individual time course and dispersion pattern of these waves at the skull. Different EEG frequency bands therefore reflect different types of information. Moreover, ICA makes it possible to filter out technical artifacts in the EEG in order to obtain an EEG with fewer artifacts caused by eye movements, muscle activity, or technical electrical noise arising from the measuring apparatus or through a broken electrical contact with the scalp.

Summary

We can measure the "cognitive evoked brain potentials" by calculating the average of a complete series of EEG segments seconds after an auditory or visual stimulus in which a coupled mental task is presented. These brain potentials form a measure of various attentional and behavioral inhibition processes. These are often aberrant in people with ADHD.

New methods of EEG analyses, such as JTFA and ICA, make it possible to monitor a more detailed structure (including fine changes in the EEG rhythms) during cognitive tasks. These new developments have lead to a unification of classical EEG research and cognitive brain potential studies.

5.

Dynamic Organization of Vigilance in EEG

5.1 "Cyclic Alternating Patterns" and Alpha Fluctuations

In 1964, the Berlin psychiatrist Bente developed a dynamic psychiatric model of the EEG in which the concept of vigilance formed an integral part. The stringent definition formed by the London neurologist Head in 1923 stimulated this work. This definition defined vigilance as the quality and degree of an individual's adaptive interaction with the environment. Bente was additionally inspired by a model of sleep deprivation formed by the French psychiatrist Ey to understand mental disintegration states. Bente applied both these concepts to build an understanding of EEG and described vigilance as a function of the dynamic state of the central nervous system as mirrored in EEG. Later, Ulrich (1994) further developed the model.

An alpha rhythm in posterior areas with fluctuating spindle formation predominantly characterizes an optimal EEG during the waking state with eyes closed. This is observed in about 80% of healthy subjects, while an EEG dominated by beta is obtained in 5-10% of subjects, and an EEG with very low voltage is observed in 4-9% of subjects (Gallinat, 1988).

During the transition to sleep, alpha activity frequently takes hold first; this activity is more monomorphic (showing less fluctuation). Often, the anterior amplitude is greater on the left than the right (A-State). Next, a state with predominately beta-2 activity (20-30 Hz) follows, which may or may not mix with theta activity (B-State).

Bente adapted sleep deprivation states as a model. Bente and Ulrich noticed types A and B EEG in psychiatric patients during wakefulness, just as in healthy sleep deprived subjects. Type A indicates a "rigid" vigilance, and type B suggests a "labile" form. The B type is seen most often in people with ADHD, however, a minority exhibits the A type. The B type with too few sleep spindles during sleep and SMR rhythms during wakefulness also typified Sterman's epilepsy patients. The sleep spindles have a vigilance-sta-bilizing influence on sleep states: when they are deficient (often the case in ADHD) sleep states are fragmented.

The classic spectrum analysis of the EEG (using Fast Fourier transform) gives the averaged EEG spectrum over a specific period. This method views the EEG as a superposition of sinusoidal frequencies, as if it is a stable state. In reality, neural networks cause spontaneous cyclic changes in EEG that are lost in classical statistical frequency analysis. The sleep spindles pro-duced cyclically in sleep provide an example. A traditional spectrum analy-sis certainly indicates the absolute quantity of sleep spindles, but yields no information about their periodicity (the average time between occurrences). Periodicities make a major contribution to the organization of the EEG, and traditional statistical frequency analyses cannot fully quantify them.

Evans (1993) found an inverse proportional relationship between manifesta-tions of sleep spindles in a sleep EEG, described by Terzano (1988) as "cyclic alternating patterns" (CAP). These recurring sequences are 3 to 7 minutes long and are comprised of periods lasting an average of 40 (range 2-60) sec-onds. If the complete sequence is described as a CAP, the interval between two periods cannot exceed a minute. Each CAP period is characterized by a short phase A and a longer phase B. Phase A is a short (2-60s) phasic EEG paroxysm, an EEG phenomenon that contrasts sharply with the background activity of the EEG. It is followed by a longer lasting deactivated interval (phase B). A normal quantity indicates sleep phase stability, but a heightened quantity is the expression of vigilance instability and occurs during sleep es-pecially just before or after a sleep phase transition. The CAPs are also asso-ciated with adaptive dynamic responses to environmental conditions. If there are not too many external disturbances, they guarantee sleep stability in a healthy person, while a greater number of external disturbances pave the way to sleep phase transition. Undoubtedly, such external factors can modulate CAPs with a certain endogenous oscillatory rhythm just as they modulate, on

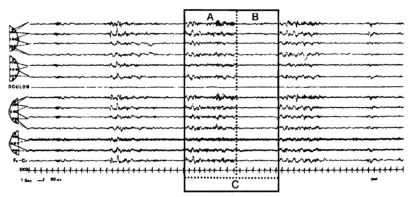

Figure 24. CAP during sleep phase II consists of two phases (A: paroxysmal, B: deactivated phase). Reprinted from Sleep Medicine, 2(6), Terzano et al., Atlas, rules and recording techniques for the scoring of cyclic alternating patterns (CAP) in human sleep, Copyright (2001), with permission from Elsevier.

a different time scale, the day-night rhythm and the basic rest activity cycle (BRAC) of an organism.

An alternation of phases A and B is observed during the transition from wakefulness to the first phase of sleep. In sleep phase A, there is a rigid, monomorphic alpha activity. In sleep phase B, there is a low voltage beta-2 activity eventually mixed with theta activity. Terzano, Parrino, Smerieri, Chervin, Chokrovertry, Guilleminault, Hishkowitz, Mahowald, Moldofsky, Rosa, Thomas, & Walters (2001) pointed out that sleep phase A, in regard to reactivity of vigilance, displays similarities with CAP phase A (low reactivity) while sleep phase B has similarities with CAP phase B (induced by external or internal factors induce a phase A reaction). Evans suggested that these alternations in wake-sleep phase transitions are analogous to a CAP. Terzano himself suggested that an intermittent continuous alpha series are analogous to the CAP during waking state. This is in agreement with recent findings (Tirsch, Keidel, Perz, Scherb, & Sommer, 2000).

The CAP cycle was originally considered an activation phenomenon, but in recent years, no unique relationship has been uncovered in clinical correlations of sleep disorders. Recently, an alternative and more nuanced conceptualization has formed describing CAPs as a process that encompasses both sleep maintenance and sleep fragmentation. This broader perspective was formed when the paroxysmal A phase of CAP sleep was subdivided into either type A1 or else the types A2 and A3. The A1 phase type is a paroxysm (upsurge) of synchronous EEG activity such as delta waves, alpha waves, and K complex (an upsurge of a higher voltage biphasic wave occurring in sleep stage 2, which may or may not be accompanied by a sleep spindle followed by a segment of not less than 20% of desynchronized low voltage activity).

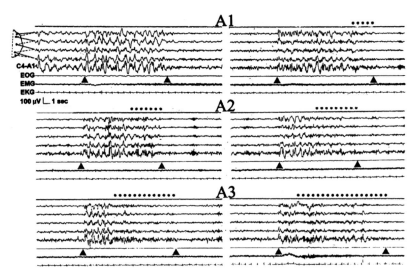

Figure 25. The three CAP phase A types: the first type (A1) is characterized by a short upsurge of synchronized EEG activity and has sleep stabilizing and integrating functions; the two other types (A2 and A3) occur after the upsurge and consist of a segment of desynchronized activity with microarousals. Reprinted from Sleep Medicine, 2(6), Terzano et al., Atlas, rules and recording techniques for the scoring of cyclic alternating patterns (CAP) in human sleep, Copyright (2001), with permission from Elsevier.

The phase types A2 and A3 are similarly paroxysmal but followed respectively by either 20-50% or by more than 50% of low voltage desynchronized EEG activity (Terzano et al., 2001).

CAP phase A1 occurs predominantly during light NREM sleep stages 1-2 during the progression towards REM sleep and deep NREM sleep stages 3-4. CAP phases A2-A3 occurs most often during the progression of deep sleep towards phases of lighter NREM sleep stages 1-2. In physiologically healthy states, sleep stabilizing subtype A1 prevails. The distribution of subtypes is associated with definite strategic functions and is certainly not based on chance as evidenced by the role they play in the synchronization or resynchronization of the EEG.

CAP phase A1 (paroxysmal high voltage synchronization such as delta waves, alpha waves, or a K complex with or without a sleep spindle) is an expression of the effort made by the brain to maintain light sleep despite the presence of internal or external stimuli. In this case, discrete destabilization accompanies a gradual increase in arousal, leading to more stabilization and, consequently, sleep maintenance. Bizarrely, the light instability of sleep stage 1-2 guarantees sleep maintenance. If this effort fails, because too few CAP phase types A1 are produced, real arousal occurs in the form of CAP phase types A2-A3 (paroxysmal low voltage desynchronization).

CAP phase type A1 is therefore a sleep stabilization phenomenon, which currently considers K complexes followed by sleep spindles as a subtype of sleep stabilizing CAP. CAP phase type A1 plays an integrating role in transient large-scale cooperation of multiple brain areas.

CAP phase types A2-A3 are recognized as microarousals and are more frequently observed in epilepsy, periodic muscle twitches of the lower limbs (classically with a periodicity of 2-60 seconds), sleep apnea, and bruxism (teeth grinding), among others. CAPs have a period of 2-60 seconds, within which sleep spindles are about the fastest, with a rhythm of 0.1 to 0.2 Hz.

A recent study (Miano, 2006) found a lowered quantity of CAPs, especially CAP phase type A1, in 20 sleeping children with ADHD (in comparison with a group of 20 children without ADHD). This suggests that during light NREM sleep stages, no discrete increase of arousal occurs in response to internal or external stimuli; therefore, no compensatory sleep maintenance processes are launched to stabilize sleep in the children with ADHD. The same study observed shorter sleep duration and an increased number of sleep phase transitions in the ADHD group. This supports an earlier small-scale sleep study of children with ADHD (Kahn, 1978).

The CAPs were associated with "infraslow" EEG rhythms of 0.02 Hz (waves with duration of about 50 seconds), which are an expression of very slow cyclical cortical and subcortical stimulus sensitivity.

Slow waves recruit large neuronal networks that generate functional connectivity between cortical and subcortical structures through rhythmic coupling (Buzsaki, 2004; Vanhatalo, 2004). During sleep, the changing activation/deactivation of a CAP cycle generates a "brain beat" that can drive synchronization between neuronal groups, thus, providing for progression between different sleep stages. Further, there are indications that faster EEG rhythms synchronize infraslow EEG rhythms, which are responsible for a slower cyclic modulation of cortical sensitivity. A routine sleep EEG does not measure infraslow EEG rhythms because the apparatus is not calibrated for frequencies lower than 0.5 Hz.

CAP patterns with a frequency of 0.02 Hz are embedded in an even slower cycle within the NREM/REM 90 minute cycle. The "brain beat" of the sleep stabilizing CAPs, of which the sleep spindles are a special subtype, contributes to the progression of these cycles. CAPs decrease around sleep phase transitions.

Sleep deprivation disrupts the performance of the sleep wake cyclical rhythm, resulting in EEG similar to the EEG of a person with ADHD. On the night following sleep deprivation, less sleep spindles and more sleep fragmentation are present, as in ADHD.

Considering that during the daytime, a "basic rest activity cycle" with cycle duration of ninety minutes also exists, it is plausible that these same principles apply to wakefulness in good agreement with Terzano's hypothesis that CAPs in the form of slow cyclic alpha wave fluctuations occur during wakefulness. Tirsch et al. (2000) investigated the cyclic nature of alpha energy fluctuations over the course of at least a minute in order to gain a better understanding of fine structure in the EEG, taking into account the never static nature of EEG. He examined the time course of occipital alpha energy for EEG data from eight healthy adult participants. A sliding window analysis was employed in which the alpha energy of partially overlapping fragments of 2.56 seconds duration was calculated to obtain 230 "windows." The windows were arranged in a time series and a frequency spectrum calculated from the resultant time series; an alpha peak occurred on average every 50 (+/- 20) seconds, thus, an average rhythm of 0.02 Hz. It is striking that the duration of this period concurs with the CAP. This dynamic method of spectrum analysis can clearly reveal the cyclic fluctuations that the clinician sometimes suspects in the raw EEG. The relative absence of these fluctuations is often discernable even by inspection of the raw EEG of someone with ADHD, which expresses either a too labile EEG (with too many alpha fluctuations or too little) or sometimes a too rigid EEG (too much alpha activity with too few fluctuations). Systematic fluctuations over the course of 50-60 seconds are of course difficult to detect visually from the raw EEG. Later, Tirsch (Tirsch, Stude, Scherb, & Keidel, 2004) demonstrated an inverse relationship between the energy of the alpha fragment and the corresponding nonlinear 'correlation dimension.' The nonlinear correlation dimension of an alpha time series in an EEG is a mathematical reconstruction of the extent to which nonlinear correlations occur in the time course of alpha series. A higher nonlinear correlation dimension is an indicator of increased system complexity. Thus, Tirsch established that a high degree of alpha synchronization reflects less complexity in the system. His interpretation was that the brain, with its reactivity to internal or external stimuli, periodically changes its activation state and the degree of "synergy" between different parallel information processing systems. He assumed that a central pattern generator ("pacemaker," "cyclic modulator," "self-organized rhythmicity") in the reticular formation of the brain stem or thalamus drives these synchronized cyclic changes in the degree of synchronization.

This makes us think of the sleep spindles and other cyclic alternating patterns in sleep that play a cyclic modulating role, originate in the reticular nucleus of the thalamus, and are themselves modulated by cholinergic reticular formation neurons in the brain stem. The reticular formation is known to play a major role in consciousness and wakefulness.

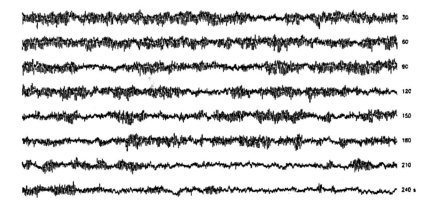

Figure 26. Raw occipital EEG of 4-minute duration (240s) from a normal adult participant in 8 consecutive fragments of about 30s. With kind permission from Springer Science+Business Media: Biological Cybernetics, Inverse covariation of spectral density and correlation dimension in cyclic EEG dynamics of the human brain, 82(1), 2000, Tirsch, Keidel, Perz, Scherb, & Sommer, fig. 1.

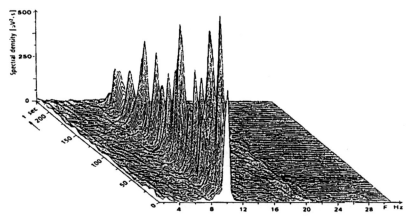

Figure 27. The course of the occipital frequency spectrum of the EEG from the previous figure over 4 minutes (240 s) in which the 50-60s cyclic fluctuations of alpha peaks are clearly seen. With kind permission from Springer Science+Business Media: Biological Cybernetics, Inverse covariation of spectral density and correlation dimension in cyclic EEG dynamics of the human brain, 82(1), 2000, Tirsch, Keidel, Perz, Scherb, & Sommer, fig. 3.

Possibly, this "pacemaker" or "cyclic modulator" in the brain stem also contributes in the generation of hippocampal theta rhythms implicated in working memory and integrative functions of REM sleep. Noradrenalin input from the locus coeruleus in the brainstem to the hippocampus also contributes to these processes.

An optimal fluctuating system provides adaptive responses to internal or external stimuli, and this is potentially reflected in a well-developed event related desynchronization (Kaiser, 2001). Kaiser noted that ERD-ERS cycles run continuously in waking states and their sequential flow reflects cognitive responses to internal and external stimuli and the subsequent restoration of a state of readiness for further inputs. Moreover, reaction times during an attention task are slower at moments of alpha synchronization when the evoked ERD is often weaker (Sterman, 1996).

Sustained fine regulation of the brain's reactivity to internal and external stimuli leads to maintenance of a certain intermediate level; thus, avoiding at the one extreme habituation and at the other over-excitability (possibly leading to epilepsy). This mechanism can also decide on optimal attentional regulation. The cycle duration of 50 to 60 seconds is, on the behavioral level, expressed in attentional tasks, fully promoting a more efficient global functioning of the system.

Tirsch assumed that lower alpha energy fragments (and thus possessing a higher correlation dimension) reflect faster parallel information processing in independently active brain areas. The highest energy fragment (and thus with the lowest correlation dimension) would therefore express synchronized data transfer over higher association cortex areas. These CAPS, formed from series with average 50-second duration, illuminate the brains integrative functions in which parallel and central information processing modes alternate with each other. From the evidence for decreased quantities of sleep spindles and CAPs during sleep, and a lowered quantity of SMR rhythm during wakefulness, one may suspect that these fluctuations in daytime will show a different pattern in disorders such as ADHD. Reduced smooth alpha synchronization in ADHD described by Kropotov (2004b) strengthens this suspicion.

Verstraeten (2002) demonstrated a different pattern of slow fluctuations of alpha in ADHD. Verstraeten measured lower left frontal (F3) alpha 8-10 Hz desynchronization during weak phasic arousal and alertness and increased synchronization of 10-12 Hz rhythms during inaccurate attention switching.

Tirsch's research into this cyclic pattern of occipital alpha activity has been described here in detail, but it should be mentioned that he also demonstrated the same 50-60 Hz cycle in sensorimotor beta rhythm in EEG (Tirsch, Stude, Scherb, & Keidel, 2004). Moreover, this phenomenon has been observed in all physiological phenomena, such as attentional quality, motor performance, and normal physiological resting tremor (Tirsch, Keidel, & Sommer, 1995).

The discovery that similar fluctuations occur in the physiological resting tremor to those in EEG strengthen the hypothesis that a pacemaker plays a moderating role in the brain stem both in ascending paths (towards the brain stem) and descending paths (towards the backbone) in which other rhythmic structures are also involved. All these discoveries persuaded Tirsch that "injuries" in temporal structure could be identified earlier than structural injuries. In the future, this new approach may be a practical method for diagnosing pathology.

Summary

As in behavioral regulation, a cyclic modulating pattern with a period of 50 to 60 seconds exists in the EEG, probably playing a "pacesetter" role. The evidence indicates that this cyclic pattern may originate in the mesencephalic reticular formation of the thalamus and may be similar, in some ways, to the cyclic alternating patterns (CAPs) in the EEG that are responsible for optimization of global functioning of the EEG.

It is very likely that this integrating pattern is disturbed in ADHD, which might explain global disturbance in the vigilance system.

5.2 Pink Noise and "Self-Organized Criticality" in Behavior

Slow cycles, lasting 30 to 60 seconds in EEG and in behavior (such as the physiological resting tremor), are also found in other behaviors.

A far-reaching phenomenon in both behavior and EEG is that both have time series (for example, the occipital alpha waves and the sensorimotor beta-1 waves) which fluctuate in a scale free manner: that is, the degree of fluctuation over short time scales is identical to the fluctuation over longer time scales. It is not yet known whether infraslow EEG waves also show similar scale free fluctuations.

A time series can be constructed by plotting consecutive reaction times from simple reaction time on vertical strips for each serial position and a connecting curve sketched through the end-points. Traditionally, the average reaction time and standard deviation is then calculated for these tasks. Although rearranging the order of the original reaction times does not alter either the average reaction time or the standard deviation, it does destroy the fine structure of the original time series as it can leave out much valuable information about functional behavior. If a frequency spectrum is obtained from the curve formed by the time series of reaction times, it is evident that the slowest frequencies have the highest energy. The spectrum slope is best evaluated by plotting the x-axis (frequency) and y-axis (amount of energy in each frequency) on a logarithmic scale (figure 28) (Van Orden, 2002).

The slope of the energy spectrum is steepest during simple tasks (less dependent on external noise). Consequently, pink noise is much more visible in a very simple behavioral task in which participants are asked to press a button whenever they subjectively feel that a second has passed for a period lasting ten minutes (Gilden, 1995). This task is self-paced, without the necessity to react to an external stimulus, and gives rise to a very clear behavior. The introduction of an external stimulus is responsible for the appearance of more white noise and, therefore, produces a less steep slope to the frequency spectrum. As tasks become more complex, more white noise combines with pink noise and the slope becomes less steep. In pathological cases, the slope is even flatter during complex tasks. That could indicate that there is too little response to external circumstances (associated with white noise); thus, indicating that organization is no more complex than during simple tasks. In summary, if the time series of reaction times mix randomly, the average reaction time and the standard deviation remain unchanged, and white noise replaces pink noise in the time series frequency spectrum.

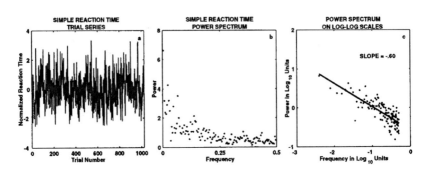

Figure 28. Left: A series of a 1000 reaction times from a healthy partici-pant. Middle: Frequency spectrum of these reaction times. Right: Loga-rithmic treatment of the frequency spectrum. There is a 1/f relation (pink noise in which the longest frequency has the most energy). Reprinted from Ecological Psychology, 14(1), Van Orden, Intentional contents and self-control, Copyright (2002), with permission from Taylor & Francis http://www.informaworld.com.

Gilden (personal communication, 2006) found that for participants with ADHD, more white noise appears in the 1/f graph (discussed in more detail below) of the time series obtained from three self-generated button push tasks over a period of ten minutes. Epstein and Orden (personal communication) have run a comparable experiment, expecting to find more white noise.

The noise in such systems is thus not completely disorganized; completely disorganized noise is white noise, analogous to the visible light spectrum in which white light consists of all component colors. Every measurement in the series is thus completely independent of the values at every other point; this is also termed uncorrelated noise. Pink noise can be observed in figure 28, in analogy with visible pink light comprising mostly long wavelength (lower frequency) light with other subcomponents present in exponentially decreas-ing amounts. An inverse proportional relationship exists between energy and frequency band (1/f), and this is termed correlated noise. Background noise, like pink noise, is expected to occur in a self-organizing behavioral system over the course of time. Pink noise indicates the internal source of variability and refers to the brain's intrinsic dynamics and mechanisms of alternation between cognitive processes. Pink noise is the signature of goal directed be-havior arising from self-organization. When "surrogate data" created from a series of measurements by placing data fragments side-by-side, white noise is obtained in place of pink noise, then absolutely no interrelationships survive. Thus, a 1/f relationship in which f has a negative exponent (with a value of roughly -1) indicated by the gradient of the slope characterizes pink noise. Pink noise occupies the space between white noise and brown noise. White noise yields a horizontal line when the logarithm of the density is plotted against the logarithm of the frequency; thus, each frequency contains on average the same amount of energy. White noise is characteristic of a stable time series that randomly fluctuates around an average value where f has an exponent of 0 in the 1/f time series. Brownian noise (Brown noise, named not after a color in the electromagnetic spectrum but after Brownian motion described by the botanist Brown) is also known as red noise (because the curve gradient is steeper than in pink noise) and is defined as the cumulative sum of a series of random movements, often said to resemble a drunkard's walk. The exponent of f in the expression 1/f is 2 for Brown noise. Pink noise is independent of time scale since on a logarithmic scale, the 2-4 Hz band possesses the same energy as the 20-40 Hz frequency band. Incidentally, human hearing also functions in accordance with this principle, which explains why every octave perceived contains the same quantity of energy. Acoustic engineering often utilizes pink noise, because the human auditory system perceives approximately the same volume at all acoustic frequencies.

Based on reaction time experiments, Van Orden (2002) hypothesized that goal directed cognitive performance develops via 1/f organization. The internal complexity and especially the personal internal history of such a system permit better adaptability to various situations via a smooth transition from one organizational state to another.

A well-developed pink noise system is constantly balanced between unpredictability and over-determination, a critical balance that Bak (1997) termed "self-organized criticality" or SOC. Out of a full range of subsystems within the global system, self-organization spontaneously establishes the critical equilibrium state optimally favorable for task adaptive behavior. The theory of SOC suggests that a system self-organizes into a complex system with fractal features (fractal: approximately the same degree of organization is found on all time scales). A sand heap provides the canonical example in that additional sand added to the top of the existing heap may suddenly subside along different break lines. Another example would be a snow avalanche that leads to further sudden shifts as further snow accumulations. According to this theory, fractal organization develops in a simple unbalanced system. An SOC system has a number of important characteristics: 1) the degree of complexity arises from self-organization and is not determined by a regulating control parameter; 2) a scale free (fractal) pattern of organization exists (the same pattern is expressed on both a small and a large scale); 3) SOC and pink noise arise through the interaction of many systems from which a global system arises spontaneously with its own dynamic that can no longer be reduced to the specific input of subsystems.

Van Orden (2002) observed that in classical linear "Newtonian" cognitive psychology where cognitive phenomena are explained using computer models in which measurements of human behavior are directly linked to assumed brain components. The products of psychological processes are not distinct from the processes themselves (attention, perception, thought, speech, and walking, among others). Van Orden named this classic approach the "component dominant dynamic." He stressed that concepts such as free will, reflex, and automaticity were developed in the seventeenth century as classificatory designations, but over time became laden with philosophical, physiological, and psychological associations with causal implications. In this connection, Van Orden cited Fearing who in 1930 wrote an article in an attempt to distinguish the knee jerk reflex from "voluntary" movement of the lower leg. Fearing thought that the "voluntary" movement was a higher form of reflex and the knee reflex a lower form of reflex. However, Fearing warned that these reflex hypotheses and related data generated from the 17th and 18th centuries should be should be considered as provisional and therefore should be viewed with caution (Fearing, 1970).

Van Orden (2002) suggested an "interaction dominant dynamic" in which interactions between neighboring processes change each other. Internal and external processes hold behavior within certain boundaries, leading to emergent behavior. The interplay between component systems over different time scales is the source of correlated noise. The behavior of subcomponents reflects the behavior of the whole system because of their underlying system dependence. Likewise, variation in the subsystems reflects variation in the whole. Goal directed intentional behavior therefore arises from self-organization in a system that, at its critical point, is strongly determined by internal and external circumstances. Choice and self-control are emergent properties arising from interactions between the organism and the environment.

On this basis, Van Orden (2002) argued that the indications of correlated "pink noise" are the signature of goal directed behavior. The characteristics of goal directed behavior such as self-control and choice are context dependent. Classical science saw noise (for example, in a reaction time experiment) as an irritating side effect. In the "interaction dominant dynamic" approach, noise represents precise information, worthwhile of study because pink noise is an indication of the system's organizational pattern.

If we equate the brain's pink noise with the brain's intrinsic dynamics then we can argue that these dynamics are responsible for the global emergence of behavior. However, isolation of certain causal mechanisms in a "component dominant dynamic" of the brain requires certain behavioral parameters that are expressed on specific scales. Composition of pink noise does not support these characteristic scales, raising the question if we will ever be able to reduce the causes of human behavior to activity within specific brain areas.

Similarly, pink noise curves have been obtained, and the resulting frequency spectrum have been calculated, from an experiment in which participants were asked to rate their mood every day over a two-year period (Gottschalk, 1995). In healthy participants, the logarithmic curve is steeper than in people with bipolar disorder.

Another study examined the frequency spectrum of the time series formed from consecutive participants' own ratings of "self-esteem" assessed twice daily over 729 days (Delignières, 2005). Here too a remarkably similar pattern formed that the authors labeled as "self-image" emerging from the nervous system in a self-organized manner.

Notice that self-organized refers not to the individual "self" but to the automatic interaction between many system components. Delignières (2005) concluded that this pattern not only demonstrated stability in an individual with a healthy self-image but also possessed enough flexibility to adapt to changing circumstances. This is possibly achieved through adequate "criticality."

Marks-Tarlow (1999) predicted that we might observe more white noise in patients with a hysterical personality disorder (which we might assume is the case in ADHD) and more brown noise in rigid obsessive-compulsive personality types.

Nowak (2000) demonstrated that self-image is an emergent property from a complex dynamic system composed of a flow of specific, linked self-thoughts. From this vantage point, the self can emerge as a coherent structure, and the process of preservation, when exposed to incongruent elements, can be understood as a process of self-organization based on multiple interactions within the system. A robust system exhibits pink noise, which means that the energy contained within every frequency of the energy spectrum of the time series is proportional to the oscillation period. Thus, energy does not concentrate within any time scale but, instead, spreads over the whole spectrum. Therefore, fluctuations on one time scale only loosely connect to fluctuations on another time scale. The relative independence of the underlying processes active at different time scales implies that a localized disturbance within a time scale does not necessarily change the stability of the whole system. In other words, pink noise (1/f) produces a system that is both stable and adaptable to internal and external disturbances.

However, Delignières (2005) remarked that in principle, this kind of analyses applies only to the adaptation of a stationary time series so that the fractal analysis of self-image is just a first step in the characterization of its nonlinear properties. Dynamic changes characterize non-stationary processes. He assumed that this happens in depressive or very anxious patients. Meanwhile, methods for analysis of non-stationary time series may usefully extend the current approach.

5.3 Pink Noise in the EEG

Brain dynamics switch constantly between the complex and the unpredictable. Friston (2000) stressed the importance of momentary transitions in the "labile brain." This switching element provides the most efficient manner for the brain to detect change in the body and in the surroundings, while at the same time, maintaining autonomous self-generated internal organization. This self-generating mechanism arises at the microscopic level from neuronal discharge and synaptic activity and keeps building up to the macroscopic level of a complex organized system at multiple coordinates of time and space within the brain.

A logarithmic x, y plot of the Fourier spectrum in the EEG follows a "power law" (1/f) in which the energy of the system is inversely proportional to the signal. The slowest frequencies contain the most energy. This is the essence of a scale free system. The brain generates a full series of EEG rhythms that allow processing and predicting of events on multiple time scales. The inverse relationship between EEG frequency and energy indicates that the interference at low frequencies is responsible for a chain reaction of energy shifts at all frequencies. It is assumed that these dynamics form the essence of a global temporal organization of the cerebral cortex. The fact that the same 1/f phenomenon occurs on every time scale is an important argument for self-organization. The speed with which energy drops from slow to fast frequencies in the EEG is a measure of the strength of the correlations and of the statistical memory of the signal. If no relationship existed between different frequency bands, the energy density over specific EEG frequency distributions would be constant and the spectrum would be flat (in other words, it would show white noise). The 1/f behavior of the EEG is the golden mean between disorder and high information maintenance on the one hand, and the predictability of low information maintenance on the other. This golden mean represents "self-organized criticality." The fact that different frequency levels are dependent on each other explains the fact that slow frequency disturbances lead to power changes at all frequency levels. During slow rhythms, slow axonal conductions and slow synaptic processes also contribute to the activity, consequently larger neuron groupings can participate in faster EEG rhythms. This shows a 1/f phenomenon. Such correlated pink noise has important consequences and advantages for perception and behavior. From this viewpoint, the brain does not demonstrate just large-scale long-term patterns because these self-organized collective patterns guide the very neuronal behavior that contributed to the existence of these patterns. The effect of properties of emergent higher levels on lower levels of organization contributes to 'circular causality' (see figure 59) (Haken, 1996; Kelso, 1995).

The corollary is that the firing patterns of single neurons occurring at any given moment do not depend solely on the external input but also on the firing pattern history and the state of the network in which they are imbedded.

The fact that the 1/f network is independent of scale implies that the macroscopic EEG patterns, which on a large scale describe the functioning of neural networks as a unified whole, are, as a globally functioning system, independent of the details of those dynamic processes that ultimately guide the sub components towards unification. It does not follow that these rules are applicable at all times to all scales in time and space. On the one hand, a small local disturbance can influence a great part of the network and exert long lasting effects. On the other, the functional history of the network does limit neuronal firing patterns.

The 1/f "power law" implies that, for the better part of the time, the brain's dynamics is in a state of 'self-organized criticality.' This unequivocal complex state is mathematically defined, and it occupies the border between predictable periodic behavior and unpredictable chaos. It enables the cerebral cortex to show transient states during certain perceptions or cognitions, allowing fast and flexible responses to inputs. In addition to response flexibility, this cerebral cortex metastability enables dynamic reorganization in response to even the smallest and weakest disturbances. The occurrence of an event related desynchronization (ERD) in the EEG after a sensory, motor, or cognitive event is a clear example of a disturbance in the brain's critical state. The ability to switch quickly from metastable pink noise to a strong predictable rhythmic EEG state is quite possibly the most important characteristic of the dynamics of the cerebral cortex. By switching to a rhythmic state, the brain immediately creates a state with linear characteristics that are a fundamental physiological necessity for the psychological processes described as "expectation," "prediction," and "anticipation." During these short transition processes, a linear time scale needs to provide stability in order to maintain and compare information within a certain time, allowing behavioral predictions on the time scale.

In order to describe the present state of the brain, it is necessary to know its recent history embodied in the time correlation and represented by the 1/f memory of scale free systems. The term "1/f memory" is a statistical concept and does not necessarily relate directly to human memory. However, the 1/f statistical measure can indicate a link between the dynamics of the cerebral cortex and behavior. Cerebral cortex dynamics constantly alternate between complex metastable pink noise and very predictable rhythmic states.

In recent years, an additional role of pink noise has been observed, that is, an increase in the continuously present noise in some nonlinear systems counter intuitively increases the sensitivity of signal detection. In the somatosensory cortex, a signal in the form of a just detectable pulse of electric current delivered to a nerve receptor in the hand was perceived better whenever alpha activity with pink noise characteristics was present in the cortex. This is known as stochastic resonance. Traditional thinking would predict that low noise accompanies better signal detection. At present, it seems that noise resonates, so to speak, in SOC systems, picking up and strengthening weak signals.

Linkenkaer-Hansen (Linkenkaer-Hansen, Nikulin, Palva, Kaila, & Limoniemi, 2004) described how this pink noise can be discovered in a time series of organization of occipital alpha waves (10 Hz) and of sensorimotor beta waves (20 Hz). Alpha and beta activity was filtered from the MEG (magnetoencephalography), the fluctuations in their amplitude were investigated by placing an "amplitude envelope" around the filtered signal, and the frequency spectrum from these envelopes was calculated. The resultant spectrum showed the characteristics of pink noise. The highest energy was observed at low frequencies and the lowest energy at the fastest frequencies of the amplitude envelope.

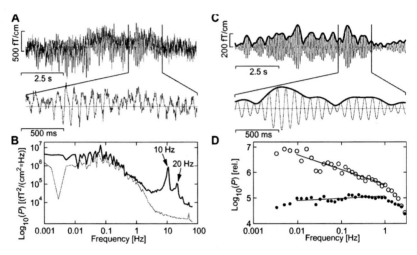

Figure 29. The frequency content of broadband signals and of the amplitude envelope of narrow frequency-band neural oscillations. (A) A representative epoch of the broadband signal as obtained from a single MEG channel at the acquisition (0.1-100 Hz) is shown at two time scales. Note from the upper trace that the high-amplitude 10-Hz oscillations are riding on slow fluctuations (< 1 Hz). (B) The slow fluctuations in the broadband signals are likely to originate mainly from environmental noise as it can be inferred from B showing the spectral density of the entire 20-min long signal in A (thick line) and reference data from the same channel (thin line). The neural signals clearly dominate at frequencies above but not below 1 Hz with prominent peaks at 10 and 20 Hz (see arrows). (C) The signal shown in A has been filtered at 10 Hz with a Morlet wavelet (passband 6.7–13.3 Hz). The thin lines are the real part and the amplitude envelopes (thick lines) are the modulus of the wavelet transform. (D) The power spectrum of the amplitude envelope of the neural data at 10 Hz exhibits a 1/fβ power spectrum (circles) with β = 0.58 in the range from 0.01 to 1 Hz, thereby indicating that the fluctuations of the amplitude envelope of these oscillations are correlated at time scales of 1–100 s. On the contrary, the 10-Hz amplitude envelope of the reference data gave rise to a white-noise spectrum characteristic of a temporally uncorrelated process (dots). Reprinted from European Journal of Neuroscience, 19, Linkenkaer-Hansen, Nikulin, Palva, Kaila, & Limoniemi, Stimulus-induced change in long-range temporal correlations and scaling behaviour of sensorimotor oscillations, Copyright (2004), with permission from John Wiley and Sons.

Plotted on a logarithmic scale, the frequency spectrum is an oblique line with high values lying to the left and low to the right (high in slow and low in fast frequencies). Calculating the negative exponent of 'f' in the 1/f expression gives us a measure of the curve gradient, that is, the steeper the curve, the more pink noise and the higher the degree of self-organized criticality.

In this way, the pink noise for different frequency patterns has been calculated (such as theta, alpha, beta, gamma) (Freeman, 2000; Stam, 2004; Linkenkaer-Hansen, Nikulin, Palva, Kaila, & Limoniemi, 2004) indicating that the energy of the frequency band is at its highest at slow frequencies of the time series spectrum for these different frequency bands.

It is not yet clear if the 0.02 Hz slow EEG waves such as CAPs participate in the scale free pink noise modulation of theta, alpha, and beta waves. The fact that they increase in the neighborhood of sleep phase transitions is certainly an indication that they correlate with these even slower cycles (an NREM/REM cycle lasts 90 minutes) of which the sleep wake cycle is an example.

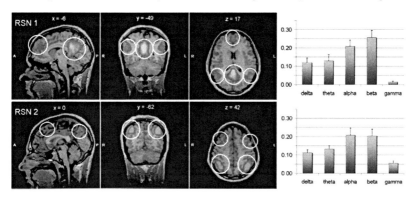

Figure 30. Left: fMRI of default network (RSN1) and dorsal attention network (RSN2). Right: EEG band correlations with slow fluctuations of the fMRI signal in both networks at rest: orange indicates positive, blue negative correlation (Mantini, et al., 2007). Copyright (2007) National Academy of Sciences, U.S.A.

We know that the highest amplitude SMR-bursts occur roughly every 50 seconds (Tirsch, 2004) and that this phenomenon has similarities with a CAP (cyclic alternating pattern), which has a stabilizing function. This slow cycle is only discernable with a chronospectrogram (see figure 27). Sterman and Lubar noticed by visual EEG inspection that the SMR rhythm (which it defined as a burst with a minimum duration of 0.5 seconds (s) and an amplitude of at least 10 µV) in normal children predominantly occurs around 10 to 20 times per minute. Smaller and more frequent short bursts of 12-15 Hz are also plainly visible in the EEG.

This may be linked to the 1/f pink noise phenomenon. The evidence that in ADHD fewer SMR bursts (and possibly less cycling alternating patterns of 0.02 Hz) are present, as Sterman and Lubar suggested, could therefore be interpreted as a manifestation of a disruption in intrinsic organization with the presence of less pink noise.

Robert Thatcher (personal communication) thinks that we could expect increased burst duration in a homeostatically regulated system. The burst duration of any frequency, not just SMR, represents a type of rapidly opening and closing "shutter" in which action potentials occur on the falling phase of each rhythm of local field potentials (LFP; excitability cycles representing a discrete action potential probability distribution; see Buzsaki's review, 2006). If bursts are too short, then more bursts per second compensate for the need to process information, which resembles the shutter opening and closing. When burst duration increases, then there is a more sustained period for processing information and for cross-frequency synchronization to occur.

The hypothesis is that in people with ADHD, the SMR rhythms (cyclic alternating patterns with a vigilance stabilizing function) contain less slow fluctuations of 0.02 Hz. Moreover, as Lubar demonstrated, short SMR-burst with a minimum duration of 0.5 s (usually occurring 10 to 20 times per minute) also has a vigilance-stabilizing role.

From a different perspective, recent research revealed that the alpha-and beta rhythms also correlate with slow fluctuations that are measurable by fMRI. These slow (0.01-0.1 Hz) blood oxygenation level-dependent functional imaging signal-fluctuations are topographically organized in discrete brain networks. This characterizes the "dorsal attention network" (mediating external goal directed stimulus-response selection) that is active during attention. This network includes bilaterally the intraparietal sulcus, the cortex at the intersection of precentral and superior frontal sulcus near and at the human frontal eye field, the ventral precentral, and middle frontal gyrus. During passive states, a different network is active: the "default network" that controls internally focused processes such as introspection. This network links the bilateral inferior parietal lobules (mainly the angular gyrus), the precuneus/ posterior cingulate, bilateral superior frontal gyrii, and medial frontal gyrus. The network is called the "default" network because fMRI research indicates it is active during passive conditions (no cognitive tasks or other functions) or, more cogently, because this network is deactivated during cognitive tasks. However, the "default" network is not in itself at rest. It reflects brain activity during introspection (medial frontal gyrus) as well as proprioception (parietal cortex), among others.

The default network has a peak frequency of 0.013 Hz in slow fMRI-signal fluctuations whereas the dormant dorsal attention network shows a peak frequency of 0.022 Hz (Mantini, Perrucci, Del Gratta, Romani, & Corbetta, 2007). Curiously, this peak frequency of 0.022 Hz is similar to that of the slow fluctuations in the occipital alpha and the sensorimotor beta rhythms that were demonstrated during rest (Tirsch, 2004), which in turn show similarities to a CAP (cyclic alternating pattern). The alpha and beta rhythms (13-30 Hz) correlate positively with slow fluctuations of the fMRI-default network and negatively with fMRI-slow fluctuations of the dorsal attention network in resting states (Mantini et al., 2007).

During cognitive tasks, the default network (especially the medial prefrontal cortex) in people with ADHD is insufficiently suppressed (Sonuga-Barke, 2007; Fassbender, 2009), which could explain increased distractibility. Sonuga-Barke advanced the hypothesis that the slow cycles of increased variability in reaction time tasks in people with ADHD may be linked to slow fluctuations of the fMRI signal of the default network. These slow default network fluctuations during attentional tasks are ineffectually suppressed. They may also correlate with slow fluctuations in reaction time variability in ADHD.

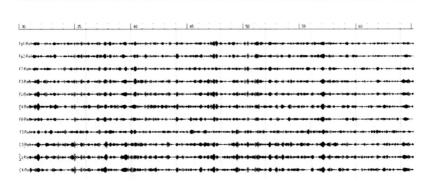

Figure 31. 12-20 Hz filtered EEG, 50 µV gain, speed 7.5 mm/s. Smaller and shorter bursts are clearly discernable between the bigger, longer bursts described by Sterman and Lubar. Image created by WinEEG, Mitsar Co. Ltd.

Summary

The discovery that frequency patterns in the EEG, and also frequency patterns of time series consisting of the consecutive intensities from certain EEG wave frequency bands, exhibit pink noise characteristics provide new insights into nonlinear relationships in the EEG. In analogy with the visible light spectrum, white noise describes the circumstance when all frequencies are present in the EEG frequency spectrum while pink noise displays more energy in the low rather than the high frequency bands of the spectrum. This indicates that the noise correlates and denotes a degree of order in the system called "self-organized criticality." In such systems, fractal organization (the same pattern is repeated on every time scale) gives rise to self-organization as the system reaches a critical threshold in which flexible state transitions are possible. This system arises purely through self-organization in which reciprocal causality is established between the global macrosystem and the activity of multiple subsystems.

There are indications that people with ADHD exhibit relatively less pink noise and relatively more white noise, which would suggest a lower degree of self-organized criticality. The system is consequently less flexible and less stable, demonstrating less adequate event related desynchronization in the EEG.

5.4 EEG Phase Resetting, 1/f Organization of Phase and Brain States

Behavioral studies have shown that poor brain state regulation plays a fundamental role in ADHD, which may explain the lack of task adaptive behavior. Nowadays, we can provide better insight into the meaning of the brain state and the determination of its organizational level. Brain state level indeed determines attention, actions, and perceptions.

At the behavioral level, sleep and wakefulness in the brain are two different states. In the first state, we are not conscious of our environment, but we are aware of our environment in the second state. However, there is also a more subtle variation of motor and cognitive capabilities over periods lasting minutes, seconds, and even over smaller time scales. This happens without an "executive network" playing a supervisory role.

We have already mentioned that variability in behavioral response does not arise from white noise in the brain, which is itself a consequence of the brain's imperfections, but from pink noise dynamic in brain activity. This indicates that the spontaneous activity of "brain states" characterizes neither stationary nor white noise. The 1/f organization of the brain is responsible for continuous phase transitions that enable the brain to react to external stimuli as effectively as possible. Brain state changes are difficult to deduce from moment-to-moment overt behavior. Nevertheless, EEG changes can be precisely monitored and associated with each other, at least temporarily. Classical research into the brain's cognitive evoked potentials assumes that the underlying activity in the EEG represents random noise, which is smoothed by calculating the average values of the curve. Consequently, only the stimulus and resultant mental processing seem to determine the evoked activity following stimulus presentation. However, more recently, it has been found that after stimulus presentation, a phase reset occurs in the brain rhythm.

Makeig (2002) performed an experiment asking participants to press a button only when a stimulus appeared inside a small green square displayed on a monitor, not if it appeared at other location. The response generated to the ignored stimuli was analyzed. If alpha waves were not present prior to stimulus presentation, alpha response was not triggered. If background alpha activity was high, then the amplitude of the evoked response was also high. The latency of the individual evoked responses varied systematically as a function of the phase of the ongoing alpha rhythm. Instead, a degree of phase adjustment was always found in connection with the neglected stimulus.

Palva (2005) examined the functional importance of background EEG activity in a study of the effect of a barely perceptible electrical stimulus on the skin of the index finger. The stimulus was just perceptible whenever sufficient alpha and theta activity, not just in the somatosensory, but also in the parietal and frontal cerebral cortex, preceded and followed the stimulus and whenever stimulus presentation occurred simultaneously to a certain phase of the ongoing rhythm. A phase reset was measurable in the EEG only under the perception of stimulus. Stimulus perception therefore depended on transient, spontaneous, rhythmic activity states in the frontoparietal network. Perception of the stimulus depended on disturbance of spontaneous brain rhythms so that the stimulus itself only partly determined the brain activity associated with stimulus perception. The consistent finding that both movement initiation and reaction times systematically vary as a function of alpha rhythm phase further supports the functional behavioral importance of phase resets (Bates, 1951; Lansing, 1959). In movement initiation and reaction times, there is no evoked phase reset so we can argue that the relevance of behavioral activity that evolves during certain EEG phases or phase reset is the same for spontaneous and for evoked EEG activity.

MEG (magnetoencephelogram) responses were measured in the cerebral cortex of participants performing a working memory task (Rizzuto, 2003) and in the hippocampus (Tesche, 2000). A string of digits was presented on a monitor, after which the participant had to recall the digits. A theta phase reset followed the stimuli, and the duration of theta activity following the stimulus increased with memory load with an upper limit of around 60 ms corresponding to 5-7 remembered digits. The firing patterns of neurons in the cerebral cortex and hippocampus were grouped together in the trough of local alpha and theta activity.

Usually, hypercoherence occurs in ADHD, suggesting that phase differences between different brain areas are more stable on average. Less phase resettings may be suspected in ADHD. A phase reset is composed of a short phase shift and a longer lasting phase lock. A phase shift is about -0.3 correlated to phase coherence while phase lock is about 0.85 correlated (Thatcher, personal communication, 2009). This would suggest that in ADHD, with usually increased hypercoherence between frontal areas, phase lock would take longer. Too few phase resets may result in less adaptive behavior, that is, over reactive to intense or exciting stimuli and under reactive to weak or boring stimuli. It would also provide an explanation for poorer working memory in people with ADHD, as they frequently cannot accurately recall 5 to 7 digits. We might suspect that the time series of phase values may demonstrate a less marked 1/f pink noise pattern in ADHD, which would correlate with less pronounced 1/f pink noise in the reaction time series. This would imply that in ADHD behavior, there is less task adaptive behavior; thus, also less exact.

Phase resettings in an EEG rhythm can usefully create an optimal temporal relationship between the discharge of neuronal groups and information carried about stimulus related activity. If information is allocated to opposite phases of the cyclic rhythm randomly, without the ability to adjust neuronal group timing, the effect induced by the stimulus may be amplified or ignored. Therefore, phase resettings can strengthen the incoming signals selectively.

A very strong or salient stimulus can influence the activities of many more neurons than can self-generate rhythms. Such salient stimuli not only exploit ongoing brain dynamics, but also alter brain state so that the newly created dynamic may be very different from the one preceding the stimulus. Sudden transition from alpha and mu to gamma rhythms during event related desynchronization is a characteristic example of such state changes in the activity of brain networks following presentation of meaningful stimuli. People with ADHD often experience the stimulus as less salient, unquestionably, this is because the brain dynamics of the phase rhythms exhibits less pink noise, resulting in less marked phase transitions and inadequate brain state (in this case, in the form of event related desynchronization).

Similar phenomena have been described in macaques (Liang, 2002) after they initiated the task sequence. After they pulled a handle, either diamond or a line appeared on a monitor and correct identification of the visual stimulus was rewarded. The energy and phase coherency of the 5-12 Hz band in the prefrontal cerebral cortex correlated highly with both amplitude and latency of the evoked potential in occipital cerebral cortex as well as with motor re-action time. These observations support the hypothesis that the brain state of prefrontal sensory areas can facilitate efficient processing of stimuli.

In general, psychological theories about selective attention have attempted to interpret all of these findings as reflecting a top down mechanism accompanied by gamma and theta rhythms. A logical consequence of this hypothesis would be that in order to maintain optimal selective attention, we must maintain our brains in an optimal condition and generate sufficient alpha and gamma rhythms. However, the brain does not operate in this way, at least not for long periods. This hypothetical executive would not be able to retain control over the long term. In the absence of a strong external stimulus, the brain falls into its programmed rhythms, such as overwhelming tiredness experienced during a long car ride, and these rhythms result in fluctuating performance levels. Consequently, there is no simple way to maintain voluntary attention, perception, memory, or motor actions over long periods. This applies even more to people with ADHD, which gives an impression that they possess a weaker will compared to other people.

Another indication that an internal mechanism is responsible for fluctuations in the state of readiness for perception and action is that the gamma and theta rhythms at the scalp demonstrate a $1/f$ pink noise pattern.

The structural basis of this brain dynamic might be the multiple parallel neuronal circuits that deliver feedback over long time scales because of progressively longer conduction times and synaptic transmission durations in longer circuits. This may indicate that these multiple systems are responsible for the global $1/f$ pink noise. On the other hand, following the principal of reciprocal causality, the global $1/f$ dynamic maintains a certain degree of order in these subsystems. These multiple scales in time and space embody the contextual dependence of input disturbance in the "situated" environment of task adaptive behavior and vigilance. This context itself is determined through the historical associations of the input and the previous responses of the brain to that input.

The signal measured in the EEG after input may well contain more information about the brain of the perceiver than about the input because perception is an "interpretation" by neuronal circuits over multiple scales in time and space in the brain rather than the aggregate of a number of unvarying physical characteristics.

Thatcher (Thatcher, North, & Biver, 2005) found a correlation between high intelligence and short frontal phase shifts. Probably, based on this correlation with intelligence, there is a higher quantity of phase resetting counts. Moreover, it is clear that there is a link between alpha and theta waves and working memory. Since working memory is often rather limited in ADHD, we may suspect that phase resettings are less frequent. Increased EEG coherence between the two hemispheres in ADHD suggests a greater grouping of phase resettings or their lower variability. This implies the probability that fewer phase resettings accompany higher coherence.

Phase resettings occur regularly and spontaneously; therefore, they are for the most part internally generated even though they are certainly triggered and modulated by internal and external stimuli. Abrupt accelerations or decelerations in the temporal course of the phase relationship between beta waves (12-30 Hz) measured between two EEG measuring points occur several times a second (with intervals corresponding to theta and alpha waves) (Freeman, 2004). Freeman demonstrated the role that these phase resettings play in sensory perception. Rizzuto (2003) observed such phase resettings in 12-16 Hz waves, especially during tasks involving working memory.

Makeig (2004) proposed a model in which phase resettings in alpha and theta waves occur with each pulse from the septohippocampal pacemaker, and that this temporal adjustment of neurotransmitter systems marks the beginning of a period of retention and analysis of information that lasts around 80 ms to 250 ms. This process is continuously repeated and the peaks of the alpha and theta rhythms reflect the phase resetting process. The stepwise phase resettings of working memory occur in the 7-16 Hz EEG frequency. A great number of cortical EEG rhythms have their pacemaker in the thalamus so that consciousness is involved in other processes in addition to working memory. It is intriguing to think that the absence of consciousness in deep sleep or anaesthesia is associated with a global uncoupling of the hippocampal cingulate complex from the thalamus and cerebral cortex. Phase resettings are still present in these states, even if at very low voltage. Perhaps, the powerful coordination between the septohippocampal cingulate and the thalamocortical system supports a central coupling between the past (as memory) and the present during consciousness expressed in the phase resetting. In ADHD, there are indications of fewer phase resettings, which in this framework can be interpreted as a discrete lowering of consciousness (in the sense of vigilance, optimal adaption of responses to circumstances) and a decreased working memory capacity.

The phase resettings are abrupt adjustments of the phase relationship within a frequency band between EEG measuring points, clearly seen when studying the curve of the first derivative of the progress of the phase difference. The first derivative gives a measure of the speed of change. The second derivative is a measure of the speed of change. In other words, the second derivative is a measure of the speed of change of the first derivative. We can understand this better by thinking about reading the speedometer when driving the car. The speedometer denotes the first derivative to the rate of distance change per unit time (miles/hour). If we suddenly break, we feel our body falling forward towards the steering wheel; this is the second derivative. Galileo discovered the importance of the second derivative in physics. Newton wrote it in his famous equation $F = m \cdot a$ (force equals mass times acceleration). The EEG is fundamentally an electromagnetic process to which all the physical laws of energy and electricity apply. An interesting property of phase resetting is that it requires only a minimal amount of energy to adjust oscillators already in motion. The phase resettings can synchronize neural networks over long distances.

When we look at the first derivative of the phase shifts in the EEG, we can see moments when simultaneous phase resettings at all 19 points are measurable separately. Between the phase resettings, we see flat segments where the first derivative is zero, signifying that the phase coupling is constant.

The frequency spectrum of the first derivative of the phase shift shows $1/f$ "pink noise" distribution. The lowest frequencies have the most energy; the highest frequencies have the least. Using this $1/f$ principle, Freeman (2004) explained the way that we may achieve long distance synchronization of neural networks. This principle points to the phenomenon of self-organized criticality, indicating self-organization occurs across the smallest to the largest time scale, guaranteeing stability of the global system and simultaneously the flexibility of adaptive responses to internal and external stimuli. The pink noise indicates the existence of mutual causality between the relative degree of phase update on short and on long time scales, involving also phase resettings of the longer sleep wake cycle. A night's sleep deprivation is a phase resetting on a grand scale, which will likely have consequences for short time scale phase resettings.

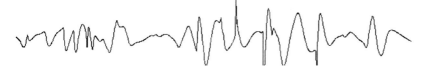

Figure 32. First derivative of the phase change between alpha waves between C3 and C4 over a 12-second period. Notice the moments of abrupt acceleration and deceleration corresponding to instants of phase resettings. The flat plateaus represent periods of phase maintenance. From Neuroguide: www.appliedneuroscience.com.

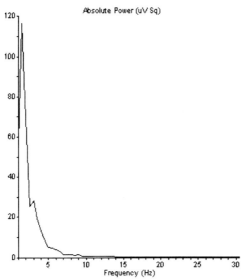

Figure 33. Frequency spectrum of the curve from the previous figure. It represents a power law (1/f) distribution, a characteristic of "self-organizing criticality." From Neuroguide: www.appliedneuroscience.com.

Summary

The phase of EEG waves in distinct frequency bands are reset regularly, both spontaneously and in reaction to external stimuli. This enables the brain system to react to internal or external inputs in an adaptive way, allowing the history of the complex brain system to determine the evoked brain activity. A "supervisor" does not control attention, certainly not over a long time. Attention arises through spontaneous self-organization via interaction with the internal and external environment to which the brain responds through its "situated" adaption.

The phase as well as the phase resettings of EEG waves demonstrate a 1/f pink noise distribution, signifying that smooth brain state changes occur as the situation requires in the form of event related desynchronization. In ADHD, there are probably less phase resettings. The time series demonstrate less pink noise. Consequently, we may expect fewer tasks adaptive functioning. Less phase resettings are characteristic of decreased vigilance and decreased working memory.

6.

Neurofeedback (EEG-Biofeedback)

6.1 Neurophysiological Effects of Ritalin and Dextroamphetamine

For over 50 years and increasingly more since the 1990s, Ritalin and dextroamphetamine have been used to treat ADHD worldwide. The scientific literature generally describes them as a safe and effective (with a beneficial effect in 80% of cases), provided the correct diagnosis (Barkley, 1997). These medicines increase the availability of dopamine and noradrenalin in the synaptic junction between connecting neurons in the caudate nucleus, resulting in improvements in attention, hyperactivity, impulsivity, and in the "executive functions" including working memory, sense of time, planning and organization, and problem solving ability, among others. Moreover, they improve adaptive motivation and decrease mood swings.

Reaction times are longer for boring tasks and decrease in response to stimulating complex tasks. Such findings in people with ADHD persuaded the Canadian psychologist Virginia Douglas (1972) that the core deficit is an impoverished ability to adapt to changing situations and task specific requirements. Ritalin bolsters the ability of children with ADHD to maintain attention when they make mistakes or are uncertain of their performance as task requirements change. Ritalin facilitates intensive information processing to challenging subtasks, reflecting better regulation.

During Ritalin treatment, the EEG shows normalization of the theta/beta-1 "distractibility index" and an increase in sleep spindles during sleep. The improvements in attention and behavior seem much greater if this index is initially more aberrant. If Ritalin does not normalize this EEG index, there is often no effect on behavior. Ritalin works predominately by increasing the availability of dopamine in the deep brain grey matter structures (striatum and caudate nucleus), which form part of a circuit that includes the DLPFC (dorsolateral prefrontal cortex), and thus improves functioning in this circuit. Studies have shown that dopamine transporter proteins are present in greater quantities in the caudate nucleus of people with ADHD. These proteins form part of the cell membrane of the neuron from which dopamine is released and bind the available dopamine in the synaptic junction connecting two neurons so that it is returned to the releasing neuron. Ritalin blocks this dopamine transporter protein as well as vacant positions on the dopamine receptors of the dopamine releasing neuron, making more dopamine available to stimulate dopamine receptor positions on the postsynaptic neuron.

This leads to an improved signal to noise relationship in the system, which in turn leads to a reduction in excessive distractibility of attentional processes and better guidance of the associated divergent thinking. More dopamine in the DLPFC can lead to better working memory and therefore improved goal focused thinking. Dopamine also strongly activates the anterior cingulate, leading to more control of attentional processes.

Dopamine intake normalizes the caudate nucleus and the putamen (basal ganglia) that are under active in the go/no-go task in ADHD, as already mentioned. Normalization of nucleus caudate activity leads to a decrease in thalamocortical "burst" activity and thus lowers frontal and central EEG theta waves. Therefore, 40 Hz activity improves and, consequently, focused attention and "conscious" perception heighten.

Ritalin does not only improve attention. We need to consider its "total effect." Adults and children with ADHD are not only more attentive and calmer, but their moods stabilize, impulsivity and emotional reactivity decrease, boring chores become easier to initiate, and organization skills become more fluent. Nevertheless, according to various articles in the popular press, medication with Ritalin remains controversial. One root of this controversy is the difficulty of our society to understand the true nature of ADHD. Our society often attributes motivational and self-regulation difficulties to psychological causes ("he can do it when he wants to") or to the consequences of upbringing. If this were truly the cause, it would indeed be inappropriate to treat this condition with medication. The truth is that Ritalin improves functioning of an inadequate brain mechanism, finally allowing the personality to develop fully in someone with ADHD.

Another misapprehension is that Ritalin is a drug comparable to cocaine. There is indeed some similarity to cocaine regarding their functioning, but otherwise Ritalin is unique in its speed, mode of action in the brain, and in normalizing these poorly functioning mechanisms. In contrast with cocaine, individuals experience longer lasting action but no "high" or immediate or intense flash effect. Thus, Ritalin is not addictive. Ritalin selectively affects areas of the caudate nucleus that relate to attentional functions while cocaine, like alcohol for example, also acts on areas such as the ventral striatum (nucleus accumbens), producing a feeling of euphoria that also contributes to the mechanism of addiction.

It is certainly true that people without ADHD can misuse Ritalin in order to work through the night, for example. This can lead to exhaustion phenomena, even depression and psychosis. However, that is a result of misuse. Precisely for this reason, prior accurate diagnosis is a necessity.

That Ritalin lowers creativity is another myth. It normalizes impulsivity and mood changes. Awareness of time also increases so that the momentary enthusiasms are less powerful. This can give the impression that the medicated individual is less inspired. In reality, the creativity of someone with ADHD is somewhat anarchic. Healthy creativity needs to be somewhat streamlined to keep the goal in mind. In fact, Ritalin has been shown to increase creativity in verbal tasks in people with ADHD.

Of course, Ritalin cannot "cure" ADHD as the symptoms reappear on ceasing medication. There may be unwelcome side effects and, as already mentioned, Ritalin does not work for everyone. The effects of long-term Ritalin use are unknown. These are all good reasons for the need to discover alternative treatments that would have as good an effect as Ritalin on the mechanisms underlying ADHD. Increasing understanding of these mechanisms has lead to the development of neurofeedback therapy.

Summary

Psychostimulants, such as Ritalin, normalize the theta/beta 1 ratio in the EEG of someone with ADHD and increase sleep spindles in the sleep EEG. This improves self-regulation, attention, and executive functions, resulting in overall more flexible, stable behavioral patterns.

6.2 Neurofeedback: Method and EEG Indications

During a neurofeedback session, a child (or an adult) with, metal electrodes attached to the scalp, sits before a computer screen displaying a simple computer game that is responsive to the moments when the targeted EEG activity is reached. Every now and then, a feedback reward signal appears onscreen when the stabilizing beta-1 or SMR activity exceeds a predetermined threshold and, at the same time, theta activity stays below a predetermined threshold. This is certainly the best-studied training protocol for people with ADHD and best suited to the most common abnormal QEEG patterns in ADHD.

Figure 34. On the left of the screen, a column indicates the theta wave strength moment by moment, on the right a column indicates momentary variations in the strength of SMR activity (or slow beta waves). The threshold value is marked on both columns. The instant that theta waves stay under the threshold while SMR waves stay above threshold, the game score increases.

In neurofeedback therapy, positive feedback is given the moment theta waves stay strictly under a threshold and SMR or beta-1-waves are clearly above threshold. This constitutes the process of operant conditioning, that is, certain "operations" ("behaviors" in the EEG) are rewarded immediately following the desired behavioral change. In this way, it is hoped to achieve a progressive and eventually permanent improvement in EEG "behaviors" and reorganization of the associated behaviors. Each session lasts about half an hour. The game score is tracked in a table and the theta/beta-1 ratio is obtained in order to monitor progress over 20 to 40 sessions. After the completion of a successful course of training, some further monthly sessions are recommended for consolidation.

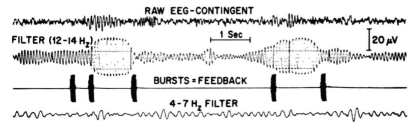

Figure 35. The raw EEG signal with the resultant filtered 12-14HZ and 4-7 Hz rhythms displayed below.

The first research studies applied SMR-neurofeedback (EEG-biofeedback) to cats in the late 1960s and found that the trained cats became more vigilant and less vulnerable to epilepsy. The first clinical treatment was given to people with epilepsy in the 1970s. In 1976, Lubar described the first clinical application to ADHD. Wider use in clinical practice did not occur until the 1990s and initially happened almost exclusively in the United States. Availability of computers enabled this broad dissemination, which was applied primarily to ADHD. Since 1976 (Lubar, 2000) an increasing number of published research studies focused on this area. The origin and early dissemination of neurofeedback was independent of QEEG. In those early years, practical applications of neurofeedback were based on loose, simple clinical models, and training protocols were applied without evaluating the EEG. Since 1995, the trend has been to use QEEG in the development and evaluation of the training protocol. The utility of QEEG has remained limited since frequency spectrum analysis enabled only certain EEG waves to be selected and strengthened or weakened by training. Many neurofeedback therapists hold the rather simple view that the EEG pattern thus marked for modification relates directly to behavioral change. A targeted reduction in theta activity is from this perspective interpreted as an expression of improved alertness. Another hypothesis is that the thalamocortical dysrhythmia is corrected based on a dysfunctional caudate nucleus. Lubar (1997) advocated another perspective, suggesting that training at the vertex (Cz) triggers an improvement in anterior cingulate functioning along the midline. This area plays a key role in "executive attention" (Posner & Dehaene, 1994) and activates the frontal areas (in which executive functions are thought to arise) and other areas from there. The anterior cingulate also plays a central role in response inhibition and stimulus conflict monitoring.

Although there are often positive objective behavioral changes and multiple studies exist that have measured a normalization of the trained EEG frequencies (Monastra, 2002), changes in the EEG or other EEG alterations that were not directly trained are not always objective. Multiple explanations have been suggested. One view is that the EEG trains mechanisms, not statistical changes; therefore, statistical QEEG measurements cannot always show these (Othmer, Othmer, & Kaiser 1999). Another, more nuanced argument is that training brings about wider changes in EEG patterns (Sterman, 1980; Cinciripini, 1984; Tansey, 1991; Rossiter, 2002; Delorme, 2002) and this can better explain the behavioral changes. The goal of the most popular training protocol is to increase the number of SMR rhythms (12-15 Hz in the sensorimotor cortex) rendering the over rigid EEG system more variable. At the same time, the SMR system can prevent derailment of the rhythm of the system. Sterman and Tansey demonstrated that the global EEG spectrum normalized in this way, showing an increase in alpha and beta-1 activity and a decrease in theta and beta-2 activity. Rossiter also found that successful training increased alpha activity and decreased beta activity. Likewise, Cinciripini (1984) demonstrated an increase in alpha waves after SMR training. All findings regarding EEG spectrum normalization can be understood within Bente's interpretive framework, which interprets such EEG stabilization as an optimization of "vigilance." In Bente's terms, this represents optimization of the individual's functional ability to adapt to internal and external changes in various circumstances. This understanding is therefore more complete than the one based on "activation level," which suggests that frontal modulation of the EEG via inhibitory neuronal circuits optimizes "vigilance."

Moreover, Lubar (1995) noted that following successful training, EEG spectrum changes were not localized to one or two points on the scalp where the electrodes were placed during training but that small changes in frequency spectra were spread over the whole scalp. Lubar (1997) remarked that many neural pathways linked these different brain areas. Those patients that showed no changes in quantity of theta after neurofeedback also showed no indications of changes in other areas in the QEEG. Therefore, the EEG pattern in ADHD, with its similarities to the EEG of a normal person after sleep deprivation, normalizes.

It is also very well known that after successful SMR/theta training, sleep quality improves, accompanied by a normalization of EEG spectra during sleep and an increase in stabilizing sleep spindles (Sterman, 1970, 1978; Hauri, 1983). Although we cannot always measure changes in the statistical EEG in rest states after a rounded EEG neurofeedback treatment, there are often changes also in cognitive electrophysiological activity. In comparison with measurements prior to training, the P300 strengthens during an attention task (Egner, 2001), and the P3 potential strengthens during the "no-go" condition in a response inhibition task (Saraev, Kropotov, & Ponomarev, 2002). Following the treatment, the event related synchronization and desynchronization normalize in the EEG (Kropotov, 2004b). There are indications that other EEG frequencies are trained often in a different location to the trained localization (Delorme, 2002). The coherence of certain EEG frequency bands between different brain areas has been found to be normalized (Cohen, 2005).

Recently, there has been a trend to examine not just the effect at different frequency bands during training, but also the degree of coherence, although this is still rather experimental to date.

6.3 Threshold Values for Neurofeedback

From the end of the 1960s until 1977, research has exclusively recognized 12-15 Hz training, which gave positive results in epilepsy and in ADHD (e.g., in many Sterman and Lubar studies in the 1970s and 1980s). In the 1970s, Sterman and Lubar had demonstrated that the SMR rhythm occurs in bursts lasting 0.5 to 2 seconds, occurring about 10 to 20 times a minute in typical controls. Based on the previous research, frequently only five bursts per minute occur in ADHD and epilepsy. Originally, feedback in the form of a light flash and a tone was given at the moment an SMR burst occurred. After a successful course of treatment that consisted of at least 60 neurofeedback sessions, the quantity of SMR bursts normalized to 10 to 20 per minute. Thus, this original method provided feedback only when an SMR burst occurred – independent of the signal strength of the burst. Graphs from these early treatment studies often clearly show that signal strength also increases. Since 1977, a decrease in 4-7 Hz was added to the treatment protocol because it was found that due to inherent problems with the analog filter method employed, 12-15 Hz rose at moments when 4-10 Hz was actually present. Afterwards, it appeared that decreasing the 4-7 Hz itself played an important functional role in bringing epilepsy and ADHD under control. Lubar was the first to produce a computer treatment protocol as a DOS computer program ("Autogenics").

In 1991, Lubar wrote that he sometimes strayed from the principle of a fixed SMR threshold. Using the original method, he had found that while learning certainly occurred, it frequently required 60 sessions. In his new method, he set the SMR threshold for the first sessions at 2 μV, followed by some sessions at 3 μV, then by 3.8 μV, 4 μV, 4.3 μV, and finally 5 μV. Likewise, the theta thresholds systematically decreased five times. Generally, 30 sessions seemed sufficient. He argued that this method produced faster learning curves with less trouble and was, therefore, a superior clinical approach. On the other hand, Lubar has elsewhere described that SMR mostly demonstrates amplitude of 5-6 μV, and that over the course of training, the number of bursts, but not their amplitude, increases. The original studies demonstrate that SMR amplitude is frequently higher in normal subjects than in people with epilepsy or ADHD.

Lubar (1995) adjusted his power or amplitude training protocol so that reward/feedback signals for children occurred during 15 to 25% of the training time and that during this feedback time, SMR (12-15 Hz) or beta (16-20 Hz) were maintained for at least 500 ms above the threshold. As soon as the feedback was consistent 25% of the time, the difficulty of threshold attainment was increased. Lubar's golden rule was that the feedback should be established in the first session to deliver a reward 30 to 50% of the time, and the inhibitory threshold should be established so that inhibition occurs 50 to 70% of the time. Lubar reported that using this method, adults scored 7 to 15 points per minute and children younger than 12 scored between 10 to 25 points per minute. Overall, trainees received about 10 rewards per minute during the first session. If the thresholds are fixed in the first session and maintained over the following sessions, then a successful training can be described as finally achieving rewards 50 to 70% of the time and inhibition 30 to 50% of the time.

Lubar set the reward threshold for children at 50%, for adolescents at 40%, and for adults at 30%. The inhibit thresholds for the three groups were respectively 50%, 60%, and 70% (Lubar, 2000). For children, it is less frustrating if the rewards follow each other quickly. However, a disadvantage is that lowered signal strength of 12-15 Hz activity is also awarded in addition to SMR bursts. With favorable training, the degree of difficulty may increase, bearing in mind the abovementioned advantages and disadvantages. Othmer decreased the degree of difficulty with a reward threshold set at 70% (see section 6.18). In this manner, rewards are easily obtained (often in the form of a progressing game or video), but doubts may be raised whether "real" SMR bursts are being rewarded. Children do enjoy a wonderful game, but the question is if it is still EEG training.

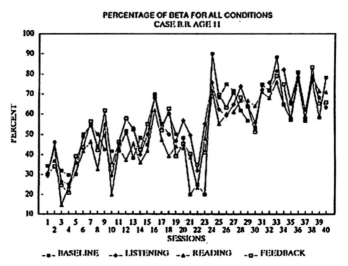

Figure 36. Case study of an 11 year old boy in which the percentage of the time that beta-1 waves rose above the reward threshold increased from around 30% to 70% over 40 sessions. With kind permission from Springer Science+Business Media: Biofeedback and Self-Regulation, 16(3), 1991, 201-225, Lubar.

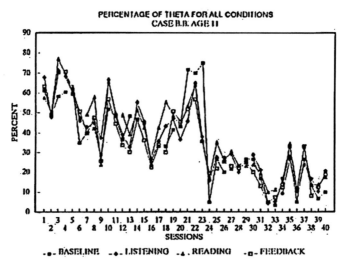

Figure 37. Case study of an 11-year-old boy with ADHD in which the percentage of the time in which theta waves rose above the inhibit threshold decreased from 70% to 20% over forty sessions. With kind permission from Springer Science+Business Media: Biofeedback and Self-Regulation, 16(3), 1991, 201-225, Lubar.

Thompson & Thompson (1998) used a minimum duration of 500 ms for power or amplitude to cross a threshold with a feedback at a rate of 15 to 20 points per minute. To combat boredom in children, a rate of 30 to 40 points a minute proved better. Sometimes it helped to set a reward threshold 0.05 μV above the SMR average value or average beta-1 baseline and an inhibit threshold 1 μV under the average theta base line.

In 2003, the prominent German/English research group (Fuchs, Birbaumer, Lutzenberger, Gruzelier, and Kaiser) set the reward threshold for SMR and beta at 60% of the time with the condition that the minimum duration of a rewarded 'burst' should be 500 ms. Similarly, theta activity had to stay below the threshold 70% of the time for a minimum duration of 500 ms. Thus, an ideal difficulty level of the training as determined by the thresholds lay between that set by Lubar and Othmer. The reward threshold increased if the reward threshold was exceeded 70% of the time for two consecutive sessions. The inhibit threshold decreased if theta amplitude stayed below threshold 85 to 90 % of the time over two sessions, which is in line with Lubar's practice with over 30 years experience. Another possibility exists to set an automatic reward threshold during the first two minutes of the initial training session at 40%, for instance, and an automatic inhibit threshold of 60%, both remaining fixed thereafter.

6.4 Evolution of the EEG Over the Course of Treatment

Lubar (Lubar & Lubar, 1999) suggested that training was completed if the theta/beta-1 ratio normalized or if the reward increased from 30% to 50% to 50% to 70% and the inhibit decreased from 70% to 50% to 50% to 30%. Over the course of training, a record in the form of tables and graphs summarized reward and inhibit percentages, average amplitude values of the trained frequency bands, and the alpha and beta-2 bands. In addition, the scores were recorded for each session. The standard deviations and the coefficient of variation were also useful. The coefficient of variation is the ratio of the standard deviation to the mean value and is thus a measure of the relative variability of the signal. The variability coefficients for theta, beta-1, and for the theta/beta-1 ratio often decline both within a session and over consecutive sessions. Changes in all of these variables are not a necessary condition for a successful course of treatment. Changes in any one will often suffice.

A decreased variability coefficient, in Lubar's view, is a major indication that a more stable state was maintained during the session and that fluctuations between consecutive sessions were also more stable. This may reveal a better balance and better homeostasis between dynamic brain systems as reflected in EEG macrosystem dynamics.

Lubar described some incidences of satisfactory treatment accompanied by little reduction in variability. In such cases, no decrease occurred in average theta or beta amplitude or in the theta/beta-1 ratio over the course of treatment, but fluctuations around the average value certainly decreased over the final six sessions.

6.5 First Neurofeedback Studies

At the end of the sixties, SMR neurofeedback was studied for the first time by Sterman. He investigated the EEG characteristics of the transition from wakefulness to sleep in cats and apes. Sterman was inspired by Pavlov's model of "internal inhibition," a process occurring during the extinction of learned behavior. Pavlov employed a classical conditioning experiment in which hearing a tone on provision of food led ultimately to the dogs salivating upon hearing the tone in the absence of food. A different tone signaled that an electric shock would follow on pulling their paw away from a handle. Whenever the two tones gradually became more and more similar to each other, the dogs no longer exhibited the conditioned behavior and eventually fell asleep. Pavlov called this process "internal inhibition." Sterman, who was initially interested in the EEG correlations during the transition from sleep to waking, saw Pavlov's "internal inhibition" as a possible model. He approached this using another method, that is, he trained cats using operant rather than classical conditioning. In the first phase, the animals received 2 cc of milk and a chicken cube if they pushed a handle. In the second phase of the experiment, a food reward was given only if they learned not to push the handle upon hearing a tone. As long as the handle was pressed, the tone continued and stopped only when the handle was released. Whenever the cats learned to refrain from pressing the handle during the tone, an SMR rhythm was measurable in the EEG. After the reward was received, a parietal post reinforcement alpha rhythm appeared.

In the next phase of his experiment, Sterman trained the cats via operant conditioning to increase the SMR rhythm directly to obtain rewards. This was accomplished easily, and, in the first session, the SMR rhythms occurred after 5 to 10 seconds. Inhibition of movement together with a lowered muscle tone was a necessary but not sufficient condition to generate SMR rhythms. After 150 to 200 conditioned SMR responses, satiety was reached and there was no interest to continue further training in the same session.

Figure 38. One of Sterman's cats during an SMR experiment (Image appears with permission from Barry Sterman).

Immediately following reward of SMR, the PRS rhythm (post reinforcement rhythm) also frequently occurred in these cats' parietal EEG (Howe and Sterman, 1972). This reflects brief moments of satiety and "drive reduction" following a reward.

If this learning process went well, the density of sleep spindles during sleep would increase, being accompanied by fewer moments of awakening in the course of sleep. The epilepsy threshold for these cats increased following injection of an epileptogenic GABA antagonist. This suggests that sensitivity of thalamocortical circuits decreased in these animals. Muscles relaxed, giving less sensory feedback from muscles to the thalamus, leading to consequent hyperpolarization of the ventroposterolateral nucleus.

This led to an increase in SMR rhythms and thus to stabilization of sleep and wake patterns.

These results prompted Sterman to apply this training to people with epilepsy. He subsequently demonstrated concomitant improvements in frontal executive functions. In 1976, Lubar described an amelioration of hyperactivity and attention disorders in a hyperactive child with epilepsy. The training protocol was refined in subsequent studies to strengthen 12-15 Hz (SMR) and weaken 4-7 Hz (theta).

In the eighties, Tansey (1985) undertook multiple studies, demonstrating positive clinical effects of this treatment for children with various types of learning difficulties comorbid with attentional problems. A typical course of treatment consisted of 20 to 40 weekly half hour sessions and boosted the quantity of SMR rhythm.

6.6 Controlled Studies

One of the legitimate criticisms of these early studies is that they did not control for confounding factors, that is, they did not make comparison with an untreated control group. This began to change in 1995 when Cartozzo examined the effects of 12-15 Hz training on eight children with ADHD in comparison with an untreated ADHD control group. He found significant improvement in the treated group, but not controls, on WISC-R IQ subscales: arithmetic, digit span, and coding. These 'load' working memory and are therefore sensitive to attentional difficulties. The treated group showed significant improvement on an attentional test (TOVA: Test of Variables of Attention). In the same year, Scheinbaum (1995) performed a controlled study providing neurofeedback training and outcomes to eight children with ADHD. The ADHD control group received training in a mathematical computer game. The treated group performed better on the TOVA and received better ratings on a behavioral scale.

Rossiter (1995) published a controlled study of a group of 46 children with ADHD. The subgroup that received neurofeedback training showed an improvement equivalent to a group treated with Ritalin or dextro-amphetamine. Nineteen of the twenty-three children who had received neurofeedback showed clear improvements. In 2004, the same author repeated this study, obtaining the same results for a group of 62 children with ADHD, half of whom received neurofeedback and the other half Ritalin or dextroamphetamine.

Linden (1996) performed a controlled single blind study (in which the researcher did not know the participants' treatment group) of 18 children with ADHD. Nine children received 40 neurofeedback sessions; the other nine were placed on a treatment waiting list. A significant improvement in attention and in aggressive and hyperactive behaviors was measured in the treated group only.

More recently, a number of large-scale studies were conducted with more than a 100 children and adult participants in the United States (Othmer, Othmer, & Kaiser, 1999; Thompson & Thompson, 1998). Neuropsychological attention tests and behavioral rating scales showed positive results, but there was no ADHD control group available for comparison. Despite this shortcoming, these results remain impressive because those children and adults who previously had little response to other treatments often resort to neurofeedback, thus, it is less probable that a placebo effect can wholly explain these results. Thompson's study included 100 child participants, 30 of whom took Ritalin from the start of the treatment. At the end of the treatment, only six of these children (20%) appeared to still need Ritalin.

Leins (2004) assessed a group of children with ADHD who had received neurofeedback training to lower the theta/beta-1 ratio at C3 and/or C4. Leins found a good response in 30% of the children.

Rossiter (2002) published an exhaustive case study of a 13-year-old boy with ADHD, who also attained a lower theta/beta-1 ratio trained at C3 or C4. Rossiter remarked on the advantage of having only a single parameter displayed on screen, in this case the theta/beta-1 ratio, as a measure of activation level thus making feedback clearer to the trainee. He set the threshold at 1.2 to 1.3 times the average ratio obtained during the first session. The very simple instruction asked to keep the column below threshold as much as possible and the screen, next to the on screen column, displayed the cumulative percentage success rate. A tone sounded if the column fell under threshold. Rossiter strongly advised against experimenting with different goal reaching strategies. After 45 sessions, good clinical outcomes were attained, i.e., the theta/beta-1 ratio was lowered from 33.21 to 28.70 and theta amplitude decreased from 11.14 µV to 9.79 µV while SMR and beta (15-18 Hz) amplitude showed virtually no change. There was a slight increase in alpha amplitude from 6.44 µV to 6.92 µV and a slight decrease in beta-2 (22-39 Hz) amplitude from 4.82 µV to 4.54 µV. This discrete global stabilization of the EEG spectrum is comparable with Sterman and Tansey's findings. The standard deviation of the theta/beta-1 ratio and theta amplitude also decreased, as did the variation coefficient (the ratio of the standard deviation to the mean value). The last variable indicates that the trained parameters decreased not only in absolute terms, but also in relative terms, pointing to an increasingly stable, less labile signal. The standard deviation of the alpha amplitude and the variability coefficient increased (and therefore signal variability).

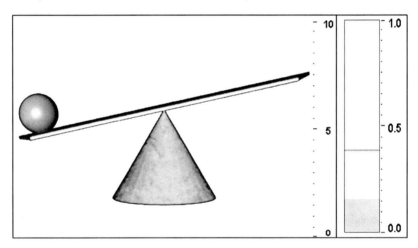

Figure 39. Screen display for training of theta/beta-1 or theta/SMR ratio. The column indicates the value of this ratio at any given moment. The goal is to keep this column under the threshold as much as possible. Success is indicated whenever the animation shows the ball rolling to the left in accordance with the instruction to keep the ball to the left as much as possible.

Linda Thompson, who scrupulously followed Lubar's training protocols in her published studies, wrote in her handbook (Thompson & Thompson, 2003) that in daily clinical practice, she used individualized training protocols, as Lubar did. She used a theta/SMR ratio and a theta/16-20 Hz ratio trainings protocol, similar to the protocol employed in Rossiter's case study.

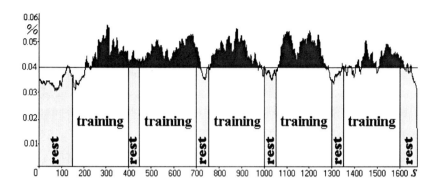

*Figure 40. Progress of a boy with ADHD during the 15th neurofeedback ses-
sion in which the ratio between beta-1 (15-18 Hz) and the rest of the frequency spectrum between 0.5 and 30 Hz was trained over 5 minute periods (300
seconds) with short rest pauses. During feedback, the ratio clearly increases,
falling back again during rest. A smooth curve joins the points in the graph,
creating false impression that there is no moment and that the ratio is above
threshold during basic measurement and during rest periods and that during
neurofeedback segments, the ratio is practically never above the threshold.
Reprinted from International Journal of Psychophysiology, 55(1), Kropotov,
Grin-Yatsenko, Ponomarev, Chutko, Yakovenko, & Nikishena, ERPs correlates of EEG relative beta training in ADHD children, Copyright (2004), with
permission from Elsevier.*

Kropotov (Kropotov, Grin-Yatsenko, Ponomarev, Chutko, Yakovenko, & Nikishena, 2004) published an analogous study in which the ratio of beta and
SMR was trained at C3-Fz or C4-Pz in a group of 86 children. The threshold
was set so that this ratio was above threshold 50% of the time during the first
baseline measurement. The ratio increased in sessions 15 through 22 but this
improvement was never maintained after the end of each session. Nevertheless 82% of the children showed clinical improvement and an improvement
in the go/no-go evoked P3 brain potential, which indicates a functional improvement in parietal stimulus evaluation and frontal response inhibition.

Monastra (2002) followed 101 children with ADHD who were treated with
Ritalin, and received parent counseling and educational support. A condition
of participation in the study was an abnormally high EEG distractibility index
(theta/beta-1) ratio. In addition, 51 of the children received neurofeedback

training aimed at normalization of this index. Overall, participants completed 43 training sessions. Twelve months later the trained group showed significant improvement on behavioral scale ratings, as assessed by parents and teachers. This improvement was seen even after the discontinuation of medication for a week! Lubar (1995) had previously shown that, following neurofeedback, 11 out of 17 children and young adults showed clear improvement and normalization of the theta/beta-1 ratio.

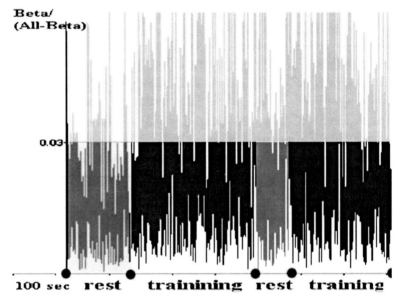

Figure 41. Fragment of neurofeedback session with the same training protocol as in figure 40 showing an increase of beta-1 compared to the rest (all-beta) of the EEG spectrum. All measurement points are displayed without smoothing the curve (as in the previous figure). It is clear that during rest moments, values of the trained ratio frequently lay under the 0.03 reward threshold, but it is also true that it is above threshold from time to time. In the very first session, the threshold was set so that the measured values were above threshold 50% of the time. During training sessions measured values were frequently above threshold, but also regularly below it. This is an early session, in contrast to the previous figure in which the reward threshold is higher. Reprinted from International Journal of Psychophysiology, 55(1), Kropotov et al., ERPs correlates of EEG relative beta training in ADHD children, Copyright (2004), with permission from Elsevier.

As far back as 1977, Lubar noticed during SMR training for epilepsy an increased quantity of SMR during early sessions, which was not maintained after the end of the sessions. During the final sessions of the treatment, the amount of SMR before and after the sessions increased, which he regarded as necessary; that is, training would have been futile if this transfer had not occurred. He emphasized, as Sterman had in the infancy of neurofeedback, that the thinking behind the training is the attainment of a permanent reorganization of the nervous system. Undoubtedly, Sterman had demonstrated in 1980 that isolated training of the SMR rhythm could lead to global normalization of the EEG (with a decrease in theta and slowed beta activity).

Tansey, who trained SMR at Cz (at the middle of the skull), found that a decrease in theta activity accompanied this change. He visualized the brain as a functional network of reciprocal links enabling the possibility that any pattern of neural activation may trigger a change in the entire matrix. Sterman (1980) had independently reached the same conclusion through his research. He considered SMR as a catalyst for a synergetic EEG normalization. Extending this line of thought, Monastra's distractibility index provides a measure of the functional integration of the unregulated subsystems in ADHD.

Lubar, Swartwood, Swartwood, & O'Donnell (1995) demonstrated that at least 20 to 40 sessions (1 to 2 times a week) are necessary to reach the desired goal followed by several monthly sessions to consolidate the training. Lubar (2003) obtained good results for 80% of treated children and adults, or 52 patients in total. Moreover, these gains appeared to be maintained after 10 years as assessed by the Conners' Behavioral Rating Scale, general attitude, ability to complete tasks, better school results, and improved relationships with friends, family, and others.

Fuchs (2003) studied a group of 34 children aged from 8 to 12 years, of whom 22 were treated with neurofeedback and 12 with Ritalin. Both groups showed similar improvement on the TOVA and behavioral scales as rated by teachers and parents.

Since 2003, a number of methodologically stronger studies published the positive effects of neurofeedback for people with ADHD. The German research group of Birbaumer, who studied slow cortical potential neurofeedback for years (see Chapter 8), published the first comparative study of slow cortical potentials neurofeedback and theta/beta neurofeedback for ADHD in 2004 (Leine, 2004). Both forms of neurofeedback appeared to deliver comparable clinical results. A later study (Strehl, 2006), in which the effects appeared to be maintained at 6 months (Leine, 2007) and at 2 years follow-up (Gani, 2008), confirmed this finding. Not only self-regulation of the EEG was maintained, but also the clinical results. After 2 years, half of the treated children no longer met the ADHD diagnostic criteria, with further improvements in the clinical situation immediately following the end of the course of treatment.

Bakhshayesh (2007) compared the effectiveness of neurofeedback among 18 children with ADHD with the results of EMG biofeedback in 17 children with ADHD (with the same visual and auditory feedback). Bakhshayesh found that the effectiveness of neurofeedback clearly surpassed EMG biofeedback.

Two new neurofeedback studies in 2009 provided comparison to computerized cognitive training (i.e., control group), which in itself was an important improvement in design. Moreover, both studies employed randomized trials, which finally addressed the shortcomings of earlier studies. Gevensleben (2009) studied 102 children with ADHD and the outcomes were clearly better for half of the children treated with neurofeedback. Neurofeedback consisted of a block of 18 sessions of theta/beta training and a block of 18 slow cortical potential training sessions. Both neurofeedback trainings gave similar results. In a later publication (Gevensleben, 2010), the changes in the EEG of these two groups of children were examined. There were no significant differences in baseline activity between the neurofeedback group and the cognitive training group, except, the former showed clear decrease in theta activity over central and theta midline (Cz, Pz). Moreover, higher theta baseline activity and a greater decline after theta/beta training were linked to clinical improvement.

Holtmann (2009) compared the outcome of theta/beta training among 20 children with ADHD with the results of a computerized cognitive training among 14 children with ADHD. In this study, the results of a neurophysiological inhibition task (stop error negativity, ERN) were clearly better in the neurofeedback group.

6.7 Neurofeedback in American Schools

"A Chance To Grow/New Visions School" program suggests a way to offer neurofeedback in schools as a supplementary program. New Visions opened their doors in America in 1991 to provide small-scale public schools that welcome children both with and without learning difficulties. These schools meet specific needs of children, including speech therapy, physical therapy, or auditory phonic training, among others.

"A Chance To Grow," the new visions school program in Minneapolis, launched a neurofeedback program in 1994. In that first year, 42 children were treated while 53 children were treated in the following school year 1995-1996. The outcome of the training of 65 pupils in the school year 1996-1997 was closely assessed. Attention tests were administered prior to the treatment. As a rule, the children received a half hour session twice a week. Overall, 33 pupils who received a minimum of 20 sessions were reassessed after treatment. All these children had struggled with the attentional tests prior to the treatment program. Following treatment, 83% of students showed significant improvement on at least four measures of the attentional tests: 44% showed improvements in attention, 39% showed decreased impulsivity, and 61% showed improvements in sustained attention.

The following case studies illustrate how training can bring about specific behavioral changes and skill improvements:

1) A 12-year-old girl was initially seen for serious attention difficulties and some impulsivity. She was stubborn, seemed angry, and suffered from low self-esteem. After 54 sessions of neurofeedback, she showed clear improvements on an attention test, showing improvements on impulsivity and sustained attention. Her reading scores improved as did her attitude and self-image.

2) A 12-year-old boy was referred for hyperactivity, impulsivity, behavioral problems, and learning difficulties. He was anxious, depressed, frustrated, and constantly busy and yet easily gave up. His class teacher reported that he was verbally and physically aggressive, had poor relations with his peers, and exhibited disruptive behavior in class. After 60 sessions of neurofeed-

back, his attentional tests markedly improved. He was less impulsive and more attentive. His impulsivity and attitude improved, though he remained a difficult pupil.

3) An 11-year-old girl diagnosed with ADHD and receiving Ritalin treatment was referred for attentional problems and hyperactivity. After a course of neurofeedback sessions, attention and sustained attention improved on testing. She took Ritalin prior to the first attentional test, but not prior to the post-training test. However, impulsivity remained a problem.

4) A 13-year-old boy was referred for attentional problems, sleep problems, low self-esteem, and temper tantrums. A diagnosis of ADHD was made. All attention scale measures showed a clear improvement after neurofeedback training. His teachers said he was more attentive in class, his sleep normalized, and self-image improved.

6.8 Double Blind Studies

Until very recently, no double blind studies (in which neither the therapist nor the patient knows for sure who is in the group which received neurofeedback, or in a control group given pseudo-neurofeedback) had been undertaken. From a scientific viewpoint, this has been a major weakness for some years; fortunately, several double blind studies have been published lately.

In 2004, DeBeus performed the first randomized double blind study of the therapeutic efficacy of neurofeedback training for children in which 53 children with ADHD (ages 7 to 11) completed 40 sessions with a cross over in treatment group after 20 sessions. During each session, every child had a metal electrode placed on the scalp (Fz) and watched a video game. For the first group, brain activity (neurofeedback) modulated the video game for 20 sessions, followed by 20 sessions in which brain activity (pseudo-neurofeedback) no longer modulated the game. The second group received the same treatment in reverse order. The real neurofeedback sessions improved attention, hyperactivity, aggressive behavior, adaptability to change, social interactions, and organizational skills. In addition, study habits and a better attitude toward school improved. The treated group scored better on computerized attention tests and the results were more salient. Moreover, only this group showed a reduction in theta and increase in beta-1 activity. About a third of the children were able to reduce their dosage of Ritalin after neurofeedback.

Greco (2004) described similar outcomes with two groups of 18 boys with the hyperactive subtype of ADHD. The children were assigned randomly to one of two groups. The experimental group received 40 sessions of neurofeedback in the form of a video game while the control group played a video game with the same complexity and duration as the neurofeedback group. For those in the control group, measurements were made with EEG electrodes without providing feedback. The therapists knew the assignment of children to groups, but the children's parents and the researchers who evaluated any behavioral changes in the children did not. Overall, 47% of the control group and only 6% of the neurofeedback group did not complete the course of 40 sessions. The treatment group showed clear improvement on behavioral scales.

A third double blind study (Picard, 2006) ran in two phases. During the first phase, 31 children with an ADHD diagnosis and a theta/beta-1 ratio greater than 2.5 were assigned randomly to either a waiting list or a 40-session neurofeedback group (training to increase SMR and decrease theta). Only the children receiving neurofeedback improved on behavioral scale measurements. Neurofeedback measurements from the first phase were used to fake neurofeedback sessions in the second phase. In this second phase, 31 children were assigned randomly to one of three groups: a wait list group, a neurofeedback group, or a pseudo-neurofeedback group. Once again, only the neurofeedback group showed improvement on behavioral scales while the ratings for the group that received pseudo-neurofeedback and the wait list group did not evidence statistically meaningful changes.

6.9 Neurofeedback in Adults with ADHD

Traditionally, ADHD has been thought of as a psychiatric disease of children, and the therapeutic effect of ADHD medication was established mostly with children. More recently, the diagnoses and treatment of adult ADHD has been greatly extended.

ADHD in adults has been misconstrued for several reasons in the past as well as in the present. One is that ADHD has been viewed for many years as a developmental disorder of childhood. Another reason is that hyperactivity frequently disappears or diminishes in adulthood, becoming less conspicuous as it often converts into an internal unrest. Finally, it is often difficult for us to understand that an adult rather than a child cannot sufficiently structure his or her life and has inadequate will to control his or her behavior.

Neurofeedback has been studied mostly in children; however, a number of studies assessed the effects of neurofeedback training on adults.

Kaiser (1997) obtained positive results in a group of 142 adults with ADHD, aged 19 to 79 years old, with the mean age of 41 years. In this study, 12-15 Hz or 15-18 Hz activity was rewarded while 4-7 Hz and 22-30 Hz activity was inhibited, with training located at C3 or C4 over the 20 to 40 sessions. The great majority of the treated adults showed normalization in the aspects of sustained attention and impulsivity, as measured by a computerized attention task.

Tinius (2000) investigated the effect of 20 sessions of neurofeedback combined with cognitive training on psychological and neuropsychological functioning in 13 adults with ADD (ADHD without hyperactivity) and a separate group of 16 adults with moderate brain trauma. A control group of 15 adults took the same psychological and neuropsychological tests as the treatment groups before and after the beginning of the treatment, but received no treatment during this period.

Prior to the treatment, both groups, relative to healthy controls, showed abnormalities on neuropsychological tests including the IVA (Integrated Visual and Auditory Continuous Performance Test) and NIS (Neuropsychological Impairment Scale with subscales consisting of Cognitive Efficiency, Attention, Memory, Frustration Tolerance, Verbal Learning, and Academic Achievement). After the treatment, average scores for both patient groups became comparable to those of healthy controls. The neurofeedback protocols were individually fashioned based on prior QEEG examination. All members of the ADD group showed lowered theta and increased SMR trained at Cz, C3, or C4. Training corrected abnormal coherency values in a number of patients with mild brain injury.

Lubar (1999) described his experience with a group of adults with ADHD that did not exhibit increased theta but increased alpha activity at Cz or Fz, which was often more marked during cognitive tasks. He obtained good therapeutic outcomes in these patients utilizing training aimed at decreasing alpha and increasing beta-1.

Thompson & Thompson (2005) described QEEG patterns in a group of adults with ADHD and their application in forming appropriate training protocols. Section 4.2 discusses QEEG research findings in individuals with ADHD.

Summary

Neurofeedback can be understood as a learning process (specifically, operant conditioning) in which rewarding feedback signals are triggered every time the desired EEG pattern occurs. Another viewpoint argues that conscious self-regulation is involved to some degree. However, practitioners have come to think that in reality, this mechanism proceeds unconsciously.

The most popular training programs aim at increasing SMR rhythms or beta-1 rhythms and simultaneously decreasing theta activity. This enables better behavioral self-regulation, which consists of, among other things, improvements in attention and executive functions.

In the 1980s, Lubar published the first neurofeedback research on children with ADHD. In the 1990s, a series of single blind studies were published in which outcomes were compared with either an untreated control group or a group treated with Ritalin. In the present decade, a number of double blind studies have also been published. These more rigorous studies have supported the beneficial effects of neurofeedback training.

6.10 Changes in Cognitive Brain Potentials Following Neurofeedback

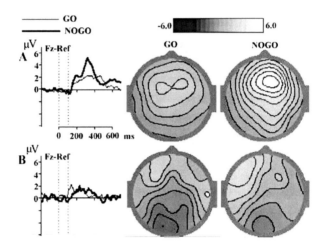

*Figure 42. **Left.** These images illustrate the average frontal potential values following neurofeedback training (uppermost trace) and preceding neurofeedback training (bottommost trace) among a group of 16 children with ADHD. Predominantly, the "no-go" P3 potential, and to a lesser degree the "go" P3 potential, is stronger after treatment. **Right.** These mappings illustrate the widely distribution of these potentials over the scalp. Reprinted from International Journal of Psychophysiology, 55(1), Kropotov et al., ERPs correlates of EEG relative beta training in ADHD children, Copyright (2004), with permission from Elsevier.*

Kropotov et al. (2004) demonstrated that the evoked frontal P3 brain potential measured in the go/no-go task (in which a response to the no-go stimulus must be suppressed) decreases following the no-go stimulus in people with ADHD. Source localization studies showed that this response-inhibition potential rises in the anterior cingulate along the midline of the inferior frontal cerebral cortex. Following successful neurofeedback training, with improvements in attentional functions and behavior, it has been found that this potential is normalizes, which reflects decreased impulsivity. Kropotov (2004b) also found normalization of the weaker beta and theta synchronization during the go/no-go task. On the other hand, successful training can lead to no improvement in EEG theta and beta activity.

Egner and Gruzelier (2001) observed a strengthened P300 (P3b) potential following neurofeedback training. As previously described, this brain potential is a measure of effective response selection in attentional tasks.

6.11 Pre- and Post-fMRI Studies of Neurofeedback for ADHD

Beauregard (2006) found that a series of 40 EEG biofeedback sessions (SMR/theta Cz protocol) improved executive functions in a group of children with ADHD. He provided further evidence by comparing fMRI brain function images before and after a course of neurofeedback. He was inspired by two previous fMRI imaging studies of children with ADHD discussed in paragraph 2.3.1 in which Vaidja (1998) observed an underactive nucleus caudate in ADHD during the go/no-go task and its normalization after Ritalin administration. Remember that for the control group, the nucleus caudate was more active and became less active after administration of Ritalin. Apparently, Ritalin had a different effect on children with ADHD in comparison to the children without ADHD.

The second study to influence Beauregard was undertaken by Bush et al. (1999) who found the anterior cingulate to be underactive in adults with ADHD performing the Stroop task (in which the participant must name the color in which a color word is printed, the print color being different from the color indicated by the word).

Beauregard (2006) investigated a group of 20 children with ADHD in which 15 followed a course of 40 neurofeedback sessions. Both groups of children took pre- and post-neuropsychological tests. Only the treated group showed clear improvements in hyperactivity and attention after the study. Both groups were imaged with pre- and post-fMRIs. Only the treated group showed increased activity in the left caudate nucleus and bilaterally in the lateral prefrontal cerebral cortex during the go/no-go task as well as increased in activity in the right frontal cerebral cortex during a Stroop task.

This corresponds with research by Kropotov et al. (2004), who found that the evoked electrical activity in the anterior cingulate, a measure of impulsivity, normalized after neurofeedback treatment.

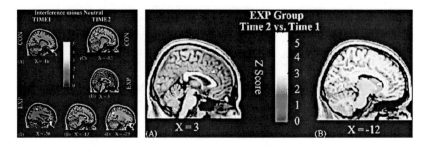

Figure 43. Small image on the left illustrates no activation of the anterior cingulate before neurofeedback in two groups of children with ADHD performing a go/no-go task. Right diagram shows only the group who received neurofeedback training, showing activation of the anterior cingulate during the Stroop task (left) after training as well as activation of the nucleus caudate after training during a go/no-go task (far right). Reprinted from Neuroscience Letters, 394(3), Beauregard, Effect of neurofeedback training on the neural substrates of selective attention in children with attention-deficit/hyperactivity disorder: a functional magnetic resonance study, Copyright (2006), with permission from Elsevier.

Beauregard's discoveries are consistent with the view that a more stable EEG is associated with better functioning of frontal executive functions and with improved global self-regulation.

SUMMARY

Research on changes in cognitive brain potentials and on functional cognitive brain activity before and after a complete course of neurofeedback sessions shows objective normalization of these values among people with ADHD.

6.12   Choice of Scalp Location and Training of EEG Frequency Bands

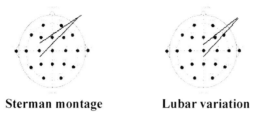

Sterman montage   **Lubar variation**

Figure 44. A comparison of montages used by Sterman and Lubar.

Sterman's original therapeutic studies, which focused on the control of epilepsy, used bipolar ("sequential") electrode montages in which one electrode is placed halfway between F3 and C3 and the other halfway between C3 and P3 because the sensororimotor rhythm (SMR, 12-15 Hz) is maximally measurable at these points. Initially, only the SMR rhythm was trained but afterwards, it was found that the global EEG pattern had normalized most notably with decreases in theta and fast beta activity. Tansey did not use a bipolar montage but an active electrode placed at Cz (with a reference electrode at the ear) to train the SMR rhythm and to target a decrease in theta waves.

Lubar was first to apply neurofeedback to the treatment of ADHD using the identical training protocol employed by Sterman. Over time, Lubar came to favor the bipolar montage Cz-Pz as a training montage, or a bipolar montage using a measuring point between Fz and Cz and another between Cz and Pz (therefore on the midline). Placement along the midline was chosen partly because the deviant theta/beta-1 ratio was maximal along the midline in Monastra's QEEG studies (1999, 2001), but also because of LORETA studies. He assumed that the anterior cingulate, which plays a role in executive attention, conflict monitoring during attention tasks, and response inhibition, would be trained in this manner. Since 1984, Lubar has trained the 16-20 Hz rhythm in ADD (subtype without hyperactivity or impulsivity), which is associated with weakening of theta waves and, in his experience, is more central to attentional control than the SMR rhythm. Lubar's followers (Linden, Monastra, and Thompson) also used this protocol. Lubar cited early research by Sheer in which he described positive outcomes with 36-44 Hz training but chose low beta (16-20 Hz) training because of the particular technical difficulties encountered in separating 40 Hz activity from the total EEG activity. Bouyer (1981) considered 16-20 Hz activity at the sensorimotor cerebral cortex as the human homologue of the 40 Hz activity shown by cats and monkeys during focused attention and immobility. Most researchers agree that 40 Hz activity correlates more powerfully with strong focused attention while the sensorimotor rhythm correlates weakly with motor inhibition.

Othmer C3

Figure 45. Othmer's C3/C4 protocol.

Othmer developed a training model on theoretical grounds described in chapter section 6.19 in which 15-18 Hz is trained at C3 (on the left) for the treatment of ADD and 12-15 Hz at C4 (right) is trained for the treatment of ADHD. It should be noted however that Sterman's original research (1980) indicated that the SMR band in the broadest sense includes 12-20 Hz and that SMR training automatically co-strengthens 15-18 Hz, and vice versa. For this reason, 13-21 Hz was chosen as the broad band, which was compared with the theta band in order to calculate Monastra's EEG distractibility index. Many researchers have followed Othmer's footsteps and have chosen C3 (15-18 Hz) and/or C4 (12-15 Hz) (Rossiter, 2000; Fuchs, 2003; Kropotov et al., 2004). However, Rossiter (2002) showed that training the theta/SMR ratio at C4 and the theta/15-18 Hz ratio at C3 gave the same indications in the EEG, in agreement with Sterman's results: lowered theta, increased alpha, and lowered beta-2 activity.

The "sequential" ("bipolar") electrode montage employed in the original studies used two positions close together on the scalp as active reference points. EEG activity can never be measured from one EEG point because the potential difference is the difference between two points, for example Cz-Pz. The development of QEEG allows for comparing individual measurements with averaged values obtained from a control group. This was often applied using the "reference" electrode method (also known as a "referential montage"), which finds the difference between a specific point on the skull and the averaged electrical activity measured at each ear, for example. Theoretically, it is assumed that no electrical brain activity is measurable around the ears and, consequently, that they offer a neutral measuring point. Thus, such reference montages are sometimes termed "monopolar" montages. However, in practice, we know that EEG temporal cerebral cortex activity is measurable around the ears; therefore, this method of measurement, strictly speaking, also constitutes a bipolar montage. Notwithstanding this limitation, this method has practical utility to make QEEG measurements. Throughout the nineties, the referential montage was increasingly applied in neurofeedback. Which of these measuring methods (i.e., sequential versus monopolar) are used in practice makes little real difference to therapeutic outcomes. Recently, there has been a trend among some researchers to revive the use of sequential montages such as Cz-Pz for a number of reasons. Firstly, if a negative and positive electrode is used, for example, at Cz and Pz respectively, both points will have similar electrical activity in common. Consequently, subtracting one from the other will smooth this activity. Furthermore, movement artifacts can have a similar effect at the two measuring points; therefore, are also smoothed out ("common mode rejection"). The use of ear electrodes as reference electrodes in a reference montage introduces a practical difficulty that can cause a major technical interference with the EEG. Furthermore, we can claim with greater certainty that a sequential montage really measures potential differences with the limitation that the values obtained are ambiguous. An increase in activity at one of the two measuring points or a change in phase relationship between the electrical activities at the two measuring points can explain an increase in measured activity. This has given rise to a view that a sequential (bipolar) training is actually a training of the difference between two measuring points (both in regard to signal strength and phase relationship). Putman (2001) referred to this as "hidden coherence training." At this point, it is worthwhile to mention that Coben (2005) showed that bipolar training led to decreased coherence. He hypothesized that an increase in bipolar amplitude could lead to greater amplitude differences between the two locations that would correlate with the lower coherence. Lubar (2001) suggested that a sequential montage delivered more learning opportunities by allowing more options for change.

In clinical practice, Lubar first trained SMR in hyperactive children either along the midline or centrally on the left or right (choosing right central if impulsivity, aggressiveness, or emotional over-reactivity were prominent). He used either a sequential or a referential electrode montage, but preferred that the greatest difference in signal intensity in theta and beta-1 activity determine the montage position. To avoid movement artifacts in the measured EEG, he did not use a referential montage with ear electrodes with the most hyperactive children.

Lubar trained children of six years old and sometimes younger most often along the parietal midline, children of seven to eight years old along the central midline, and children of 15 or older along the central mid line. QEEG can often indicate which method to use. Kropotov and Clarke showed that in older children and adolescents, maximal theta was more often measured along the midline. To improve attention and motivation, Lubar trained 14-18 Hz along the centroparietal midline in children and along the frontoparietal midline in adults. Locked phase 14-18 Hz training often proceeds well in adults at left frontal areas, areas that correspond to the dorsolateral cerebral cortex (DLPFC), which play a central role in a number of frontal executive functions and in positive mood.

Summary

Lubar and his followers (Linden, Thompson, and Monastra) chiefly trained 16-20 Hz (together with decreasing theta waves) at Cz. They argued that the most consistent abnormality found in ADHD (theta/beta-1 ratio) was maximal at Cz.

Othmer and his followers trained 12-15 Hz (SMR) at C4 (right) to treat hyperactivity and 15-18 Hz at C3 (left) to treat attentional difficulties.

There is no strong argument or research that overwhelmingly differentiates between these two neurofeedback protocols; as of now, 12-15 Hz is functionally similar to 12-20 Hz (and thus also 16-20 Hz) and this applies to C3, C4 and Cz.

6.13 The Neurofeedback Process: Conscious and/or Unconscious?

Within behavioral therapy, operant conditioning was defined as an alteration in an "operant," which is a "freely willed" behavior. The systematic association of a reward with the desired behavior brings about this change. In neurofeedback, a particular EEG pattern is the "operant" or the "freely willed" behavior. Feedback provided at specific instances rewards desired EEG patterns. In many instances, the trainee uses neither computer keyboard nor mouse to play the computer game. It is sufficient to watch attentively and enjoy the reward that the mounting score offers. The question arises: is this acquisition of points in itself rewarding enough to become operant conditioning? Originally, Sterman studied the SMR rhythm in cats and monkeys, rewarding them with milk and morsels of food. The wider behavioral literature describes how "knowing" about the occurrence of the desired behavior is in itself reinforcing. Clinical experience of neurofeedback teaches that it is best to find a balance between highly motivating SMR feedback (e.g., offered by an exciting computer game) and the practical limitation that SMR bursts frequently occur barely 5 to 10 times a minute in people with ADHD.

We do not fully know what exactly happens in neurophysiological operant conditioning. Imaging research has shown an association with increased activity in the orbitofrontal cerebral cortex. All forms of learning are known to be associated with neuroplasticity or alterations in connections within neural networks. Sleep has a role in consolidation of these changes with both the slow waves of deep sleep and sleep spindles having particular roles in learning. An increase in sleep spindles the following night has been found to follow all learning (Schabus, 2004). A noteworthy observation is that a goal of SMR neurofeedback is to increase sleep spindles because these spindles are viewed as equivalent to the daytime SMR rhythm. In fact, SMR neurofeedback targets a permanent increase in spindle number.

There remains the extremely tricky question of how exactly operant conditioning of the EEG pattern occurs. In operant behavioral conditioning, it is easy to identify the goals and the patient has the feeling of steering the self towards those goals. The individual can consciously experience the behavior that leads to reward. It is uncertain how rewarding the occurrence of certain EEG patterns in an individual can strengthen that pattern without either awareness of the experience or conscious awareness of what is happening at moments of reward. There must be an input to the conditioned EEG pattern from another part of the nervous system over which the individual has control (Rosenfeld & Baehr, 2004). It has certainly been shown that the state of consciousness has an effect on susceptibility to conditioning for some EEG patterns possessing a degree of complexity (Fox, 1970).

There is vigorous debate about how we can understand the mechanism by which such conditioning is achieved and if individuals can provide conscious input into this process. As already mentioned, can "knowing" that feedback information rewards the desired behavior itself strengthen the desired EEG pattern without conscious knowing or any feeling about how the change occurs? On the one hand, it is possible that the sensation of acquisition of control is part of the process of operant conditioning; after all, operant conditioning refers to a "voluntary behavior." The desired EEG pattern develops alongside greater vigilance, implying better functioning of the frontal executive functions. We can characterize this discussion over voluntary control as an extension of the debate about whether executive functions are things that we do or things that happen to us. Chapter 3 described self-regulation and executive functions as assemblies built from basic elementary processes and not by the agency of a supervisory, guiding "I."

This train of thought can be extended to argue that the framework of neurofeedback research provides a medium for further investigation into the nature of the executive functions. Neurofeedback can provide a powerful method with which to examine the limits of conscious control over a number of cognitive processes. This new learning process of neurofeedback allows us to access some network relations in the brain (Kotchoubey, 2002), showing that the ability to control a specific EEG parameter develops before the knowledge of how it is created is acquired.

Traditionally, it was assumed that we possess conscious control over skeletal muscles, over cognitive strategies including certain executive functions, and to some extent over the vigilance level, which incorporates cortical sensitivity to stimuli. The degree of control over these functions is problematic in ADHD; therefore, neurofeedback therapy aims at optimizing this control.

This consideration persuaded Barkley (Loo & Barkley, 2005) to challenge the utility of the principle application of neurofeedback. That neurofeedback indeed leads to improvement in attention and frontal executive functions can be explained, in his opinion, by the fact that cognitive strategies were trained. Barkley concluded that the acquisition of conscious cognitive strategies triggered the changes in the EEG and, therefore, it seemed simpler to him to train cognitive strategies directly with neurofeedback being superfluous. Several arguments can refute Barkley's opinion. First, research has repeatedly shown that teaching cognitive strategies and, above all, the transfer of such strategies to daily life is an ineffective approach to ADHD. Second, growing insights from practitioners of neurofeedback training suggest that for people with ADHD, cognitive strategies do not play a decisive role in the training process. This type of training moreover is slightly different from other forms of EEG biofeedback, such as alpha training, which goal is to target relaxation. Cognitive strategies can certainly play a key role in this application and this is sometimes described as a "top down" training in which the mental state actively directs the process. One of the leading arguments that cognitive strategies do not play a key role in neurofeedback training of the SMR rhythm is the fact that a lasting change can occur in the EEG pattern following successful training (Sterman, 1980; Tansey, 1986; Rossiter, 2002), and in the dynamic EEG pattern such as ERD/ERS and ERP (Kropotov et al, 2004; Kropotov, 2004b). Eloquently, the quantity of sleep spindles during sleep also remains increased (Sterman, 1981; Hauri, 1981; Lubar, Shabsin, Natelson, Holder, Whitsett, Pamplin, & Krulikowski, 1981) and associated with improved quality of sleep, which in and of itself has a beneficial effect on daily functioning. Sterman and a number of other scientists demonstrated in multiple studies that the susceptibility to epilepsy decreases permanently after training, an effect that can be explained by the stabilizing influence of an increased number of sleep spindles. It is not just that one or another consciously experienced learned strategy is consciously applied in everyday circumstances. The well-known problems of inadequate transfer of trained cognitive skills (encountered with cognitive training programs such as "learning learning" and Meichenbaum's "stop-think-do" strategy learning) are not observed here. Neurofeedback training produces a lasting, fundamental, and global EEG reorganization. Training a specific EEG frequency rather than the trained change of frequency alone thus sets in motion broader effects, reflecting reorganization of the global regulation state of the behavioral adaption system. SMR rhythms and sleep spindles both have a vigilance stabilizing function in this regard, protecting against system disruption (Pavlov's principle of internal inhibition). In fact, these modifications are frequently more clearly discernable in the form of an increase in the amount of sleep spindles in the sleep EEG than in the form of the SMR rhythm in the waking EEG. Often, no distinct increase in the SMR rhythm is visible in the waking EEG. Sterman offered two reasons for this observation; first, the human waking EEG, in comparison with that observed in cats and macaques, often has no clearly detectable SMR rhythm, and second, during wakefulness, the SMR rhythm is often very variable during intervening cognitive activities.

We are left to answer the frequently asked question: is there anything the individual can do to increase the number of feedback rewards? Only to an extent because for the individual, this directly relates not only to the quality of focused attention experienced, but also to indirect conscious experience of the flexible and global stability of alertness level, or in other words the degree of flexible behavioral adaptability possessed by the individual. The term 'activation states' refers to the state of preparation for adaptive action, as described earlier. We recognize here the same twofold phenomenon encountered when examining changes in healthy participants' EEG following sleep deprivation: wakefulness becomes less differentiated and subject to increased disturbances, and, consequentially, specific attentional weaknesses are manifested. Section 4.2 examined the occurrence of a similar EEG pattern in people with ADHD (Brunner, 1993) - a pattern that is most prominent at moments of weakened attention during attentional tests (Townsend, 1979; Achim, 2004).

Monastra explained the neurofeedback process to his patients by comparing it to the experience of learning to ride a bike. Indeed, we have no cognitive strategies to use in learning bike riding; instead, learning to ride involves the acquisition of coordination and balance skills enabled by pattern learning of concerned muscle groups and reflexive neural networks. However, motor skills are involved in learning to ride a bike so that these two processes are certainly not entirely comparable. As we master these skills, we have the feeling that we are guiding our learning and everything is under our control. However, in an individual without ADHD, the same can be said about regulation of attention and vigilance (in the sense of adaptive ability, level of wakefulness and frontal executive functions), which are linked to a feeling of being independent and in control. Here lies the problem for people with ADHD. Monastra's analogy implies that at the neurophysiological level acquired skills can subsequently be utilized as circumstances require. Once again, we should not assume that there is an "I" that exercises direct cognitive control; instead, we speak more of "bottom up" rather than "top down" processes. In experimental participants without ADHD, we can surely speak of an "I" because the underlying neurophysiology that supports adaptive skills makes the "I" possible. Rewarding feedback can modify this is in the self-regulatory system in the brain. The brain begins to react to the on-screen display gradually and thereby "learns" a new, more normal brainwave pattern. As the training progresses, some patients report that their mind is clearer and that their restless stream of thoughts is slowing. Some patients say that they "know" when the training is going well but cannot say what it is they have done to improve the training. Neurofeedback is more a process of experience than of active intervention. However, this is not the case every time. A number of studies have shown that both in pseudo sessions and during training to strengthen or weaken a pattern (in which neither the child nor the therapist knows in which direction the EEG pattern is being trained), the child claims that he or she has a hold on the process via a particular mental strategy (Siniatchkin, 2000). Moreover, some research shows that the use of other more or less conscious strategies can be strikingly counterproductive. It appears that effort towards cognitive control can negatively interfere with the learning process. This is consistent with the finding that frequently during cognitive activation only an increase in theta or alpha waves is seen, particularly in people with ADD (Gurnee, 2000), or a more pronounced hyperactivity in frontal areas is identified using functional brain imaging methods. It has been observed that paying attention is often even more difficult than trying to make an extra effort, which sits well within the current conception of a lack of self-regulation in ADHD (see chapter 9).

It may be best to instruct the patient explicitly not to try to influence the process consciously, and to offer simply a brief comparison with the experience of learning to ride a bike, together with the instruction to relax and watch. This instruction is in reality aimed at avoiding movement artifacts during the training session. If indeed the instructions require paying attention, it quickly appears that the response is not proportional to the apparent degree of voluntary effort. Such instructions can surely impede the learning process at a neural level. The optimal direction should be limited to asking the participant to try to keep the mission on the game screen going, without too much explanation of exactly what that entails and without offering mental "tricks." Thus, Rossiter (2002) wrote that the best results were obtained when only the simplified instruction was given to decrease the theta/beta ratio (indicated by the on screen column) and to maintain the feedback sounds and images. Sterman's cats received no instructions at all. They were trained purely by the conditioning brought about by their rewards. However, rewards must be sufficiently motivating. Milk alone was not enough, meat cubes were necessary for effective conditioning.

Patients often ask during training sessions what they must do to obtain a better score on the screen. The answer is that individuals cannot directly control these brain processes.

Some pragmatic instructions can however be useful for some patients (older children and adults) so that they know how the training can be approached practically. It is integral to our culture to think of ourselves as active agents, we get things done via our will and actions. Nevertheless, we discover more and more that the human mind and brain form a passive rather than active entity. Thoughts and mental development are things that we experience rather than things we initiate. Often, they occur despite our attempts to intervene, without interventions. In mentally typical individuals, adaptive abilities usually run smoothly, undoubtedly accompanied by a subjective feeling of steering most of their affairs. This is certainly because the underlying neurophysiology is well balanced. However, this is not the case for people with ADHD, in whom self-guidance and optimal adaptive ability are inadequate. This is why neurofeedback aims at heightening the structure of consciousness as the employment of conscious strategies is more of an obstacle than a help.

The general instruction to someone following a course of neurofeedback might be "relax and let it happen," "let the computer tell your brain when you do the right thing," and "don't try, just let it happen." When the trainee is asked what he did, he might say, "I don't know how I am doing it, but I know when it happens." However, this is certainly not always the case (Siniatchkin, 2000).

Once progress begins to be made during the game, it often seems as if the patient becomes part of a circle. There is a viewpoint that the rewarding feedback provides the driving force in the first phase of training but during subsequent phases, the complete experience, whether conscious or not, provides the greatest rewarding value.

When neurofeedback training begins, the mind is supplied with information about the state of the brain. When this information is processed, phenomena that we do not usually know become known and subject to learning mechanisms in the brain. It seems more like a process of experiencing what happens after the learning process during biofeedback as training redirects these brain functions. Becoming aware of the feedback to the desired brain wave patterns seems to be an integral part of acquiring biofeedback control, even though the neural processes themselves remain fully unconscious. It is as if awareness of the outcome allows access to the unconscious neuronal systems that are normally inaccessible and autonomous.

In the 1970s, research by Hardt and Langley at the Langley Porter Neuropsychiatric Institute showed that acquiring the desired EEG pattern during neurofeedback training demonstrates a learning curve. Throughout the early EEG sessions, improvements in the theta/beta-1 ratio are often rapid via habituation in the training session. This often followed by a deceleration in the learning curve often associated with the patients feeling that they actively guide the learning process or that they must (counterproductively) work hard to relax. Only in the final sessions, when the patient is actively engaged, does the learning curve show an exponential upsurge, often accompanied by a feeling of passive will - a spontaneous, unforced, blooming of the will. It seems that the will in general becomes more smoothly self-directed, needing no extra effort to be exercised. In a way, the individual can be considered a captain of a team, made up of all the mental and emotional systems of the brain (such as the anterior cingulate and the DLPFC). Neurofeedback training makes a better captain from the individual and makes the team players work and perform better together. When neurofeedback successfully trains the brain in the behavior that required much effort prior to the training, this behavior becomes less effortful, almost automatic. Neurofeedback trains the process of voluntary self-control, the foundation of conscious control. This training process takes place without explicit, conscious, voluntary control.

Consequent improvements in self-control in people with ADHD occur without the patient knowing for sure what he or she has done to reach a homeostatic balance. There are many indications that in some or most cases, the attempt to exercise conscious control itself changes the EEG and therefore can hinder the neurofeedback process. The effort to exercise voluntary control is thus not only trivial but can also be counterproductive. Towards the end of the training process, a feeling of heightened self-control in daily life evolves with an improvement of executive functioning. Ultimately, the goal is an improvement in ADHD symptoms. Although the executive functions operate more fluently, and the individual feels more in control of his life, one could argue that in reality, this adaptive process just happens to him or her. As an example, once the client manages the go/no-go task better after completing the training course, these gains are not attributable to something that he or she consciously does to improve previous performance. This is also true of the normalization of the go/no-go evoked brain potentials and of the event related synchronization and desynchronization of the EEG, all of which are associated with this task (Kropotov et al., 2004; Kropotov, 2004b). This argument can be extended to improved organizational ability and increased robustness of goal motivation. The individual cannot verbalize what it is that he or she is doing that enables him or her to succeed better now than before the neurofeedback training.

Although a number of researchers (among them Leins, 2004) have demonstrated a link between mental effort and cognitive strategies on the one hand and neurofeedback results on the other, we can conclude that for a number of patients, a mix of top down and bottom up processes can usefully contribute to the learning process.

Another element to consider is that both Lubar and Thompson introduced intervals during which they administered cognitive tasks within the neurofeedback therapy sessions. They reasoned that learning tasks performed during training sessions would enable classical conditioning because a better quality of attention would be stimulated during the neurofeedback session, which could then be applied to the learning strategy. This requires a sufficient improvement in theta/beta-1 activity in the early training sessions so that cognitive training can become associated with these improvements in subsequent sessions. Children with learning difficulties can read or solve math problems during a part of the session. Classical conditioning, as described by Pavlov, is achieved easily if a concomitant behavior occurs in and becomes associated with certain circumstances without the presence of a rewarding factor.

6.14. What is Rewarding and Therefore Conditioning During a Neurofeedback Session?

Regardless of whether or not conscious cognitive strategies promote the learning process, the question remains as to what incentives are rewarding enough to promote the learning process. Currently, many therapists opt for an exciting video game to be played during more than 70% of the feedback session. This is assumed more motivating and rewarding, particularly when training hyperactive children. However, if we bear in mind that SMR sequences occur no more often then 10-20 times a minute in healthy people, and even less frequently in people with ADHD, we must question the efficacy of offering positive feedback 70% of the time during SMR training. An alternative approach aims at the gradual constructive shaping of the SMR rhythm (shaping refers to successive approximations to the target pattern) by setting a progressively higher amplitude threshold. In their early studies from the 1970s, Sterman and Lubar stressed that the number of SMR bursts per minute increased in human subjects post-training but from their published EEG traces, it appears that the amplitude of SMR was higher in people without epilepsy or ADHD than in people with the disorders. In this light, Burner's (2006) investigation is interesting; he examined the effect of SMR neurofeedback training on learning of a paired associate word list, finding an improvement in list recall on the following day. Subjects studied the word pairs and subsequently received a session consisting of either four SMR neurofeedback periods or four pseudo neurofeedback periods. No increase in the number of sleep spindles during NREM was evident in the sleep EEG subsequent to training, possibly because the number of training sessions were limited. However, it was very clear that 12-15 Hz global activity increased in the frequency spectrum of the sleep EEG. Thus, in this single training session, consisting of four 10-minute periods, there was initially an increase in 12-15 Hz amplitude. We can surmise that later in the training phase this would lead to an increased quantity of sleep spindles. This research also identified a direct correlation between the number of sleep spindles and the quantity of remembered information from tasks studied the previous day. However, there was no link between the global quantity of 12-15 Hz activity and the amount of remembered information. Sterman (2006) has also described setting the reward threshold 20% above the average initial values, which can, if progressively increased after further sessions, lead to greater feedback reward. According to Sterman, this threshold increase contributes to shaping of the SMR.

In contrast, the broader beta-1 band (12-20Hz) is more likely to be continuously present as well as some indications of a proportional relationship at this frequency between amplitude and mental activation (Townsend, 1979). Therefore, a more continuous type of feedback may work well at this particular frequency band.

A reward too easily obtained is no longer truly a reward. Sporadic rewards can be more motivating, especially for older children or adults who can develop an interest in their own learning curve and in the real time coaching during a session. Thus, it can be beneficial if the therapist explains the feedback process and explores, together with the trainee, any possible cognitive or competitive strategies that sometimes arise from the experience. The therapist who actively accompanies the patient through this process becomes part of the feedback cycle. In a sense, the strongest rewards are in the end internal, namely the individual's recognition that he is master of his or her own self-regulation as the receipt of an external reward evolves into an internal "aha!" feeling of reward.

Lubar described the establishment of a group protocol during carefully designed group studies in which operant conditioning was the critical factor and the intervention of the therapist not a decisive factor. These studies achieved an 80% success rate over 40 to 60 sessions. However, in order to individualize training, clinical practice can diverge from strict research protocol by adjusting various elements including the precise training location on the skull, the percentage reward, the reward type, the active interventions of the therapist to make the reward more motivating, explanatory interventions that can make the reward experience more meaningful, and/or a training variant in which a short break is taken to examine and discuss the results with the patient after three minutes in the early sessions or in the final sessions after 10 minutes. Lubar found this variant resulted in a training that was more effective, less boring, and required fewer (20 to 40) sessions with a greater success rate of

90%. In Lubar's footsteps, Thompson & Thompson (2003) also described the advantages of individualization of the training protocol in clinical practice.

Computer screen feedback can be sufficiently powerfully motivating to adults and adolescents with ADHD because such feedback indicates progress towards personal goals such as amelioration of symptoms and symptom control. As the novelty wanes, however, this feedback can be extremely dull, in particular for children who are moreover less likely understand about the nature of their ADHD, the negative effects of ADHD on their lives, or the possible long-term gains from neurofeedback. If feedback becomes boring, the feedback would likely not be rewarding enough for conditioning to happen.

It is clear that milk and food rewards can be sufficient to condition a hungry cat. For children, however, a therapist's stimulating approach offers an additional motivating aspect that can form part of the reward. Thompson & Thompson (2000, 2003), Rossiter (Rossiter & La Vaque, 1995), and Leins (2004) have described how rewards can be enhanced using a supplementary reward system in the form of small prizes the children can earn by obtaining a certain number of points during a single session.

Rossiter's sessions consisted of two parts. During one section, the child received 100 points whenever he attained a theta/beta ratio lower than the median value from previous sessions. An additional 50 points were available if he attained this ratio in both sections of the segment and 100 points were available for a new minimum theta/beta ratio. If the child accumulated 500 points, he received a certificate with a value of $5 that was exchangeable for a prize.

Thompson & Thompson (2000, 2003) asked the child to keep a record by writing down every two to five minutes the percentage of the time that the theta/beta ratio was below threshold. A certain number of points were awarded for this percentage and performance, with the therapist softly counting the passing seconds aloud. Another strategy sometimes employed is the use of neurofeedback exercises in a "work-rest" protocol where the child must try to decrease theta activity as much as possible or increase beta activity as much as possible during a 45-second period or sometimes during 3-minute periods alternating with 15-second rest breaks. The use of five or more period repetitions encourage the child to compete with his or her own performance. Conscious control of theta or beta activity can be acquired in this manner. Short periods of two to five minutes are chosen because the percentage of time that the threshold is crossed is calculated from the average for several periods, making it harder to change the threshold over longer periods. Like Rossiter, Thompson linked total points to small prizes such as pens, bookmarks, action figures, or games. Thus, using the "work-rest" protocol, Thompson consciously trained and, subsequently, rewarded skills with small prizes. This is very similar to the method used by Leins, both to train theta/beta ratio and to train the slow cortical potential. Kropotov's method was also similar.

As mentioned previously, doubts exist about the development of neurofeedback in the form of exciting new video games. One objection is that children with ADHD have no problem paying attention to such games but adequate training should aim to maintain attention even in dull tasks. However, there are promising initiatives to develop videogames with an intelligent design for neurofeedback specifically designed to provide a varied and, above all, graded manner to deliver neurofeedback, giving for example extra bonus points if the desired EEG activity persists for a certain period.

6.15 Neuronal Changes During Neurofeedback

Research shows that SMR rhythm originates in the thalamic ventrobasal relay neuron (responsible for transferring sensorimotor information) in the form of systematic electrical discharges and that it occurs because of the intrinsic electrical properties of thalamic relay neurons. Cell membrane changes enable communication between neurons. Activated impulses trigger release of certain neurotransmitters on reaching the cell, consequently the membrane potential decreases (that is, depolarizes). If polarization reaches the activation threshold of the neuron, the cell discharge and the signal are guided along the cell axon. Other neurotransmitters work to increase the resting potential (hyperpolarization), thus, inhibiting the neuron.

If thalamic ventrobasal relay neurons are hyperpolarized, the hyperpolarization gradually falls because of slow calcium flux until the cell is depolarized. This consequent low threshold calcium depolarization causes the discharge of cell membrane, leading to a potential discharge of high voltage sodium. The discharge is then propagated to the sensorimotor cerebral cortex and cells of the thalamic reticular nucleus connected thereby. The output from the evoked discharge of these latter cells is transmitted back to the originating ventro-basal relay cells, triggering the inhibitory release of GABA (gamma amino butyric acid) causing, again, the hyperpolarization of relay cells such that the whole process repeats itself. Feedback between these thalamic cells triggers a repeating rhythmic discharge to transmit between relay cells. This discharge can last many seconds and is measurable as the sensorimotor rhythm in the cerebral cortex. The SMR rhythm can be considered as a reflection of the balance between thalamic activation and thalamic inhibitory functions. It is also associated with activation level, cognitive programming, and motor behavior. During SMR training, animals are motionless, alert, and expectant. Sterman has said that to be motionless and alert is a necessary but not sufficient condition for the generation of SMR.

Normally, during excitation of the reticular nucleus of the thalamus, the nucleus exercises an inhibitory influence on the thalamic ventrobasal nucleus; thus, attaining moderate hyperpolarization. This triggers the SMR rhythm of 12-15 (or more comprehensively 12-20) Hz that presents itself behaviorally as decreased mobility and focused attention.

If strong excitation of the reticular nucleus in the thalamus occurs, hyperpolarization of the ventrobasal relay nucleus will be strengthened. If hyperpolarization is stronger, the frequency of fluctuations in the membrane potential in the thalamic relay neurons decreases. This produces theta activity at the cerebral cortex, measurable most easily centrally (sensorimotor cortex) alone with a decreased quantity of SMR rhythm. Behaviorally, this is manifested as attentional impairment whether or not there is hyperactivity as in the case in ADHD. Normally, during tasks that require focused attention, the thalamic relay neurons synchronize different informational aspects between different areas of the association cortex. The reticular nucleus enables this selective processing via selective inhibition. However, the reticular nucleus of the thalamus modulates the thalamic relay neurons insufficiently in people with ADHD such that signal processing is only more or less focused; that is, the reticular nucleus inhibits too strongly, which is expressed by theta activity. The primary cause of this overactive reticular nucleus is yet unclear. It is known that the caudate nucleus has a stimulating effect on the reticular nucleus and in this way strengthens the SMR rhythm. On the other hand, one of the most consistent findings in ADHD is that the caudate nucleus is smaller and functionally less active. This suggests a theoretical explanation for the known decrease in SMR rhythm in people with ADHD. However, the caudate nucleus, like the reticular nucleus, forms a very complex system. Thus, attempts at simple straightforward explanations may prove misleading. Moreover, there are other dysfunctional systems in ADHD in addition to this one, for example, the noradrenalin system is less active presumably because the locus coeruleus in the brainstem is also less active.

We do not know the exact mechanism that would permit good outcomes via EEG training. Modulation of individual synaptic receptors ("neuroplasticity") and reorganization of neural networks are probably among the implicated explanations.

Examined from a more contemporary systemic perspective, the learning process during SMR neurofeedback can be compared to that promoted by parents who exploit the speech sounds spontaneously generated by the internal dynamics of their young child's brain by encouraging the development with praise or rewards. This external "disturbance" gives new meaning to the child's self-generated language sounds. Likewise, neurofeedback can also be understood as offering an external "disturbance" through which the medium of the brain's internal self regulating dynamic is addressed and triggered with the intention of optimizing the internal dynamic (if SMR is trained). This internal self-generating dynamic exhibits the 1/f pink noise pattern (Chapter 5). The momentary external "disturbances" delivered by feedback can allow the conditioned SMR fragments in the EEG to spread out over multiple neuronal circuits and, therefore, disseminate pink noise to a greater degree.

We can make a rough comparison to the function of sleep in which an increase in the number of sleep spindles during sleep appears to strengthen all learning. As neurofeedback currently focuses on training to produce more SMR, sleep spindles can also increase. Strengthening of SMR and sleep spindles might describe this optimization of the brain's internal dynamics in terms of "situating" and "embedding" the brain in the sensorimotor coordination dynamic between the body and environmental processes (Varela, 1971), described previously as a general role of sleep. Bottom-up causal processes (sensorimotor and attention input) are just as important here as top down causal processes (the macroscopic EEG rhythms that as an order parameter hold underlying micro processes within certain degrees of freedom (see also figure 59).

Inevitably, this brings us to contemplate about what kind of electrical brain activities could operant conditioning train. In the early seventies, Fox (1970) used operant conditioning to investigate the degree of complexity and type of neural system that can be trained in the cat. He did not succeed in training the visually evoked potential in the optic tract but did succeed in the lateral corpus geniculate and in the thalamic visual relay station. He concluded that a minimum degree of complexity is necessary to allow operant conditioning of the brain. This is in agreement with the recent understanding that many parallel neuronal circuits are involved in complex brain activity and that this activity is variable and influenced by mental states. It is for these reasons that this complex activity exhibits a 1/f pink noise pattern; therefore, is probably responsive to rewards.

6.16 Neurofeedback Training Effects on Intelligence and Learning Difficulties

Many people with ADHD have comorbid learning difficulties such as dyslexia and dyscalculia, among others. Scores on intelligence tests are frequently lower than expected. Attentional difficulties may partially explain these low scores. A number of researchers have investigated the effects of neurofeedback training on intelligence tests administered to children with ADHD.

Othmer (Othmer & Othmer, 1991) treated a group of 15 children with ADHD (between 6 to 16 years old), of whom seven had hyperactivity, four dyslexia, six oppositional behavioral disorders, two conduct disorders (a precursor for antisocial personality disorder), 13 sleep disorders, five chronic headache, four depression or dysthymia, three chronic anxiety, and one had motor tics. Treatment consisted of 30 to 40 sessions delivered at the rate of two or three sessions per week (aimed at strengthening 15-18 Hz and weakening 4-7 Hz and 22-30 Hz) measured at C1-C5 (therefore, at the front and rear of C3) on the left, or C2-C6 (front and rear of C4) on the right (depending on which side showed the most abnormal EEG pattern).

Tansey (1990) treated a group of eight children (7 to 15 years) with attention disorders and dyslexia with 10 to 34 sessions (strengthening 12-14 Hz, measured at C4). Notwithstanding that Tansey's group demonstrated more severe cognitive impairment, it appeared that both Tansey's and Othmer's groups showed weaknesses on the subscales Calculation, Substitution, Information, and Digit Span. These subscales are known to load on an attention factor (Kaufman, 1979) on the WISC-R intelligence tests. Following the neurofeedback, the mean IQ increased from 114 to 137 in Othmer's group and from 94 to 113 in Tansey's group.

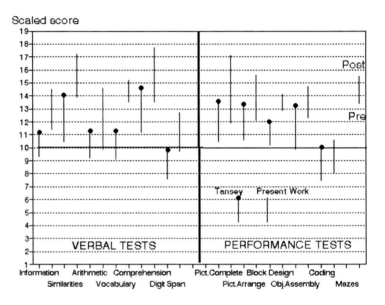

Figure 46. Mean WISC IQ measurements: For each of the 12 subscales, the values obtained by Tansey (1990) and Othmer & Othmer (1991) (labeled "present work") are displayed; both demonstrated lower pre neurofeedback than post neurofeedback scores. (Figure appears with kind permission from Othmer & Othmer).

Othmer (Othmer & Othmer, 1991) found the greatest improvement (an average increase of 33 points!) in the subgroup with an initial IQ lower than 100. The subscales with the greatest deficit showed the greatest improvements. The average increase per subscale was 5.1 points. The four subscales contributing to the Kaufman attention factor were quite consistent in their growth (4 to 6 points). Two of the four children with ADHD and comorbid dyslexia showed

160

significant amelioration of the dyslexia. In Othmer's group, the Kaufman attention factor was below the norm (= 10) in four children before training. These four children received average values on the subscales Information, Arithmetic and Digit Span, and scores of 7 and 6 on the subscale Substitution, suggesting a common underlying mechanism. In these four children, the first three subscales increased by 4 to 6 points and the Substitution subscale by 3 points after training. Othmer argued that this improvement in IQ score could not be attributed merely to the retest effect because there was an interval of nine months between the tests. In addition, these improvements cannot be attributed solely to the effects of better attention, decreased impulsivity, and less anxiety. There were also significant improvements on subscales that rely on verbal understanding and perceptual organization: memory (Information, Vocabulary), sequential processing (Arithmetic, Substitution), inferential thinking (Similarities), verbal concept formation and expression (Understanding), and visual perception (Picture Completion, Picture Arrangement). Both improvements in behavior and cognition seemed directly related to the EEG training rather than to interactions between the new skill areas. Pronounced improvements on the Arithmetic subscale (on average from 9.9 to 14.6 points) can probably be attributed to a combination of factors, such as improved attention span and enhanced sequential symbolic processing skills and also to behavioral changes, such as decreased anxiety and impulsivity. Othmer himself attributed these effects to global cortical activation or stabilization, regulated from the brain stem and the non-specific thalamic nuclei.

Follow up with the parents was maintained for more than a year after treatment, and improvements in self-esteem were most noticeable. Improvements in hyperactivity, concentration, and sleep disturbances (including bed-wetting) were maintained, and absence of headaches in children that had previously suffered headaches was noticeable. Social relationships with brothers, sisters, peers, as well as with authority figures, such as parents and teachers, improved.

Cartozzo (1995) evaluated the results from 30 neurofeedback sessions (weakening 4-7 Hz, strengthening 12-15 Hz, weakening 22-30 Hz) taken by eight children with ADHD. After the treatment, there was significant improvement on the Arithmetic, Digit Span, and Substitution subscales of the WISC-R intelligence test.

A case study illustrates these changes (Tansey, 1985): *A 12-year-old boy had hyperactivity and problems with sustained attention in class. His play skills were below the norm; he had a negative attitude towards learning in general and met little success working either alone or in a group. An evaluation confirmed the hyperactivity and revealed deficits in verbal expression and word memory. In addition, he had difficulties with fine motor control, exhibited by a very clumsy pencil grip. His WISC-R global IQ was 85 with a verbal IQ of 79 and a performance IQ of 93. SMR training was given with a base value of 5.6 µV. This value was 13 µV by the 19th session. Improvements in behavioral, educational, and intellectual functioning were already apparent. He was able to stay seated longer in class. At school, improvements were noted in his pen grip by the fifteenth session, his vocabulary had expanded significantly, and he worked hard in class to complete written assignments. His achievements at school clearly improved and he was calmer at home. The WISC-R was re-administered after the completion of training. Verbal IQ was found to have increased from 79 to 98, an increase of 19 points in total, performance IQ increased from 93 to 109, an increase of 16 points, global IQ increased from 85 to 103, an 18 point increase.*

It is useful to mention the studies of Giannitrapani (1988) and Patterson (1983) who found clear correlations between the quantity of 12-15 Hz measured in central brain areas (especially Cz) and global intelligence in children and in the elderly. Moreover, a decreased quantity of sleep spindles (the equivalent of SMR during sleep) has been demonstrated in elderly people with cognitive decline (Wauquier, 1991) and in children with mental retardation (Shibagaki, 1980).

In a later study, Tansey (1991) investigated the effects of SMR training (an average 28 weekly sessions) on a group of 24 children between 7 and 15 years old with learning difficulties (just two had a formal diagnosis of ADHD). In this case, he was especially interested in the effect of SMR training on the various subscales of IQ tests. Average global IQ rose from 98 to 118. In 22 of the 24 children, the increase in global IQ was at least one standard deviation (15 IQ points). The other two children showed an increase in IQ of 14 and 13 points respectively. Prior to the treatment, the children with the lowest IQ (70 to 79) had a marked tendency to show the most theta activity in the EEG. These improvements are greater than might be predicted from a retest effect (the global IQ retest effect is about 7 points). Both the total and verbal performance IQ scores improved and the difference between verbal and performance IQ decreased.

The Bannatyne pattern of WISC-R sub-scales is well documented in terms of inconsistency with a learning difficulty diagnosis. There are four Bannatyne categories: Spatial, Verbal Conceptualization, Sequencing, and Acquired Knowledge. The score in each of these categories increased after the treatment. The Kaufman attention factor in the WISC-R clearly improved following the treatment. After training, the learning difficulties were significantly ameliorated.

Tansey cited Robinson's hypothesis (1989) that there is a neurological base for variations in intelligence (for a long time, there has been no doubt about the decisive role of genetic predisposition). Robinson suggested that the relative balance within thalamocortical activities decides the natural frequencies of free, spontaneous fluctuations in thalamocortical circuits, which themselves determine the EEG frequency spectrum. SMR neurofeedback activates increases in excitation and a positive shift in the peak frequency (and activity level in general) towards a more optimal level, which according to Robinson's theory will express itself with a higher IQ. The promotion of a positive balance of EEG frequencies above 10 Hz (neural excitation), with respect to EEG frequencies lower than 10 Hz (neural inhibition), is crucial for the acquirement of a higher order of learning and IQ.

Tansey thought that SMR training leads to a synergistic training of the EEG (accompanied by a decrease in theta activity) because no strong correlation is demonstrable between the strength of an EEG band and the global IQ or subscale scores. In this formulation, he viewed the brain as a matrix of interconnected functional networks within which any pattern of neural activation can trigger a change in the whole matrix. Localized functionally, specific areas can be considered sub networks within the larger matrix within which neuronal activity reflects only a part of the great symphony of brain rhythm, which itself echoes the global matrix's functional neuroanatomy. A shift in the whole EEG pattern reflects the neurological substrate of improved functioning and suggests the functional reorganization of brain activity. Improved SMR activity appears to catalyze the synergistic efficient EEG normalization of the pre-treatment pathological balance of thalamocortical activation/ inhibition. Sterman had already proposed in 1980 that SMR training leads to a normalization of the global EEG pattern. A recent study (Hanslmayr, 2005) demonstrated that cognitive skills improved in normal participants following the application of neurofeedback protocols to strengthen the fast alpha waves (10-12 Hz) and weaken theta. The experimental subjects were assessed with a request to mentally rotate complex three dimensional block patterns before and after training to assess changes in these mental rotation skills. Only those participants who had succeeded in strengthening fast alpha activity showed improvements in this test following training. Moreover, there appeared to be a link between the two. During the time interval just before the task, fast alpha waves increased in those patients who had obtained good results from neurofeedback. This is consistent with studies demonstrating that a better cognitive performance follows fast alpha activity immediately preceding a stimulus.

Thatcher (Thatcher, North, & Biver, 2005) developed a practical application in which individual coherencies can be calculated from the QEEG pattern of phase delays. These patterns can then be compared with a statistical QEEG database derived from 442 typical individuals between 5 and 52 years of age. With this method, it is possible to predict the intelligence profile and eight verbal and performance subscale scores quite accurately. A high IQ is said to correspond with a frontal phase delay close to zero, long phase delays in the posterior cerebral cortex, lowered coherence, and global increases in EEG spectrum values. Shorter frontal phase-delays reflect faster frontal command processes and a more efficient control of information in posterior areas of the cerebral cortex. Longer phase-delays in these posterior areas mirror increased local processing time and integration of increased quantities of information. As described earlier, these values indicate greater neural efficiency and increased functional complexity. The combined values give a "discriminant score" for each individual. Research has found a direct link between this score and IQ. These findings are in agreement with the network model of intelligence in which the frontal areas orchestrate the information sources processed in posterior and temporal areas. This can have useful practical applications, including monitoring of changes following the treatment. Now, in addition to psychological IQ tests, to assess the effects of neurofeedback, changes in the QEEG obtained after the neurofeedback can be directly analyzed to detect any changes in the EEG correlations of IQ.

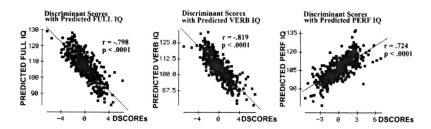

*Figure 47. Direct relationship between the discriminant score of the QEEG and predicted IQ; **left:** global IQ, **middle:** verbal IQ, **right:** performance IQ. Reprinted from Clinical Neurophysiology, 116(9), Thatcher, North, & Biver, EEG and intelligence: Relations between EEG coherence, Copyright (2005), with permission from Elsevier.*

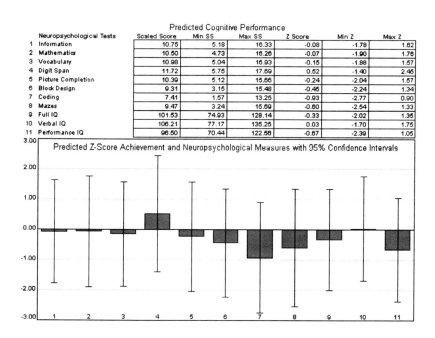

Figure 48. Graphed IQ profile of a 20-year-old woman calculated using QEEG (Neuroguide): total IQ 101.53. From Neuroguide, www.appliedneuroscience.com.

Summary

A significant increase in intelligence and improvement in learning problems also accompany the neurofeedback therapy for people with ADHD, presumably because of global EEG normalization via a synergistic mechanism.

Employing statistical correlations between QEEG patterns and measures of intelligence (global intelligence as well as subscales), it is presently possible to make a good estimate of intelligence. Testing can be repeated after the neurofeedback therapy, allowing for the assessment of changes in QEEG associated with increases in intelligence scale measurements.

6.17 Dynamic Neurofeedback Leads to Self-Regulation: Regulatory Challenge Model

Othmer developed his neurofeedback system, Neurocybernetics, starting in 1998. He emphasized several different priorities based on his clinical experience in neurofeedback and ADHD. It was clear to him that it is easier to detect human SMR rhythm of very low voltage. Furthermore, some quantity of theta waves is very often present in patients with ADHD. Lastly, although only sporadic feedback reward signals sufficiently motivated the original adult patients with epilepsy, the psychological problem remained that such signals quickly lead to boredom in younger, playful, inattentive children. For this reason, Othmer choose to set the thresholds so that reward signals occurred 70% of the time and inhibition signals 20% of the time, in contrast to the threshold use of Lubar and followers, respectively 30 to 50% and 50 to 70% of session time. It was also a condition for a reward or inhibition that the signal must remain over (or under) the set threshold for at least 0.5 seconds, in accordance with Sterman and Lubar's protocols. In this manner, boredom is averted while, at the same time, more feedback information is offered. Othmer thought that training efficiency increased when the brain received more information. Traditional researchers have doubts about this, arguing that although more feedback rewards may be very well received, they may decrease the effectiveness of a course of training just because of that reason. Sterman and Lubar chose to give feedback rewards sparingly mainly because they thought that there must be a real link between the feedback and the moments when SMR occurs. Research suggests this occurs just 10 to 20 times a minute, or in people with ADHD, around five times per minute.

Othmer thought that this continuous, dynamic, proportional stream of information carried to the brain, which at certain moments (40 times per second) reflects how much theta or SMR activity is present, offers more effective training than brief moments of feedback given when thresholds are crossed. The brain is informed about its own state through this external feedback loop, as if by a mirror. The brain moreover can develop its own control loops via this continual feedback exercise, which challenges the brain to improve its own internal self-regulation of arousal. The patient is enabled to form an association between what he or she experiences and the feeling of control over the environment (even if this is only a subjective feeling that is created as a secondary effect).

Othmer's setting of thresholds at 20% and 70% has proved another controversial aspect, amounting to an autothresholding method. In this way, an automatic dynamic threshold setting happens in the software program so that at every moment of training, a reward is delivered an average of 70% of the time and inhibition an average of 20% of the time throughout the game session and, moreover, throughout all the game sessions. The cornerstone is that continuous adjustment of the absolute threshold values during a successful learning process holds the degree of difficulty constant. The weakness is that this method always delivers the same amount of feedback to the patient, even if the patient ignores the feedback and makes no improvement. Therefore, Lubar (2000) thought that the patient could become lazy with use of such automatic threshold adjustments, which render absolute thresholds even easier to attain and the feedback rather meaningless.

Othmer cited Lubar's views that decreased SMR in ADHD generally indicates decreased arousal (activation level) and that children with ADHD with a normal quantity of SMR show clinical improvement using the same training protocol. Lubar's idea that insufficient arousal in ADHD is manifested in the form of lowered SMR contradicts Sterman's finding of increased SMR in motor rest, indicating that motor rest is associated with lower arousal. To resolve this contradiction, Othmer proposed that neurofeedback does not train the SMR up to a theoretical norm but trains the underlying neural system that produces SMR to change the moment-to-moment activation state. It is this ability to dexterously change the overall state that responds to sustained training (SMR rewarded) and leads to better self-regulation. Overall, SMR strength is very dependent on situation. There is no an optimal SMR strength. The brain's regulation system skillfully adjusts SMR to a broad set of circumstances. Training provides a subtle challenge to and exercise for those EEG frequencies implicated in regulation of arousal. Othmer goes so far as to say that in this "regulatory challenge model" or "exercising model" the inhibition of SMR and the rewarding of SMR equally challenge the system. Therefore, we cannot expect changes in the EEG to vary with the training protocol. We can expect a tendency towards EEG normalization and that the effects of such normalization will not be locally detectable at the trained site, but instead at other locations on the skull. Although the state trained does not in itself reflect a functional change, this training facilitates smooth functioning. Othmer cited Sterman's observation that reaction time is slower during a continuous performance task when increased alpha synchronization in occipital areas precedes the response (Sterman, 1996). Further, the event related desynchronization, which follows such slow reaction times, is less pronounced. Othmer thought the cyclic occurrence of occipital alpha spindles expressed the degree of vigilance organization, a conclusion also supported by Tirsch (2000, 2004). This applies not only to global background vigilance but also to handling of transient tasks. This prompted Othmer to describe neurofeedback as training in rhythmicity, which trains the brain's regulatory mechanisms slightly more than it trains the client to attain a particular brain state. The rhythmicity of the EEG is described as an expression of the self-regulatory capacity of the brain. Certainly, training conducts the brain momentarily to another operational state; however, that plays only a secondary role in the process of achieving better self-regulation.

Considering these various aspects drew Othmer to the conclusion that QEEG can often be superfluous in the design of the neurofeedback protocol. He argued that QEEG is frequently insensitive to small dysfunctions and that the patient himself can frequently provide richer and more salient information. As an example, he cited epilepsy in which a description of manifestations during a seizure is decisive but the EEG can only sometimes confirm a dysfunction and, at other times, it cannot. In deciding the neurofeedback protocol, Othmer was therefore guided more by symptoms and by those operating mechanisms he assumed to be trained via neurofeedback as well as by indications of symptomatic changes in the patient during training sessions and in the days between consecutive sessions. Great importance was attached to the patient's communications during a session about changes in their experience of self (such as changes in mood, alertness, irritability, among others), immediate and long-term. In this process, the patient gains self-knowledge and, consequently, improves self-belief. Othmer suggested that EEG abnormalities might frequently be indiscernible for a number of reasons, for example, because all functional states are calculated into statistical averages, QEEG is often too insensitive to detect slight dysfunctions, and changes brought about by neurofeedback probably play out subcortically and are thus not always detectable by scalp EEG. Othmer's clinical experience convinced him that the theta/beta-1 ratio measure was less important than the patients' own rich personal observations during training. He invoked the functional dynamic of the EEG, which is better reflected by event related synchronization and desynchronization and transient event related coherence indications that carry more dynamic EEG information than statistical QEEG measures such as the theta/beta-1 ratio. In this respect, his ideas correspond with Kropotov's (2004b) research who found little indication of change in theta/beta-1 ratio following successful training but did find normalization of the event related synchronization or desynchronization during the go/no-go task.

Othmer interpreted symptoms within an arousal framework some of which, such as poor sustained attention, reflect low arousal, some, such as hyperactivity and impulsivity, reflect over-arousal, and others, such as mood changes, reflect unstable arousal. His global model of "personal autonomy" broadly corresponded with Bente's understanding of vigilance. Healthy personal autonomy possesses the flexibility to adapt the level of arousal and attention mechanisms to immediate circumstances. It is sufficient for the client to try the training and receive feedback in order to reach other physiological states. The specific states trained strengthen and stabilize the mechanisms that maintain these different states. Three goals are targeted in this way:
1. The ability of the individual to access and maintain specific arousal states (competence).
2. The mechanism with which the brain handles arousal (flexibility).
3. Strengthening of equilibrium maintenance (homeostasis - the mechanism of stability). Here, the emphasis lies on the process of equilibrium and remediation (which is not the same as "healing").

In the 1990s, Othmer developed two different treatment protocols on the basis of theoretical principles and his garnered clinical experience, i.e., for ADD he trained beta (15-18 Hz) at C3 (left) in order to focus on attentional improvements and for ADHD he trained SMR (12-15 Hz) at C4 (right) targeting impulsivity, hyperactivity, tics, and bruxism (i.e., teeth grinding during sleep). SMR training can decrease the degree of distractibility of attention, while beta training can improve sustained attention, concentration, and attentional focus. Beta training can also improve planning, behavioral organization, motivation, and emotional well-being. SMR training can also decrease angst, agitation, and hypomania.

Over the course of consecutive sessions, as well as within sessions, both protocols were frequently adjusted depending on the physiological response and any indications of the nature of the child's problems. The ear was used as a reference measuring point, as Othmer pointed out, Lubar and Tansey preferred to use the central measuring point Cz in their neurofeedback method because the most abnormal values of theta/beta-1 ratio in people with ADHD were measurable at that point. This was determined by QEEG measurements using "linked ears" as QEEG reference measuring points. The use of "linked ears" reference is known to maximize deviant values along the midline. Othmer presumed that this anomalous activity actually originated in subcortical areas (basal ganglia, thalamus). Othmer favored C3 and C4 as neurofeedback measuring points because the EEG is more desynchronized at Cz during motor activity (Mann, 1996). Neurofeedback training certainly has an influence on the dynamics of synchronization and desynchronization. Sterman hypothesized that rhythmicity is trained in the thalamocortical regulatory circuit. Since the greatest thalamocortical fiber density is found in the primary sensory motor cortex, it is plausible that rhythmicity can most easily be trained in these areas.

The theoretical basis for Othmer's protocol originated in theories about functional differentiation between the two cerebral hemispheres as described, for example, by Tucker and Williamson (1984). The left cerebral cortex is especially active in sequential information processing; thus, playing a role in language, but also in planning, especially long-term planning (in which the frontal cerebral cortex is particularly active). The right hemisphere is more active in processing parallel information and simultaneously presenting phenomena. In essence, the right hemisphere attends to processing of novelty and strongly links with the association areas of the parietal cortex. Othmer concluded that dysfunction of the left cerebral cortex may lead to problems with focusing of attention. Dysfunction of the right cerebral hemisphere may lead to distractibility, impulsivity, and stimulus seeking behavior. Malone (1994) developed a model of ADHD based on these ideas. He postulated that ADHD involved dopermergenic and cholinergic deficits in the left frontal cerebral hemisphere, and noradrenergic excess as well as serotonergic deficits in the right parietal cerebral cortex. The left cerebral hemisphere is responsible for tonic activity, which includes focused attention, the right for phasic arousal, necessary for registering and processing new information. The up regulation of the dopamine system and down regulation of the noradrenic system mediates the efficacy of Ritalin in this model. This appears to be consistent with Othmer's empirical findings that training of C3 (left) predominately improves focused attention while training of C4 (right) predominately (but not exclusively) treats distractibility and impulsivity. Othmer also found that 15-18 Hz (beta) training on the left can ameliorate problems with focused attention and 12-15 Hz (SMR) training on the right can ameliorate impulsivity. Indeed, he concluded that beta training leads to a greater orthosympathetic arousal (also called ergotropy or arousal stimulation), and that SMR training leads to parasympathetic arousal (decreasing arousal or trophotropy). These reciprocal relationships have been recognized since Hess demonstrated in 1954 that electrical stimulation of specific areas of the hypothalamus could trigger these shifts (arousal, rest, sleep) in cats.

Othmer had proposed additional ideas based on his clinical experience of neurofeedback treatment applied to other problems. He had found that beta training on the left often improved depression while SMR training, also on the left, aggravated depression. Conversely, SMR training on the right side can decrease anxiety but beta training can lead to agitation or mania. Othmer found that the ADHD subtype with excessive frontal alpha activity is best trained left at 15-18 Hz eventually in combination with alpha inhibition training. Suffin (1995) had shown that antidepressants were the most effective medication for this group. This training protocol is comparable to the neurofeedback protocol developed by Rosenfeld (Rosenfeld, Cha, Blair, & Gotlib, 1995; Rosenfeld, 1997) for the treatment of depression. On the other hand, most people with the hyperactive subtype of ADHD showed an excess of theta activity in Othmer's experience; therefore, he favored right sided SMR training. At the onset, the subtype of ADHD with excessive beta activity, which is mostly associated with hyperactive behavior, was demonstrated to be an expression of hyperarousal. Originally, treatment with Ritalin seemed inappropriate in these cases. However, Clark (2003) subsequently showed that Ritalin worked in the treatment of this excessive beta subtype to the same extent as in the treatment of the classic subtype with excess theta activity. Clark hypothesized that low arousal, impulsivity, and hyperactivity, which are often associated, do not explain beta activity in the excessive beta subtype of ADHD; instead, these behavioral characteristics probably come about through other disrupted frontal mechanisms. This was not known when Othmer developed his model; therefore, it does not have a place within that framework.

In summary, Othmer thought that deficits in the left hemisphere leads to underactivation, causing an 'implosion' of behavior that is best treated by training beta (15-18 Hz) which has a strengthening effect on behavior. Conversely, deficits in the right hemisphere often lead to overactivation and explosive behavior, which is best treated by training SMR (12-15 Hz), which has a calming effect on behavior. This protocol has many followers, including Egner and Gruzelier, and Rossiter and Fuchs. Rossiter (2002) also followed two protocols with slightly different rationales. He trained the excess of theta activity with SMR at C4 (right central) and excessive alpha activity with beta (15-18 Hz) at C3 (left central). As Othmer, he cited Suffin's research showing that increased alpha activity responded best to antidepressants and heightened SMR activity to traditional psychostimulants.

The pharmacological functional anatomic ADHD model developed by Malone (Malone, Kershner, & Swanson, 1994) prompted Othmer in 1995 to further customize his training protocol. He replaced "monopolar" measuring points (in which the ear is used as reference point) with bipolar measuring points at left C3-Fpz and right C4-Pz, bringing a new element into the training. A bipolar measurement is not only a mixture of the amplitude of the trained frequency at the two measuring points but also the net result of the phase angle between the sinusoidal waves at the two measuring points. The measured angle is greatest in antiphase, that is, at 180 degrees. It seems counter intuitive to train such antiphase because it has been demonstrated that the process of communication between cortical locations establishes greater synchronization (Rappelsberger, 1994). Othmer argued that the empirical experience showed this training to be effective. He theorized that in the regulatory challenge model of neurofeedback, the feedback signal temporarily shifts the brain from its dominant equilibrium to which it subsequently returns. It does not matter in what direction the imbalance occurs, improved regulatory function follows in either case.

Neurofeedback facilitates a process of change, the capacity for which it already exists in the brain. Othmer conjectured, for example, that the fact that impulsivity is present in behavior implies that a functional mechanism exists to better control the behavior, that is, in a more functional and less dysfunctional manner. Othmer evinced a basal regulating mechanism, whose dysfunction leads to problems such as ADHD. Challenging the system leads to greater system stability. The three dimensions of arousal, attention, and affectivity are viewed as coupled systems; therefore, neurofeedback training of one system has implications for the other three. Hess (1954) was the first to conceptualize brain functions in terms of coupled systems. In Othmer's opinion, prolonged neurofeedback training leads to exercising and expanding the ability of the brain to move freely along the continuum from ergotropic to trophotropic dominance, with all the implications for attention, arousal, and regulation of affect. Not only an increase in stability, but also an improvement in the ability to achieve stability makes this possible. Keeping the dynamic balance between ergotropic and trophotropic domination is sometimes referred to as "tuning" of the nervous system. Neurofeedback can optimize this tuning and contribute to a global balance (homeostasis).

Othmer (1992) provides an illustration: *AK is a thirteen-year-old girl with ADHD. She had very low self-esteem, difficulties understanding written material, and was very immature. In fifth grade, she had a concussion. Her neurofeedback protocol was beta (15-18 Hz) training over 20 sessions because her reading problems were her most urgent difficulty. While slight improvements occurred in her reading difficulties, her impulsivity was aggravated so that after 20 sessions, she received a further 20 sessions of SMR (12-15 Hz) training. Only during the course of the second treatment phase were improvements in impulsivity and the disorders of attention observed and AK's behavior began to mature.*

173

Othmer, and more recently Kropotov, have found that although a learning curve occurs during a training session, after the end of a session, as well as after the end of a course of sessions, there is often no change in theta/beta-1 ratio observed in passive states. They defended their judgment stating that the mechanism supporting improved attention and more adaptive behavioral skills improved substantially following the treatment. Behavioral observations, neuropsychological tests, and the results of more dynamic neurophysiological research, such as the go/no-go task, supported their argument (Kropotov et al., 2004). Both the go and the no-go evoked P3 brain potential improved following training. Using fMRI imaging Beauregard (2006) recently demonstrated that the executive functions (associated with the anterior cingulate, the lateral prefrontal cortex, and the caudate nucleus) improved after the treatment. Kropotov (2004b) demonstrated that neurofeedback therapy also led to normalization of weak beta and theta synchronization during the go/no-go task. Othmer thought that during neurofeedback, long cortico-cortical circuits are trained, which express their function in fluctuating rhythms.

Based on this conceptualization, neurofeedback training is viewed as a challenge to these rhythmic control mechanisms. It is directed rather towards a modified theta/beta-1 ratio than towards reaching those stable states measurable in passive conditions. The latter is occasionally the case, but is not the primary goal of training. The primary goal from this standpoint is to further improve the dynamic functioning during active attention and in the associated executive functions.

6.18 The Potential Importance of a Global Timing Mechanism (Global Self-Regulation Model)

From 2002 onwards, Othmer has favored the treatment of more severe forms of ADHD associated with emotional and mood instability using a bipolar homologous interhemispheric training protocol that leads to better outcomes with greater efficiency, in his experience. He was prompted to use this method partly based on Suffin's observation (1995) that the best antiepileptic therapeutic outcomes were obtained in patients with ADHD who demonstrated increased interhemispheric coherence. Othmer referred to this as cortical instability. The relationship between cortical instability and disorders such as bipolar disorder, borderline personality disorder, and dissociative disorder is transparent and supported by the known therapeutic stabilizing effect of antiepileptics on these disorders.

Othmer noted that the designated reward frequency band for this training was very much more specific and often very narrow (for example 10 Hz). The first session usually began with setting SMR as the reward frequency in a bipolar recording of T3-T4. This is adjusted around every three minutes when a slightly narrower, lower (or more rarely, slightly higher) frequency band is chosen as the new reward frequency, until a frequency is found at which the patient indicates that he or she subjectively feels better (calmer and more comfortable). Although the optimal reward frequency is normally SMR or alpha, it often shows rather surprisingly as delta. To Othmer, this suggested a method for training slow cortical potentials. (See chapter 8).

Taking into account that bipolar recording (in which the electrical polarity of the EEG signal at both measuring points is contrasted) is used, together with the fact that this type of training is very sensitive to frequency, indicated to Othmer that the relevant variable in this training is the phase angle between the EEG waves of the specific rewarded frequency, both left and right, and therefore implying that this type of training challenges the phase regulating mechanism. The amplitude of the measured signal in bipolar training has thus a different significance than in monopolar training. If a clear change in amplitude is observed, then a change in phase between the signals between the two measuring points also occurs. Thus, in order to obtain rewarding feedback, the brain is challenged to change its activity in a more complex manner rather than in monopolar training. A more interactive, coupled activity is required of the brain, possibly explaining why the patient experiences the effects immediately. The therapist takes into account the patient's own experiences of the training (when it is relevant) to assesses the optimal reward frequency. If signs of labored effort are evident, the reward frequency is decreased. Nevertheless, it remains difficult to find an optimal reward frequency for patients with emotional instability.

Othmer's formulation was that the phase between the two hemispheres is trained during this interhemispheric homologous bipolar training, and this trained phase plays a central role in the large-scale timing mechanism within the brain. He obtained remarkably good results in comparison with his original method, especially in more severe ADHD cases that are frequently comorbid with other psychiatric problems. Othmer thought these comorbid problems could also be grouped under the umbrella of cortical instability, including panic attacks, bipolar disorder, dissociative states, and borderline personality disorders. The temporal lobe locations T3 and T4 were used in the training.

In contrast to the earlier method employing standard protocols, this new method was based on a clinical model in which the therapist continuously adjusts the selected reward frequency. At the outset, the rewarded frequency band is the SMR rhythm. The rewarded band is subsequently continuously modified. The therapist searches for the optimal frequency in a process of adjustment that is more interactive than the traditional method. Even during the first session, the patient is often aware of the brain state changes that correspond to reward. In this way, the patient is reassured that something is really changing, and therefore he becomes more active in the feedback process. For all these reasons, even the more challenging patient becomes more likely to complete the course of training. Othmer observed that improvements in symptoms over the course of sessions appeared more quickly using this newer method, especially in patients with the most pronounced symptoms. In total, 106 patients took part in his published study (Putman, Othmer, & Othmer, 2005).

No more than three synapses link every brain area to every other brain area. Each link has a role in the "timing" of the communication between different brain areas. The timing of EEG signals at different points can be seen as the net result of timing mechanisms acting at the micro level (that is, the neurons). In addition to specific local timing aspects, there are also global timing principles that produce the same proportional pattern at every time scale. In other words, a reverse proportional ratio, the power law distribution, exists between the cyclic frequencies that occur at particular phase changes and the degree to which they occur. These distributions are repeated on different time and space scales, producing a fractal pattern. The brain stem and hypothalamus probably regulate simultaneous bihemispheric processes. Interhemispheric training of timing mechanisms happens at the highest and probably the most efficient scale that challenges the brain's reorganization. Coordination of timing is one of the brain's key functions at both a local and global level and is essential to good communication between different brain areas. Othmer used the analogy of an orchestra, which produces global timing and a rhythmic pattern into which each individual instrument (which have their own local location and frequency characteristics) must fit. We can ascribe to a "virtual conductor" in the brain the self-organized functions that manage and coordinate global timing. The function of this 'conductor' can be most likely attributed to the thalamus, which possesses the reciprocal thalamocortical circuits. This regulating activity is measured in the EEG, and the timing mechanism (the phase) is measured during neurofeedback. The brain is thus challenged to optimize its less than optimal functioning in the patient. The self-regulation of the brain is challenged to attain a better level. By rewarding the individual at every moment that the brain reaches this more optimal state, the chance that this state will be repeated most likely increases (Thorndike's Law of Effect). Othmer thought that a more effective regulation of neuronal networks develops out of this process of challenge, regardless of whether or not these networks are involved in the regulation of attention or mood.

Symptoms can be considered in terms of physiological mechanisms that are reflected in the dynamics of the EEG. Suggested mechanisms can be confirmed or refuted during neurofeedback training by observing the dynamics of the EEG from moment to moment and, at the same time, by observing the response to adaptive feedback. Training leads to changes in the EEG dynamic, resulting in improved self-regulation and diminishing symptoms. During training, the neurofeedback protocol is adapted in accordance with indications of changes in the dynamic and the desired parameters originally targeted.

Othmer emphasized that the search for a specific narrow reward frequency band entails rewarding an antiphase mechanism at that EEG frequency. Consequently, the phase mechanism is challenged and strengthened.

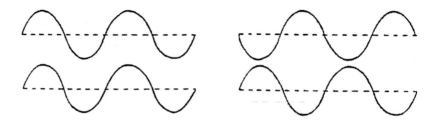

Figure 49. **Left:** *Phase synchronization, the use of bipolar measurement would give a flat signal.* **Right:** *Antiphase (180 degrees), the use of bipolar measurement would give high amplitude.*

Othmer thought those proportional relationships that remain constant during training of a highly dynamic process indicated the most efficient training. That single narrow frequency band that designated for feedback reward becomes a kind of rudder to follow the higher EEG dynamic.

Othmer emphasized that the EEG dynamic is often only partially, or even not at all, traceable in the statistical QEEG. Othmer used a bipolar hemispheric homologous EEG montage (for example T3-T4: left and right amplitudes mid temporal) to detect and to train the global phase dynamic. The amplitude of each frequency was determined not only by the degree of synchronization (phase) amplitude at each of the two points, but also by the degree of synchronization (phase) between the two frequencies. The electrical positivity is recorded in one channel as an upward deflection and in the other channel as a downward deflection during bipolar measurement; the synchronization (phase difference 0°) of the amplitude of this frequency is therefore zero.

The amplitude is maximal in antiphase (180°). Othmer described a bipolar montage as an instrument for changing phase to net amplitude information. While the phase difference can only be partially measured in this way, in the training context, it is not necessary to know the exact values. We need to know only the speed of phase reversals to know how well the training is progressing at any particular moment. Some neurofeedback therapists have observed that following reward of the optimal frequency, a sudden increase in amplitude, synchronous with a very low amplitude in all the other frequencies (corresponding to a tendency to phase synchronization), occurs at that frequency (corresponding to the antiphase). Othmer himself never observed this. Rewarding the optimal frequency can be seen as a subtle challenge of the brain state at that moment. Although very speculative, the brain reacts to the reward with a response in the opposite direction.

Nevertheless, Othmer allowed QEEG to play a role in the identification of a specific dysfunction. He also emphasized that positive consequences obtained from the use of the challenge model can occur at the cost of limitations imposed on the brain by the feedback. In 2005, he integrated both approaches, arguing that classical neurofeedback (that is, operant conditioning based on a training protocol determined by QEEG findings) may be complementary to the dynamic challenge neurofeedback method (developed based on both hypothesized and established mechanisms). He reappraised the balance of positive perspective and the limitations of the earlier model from a different perspective.

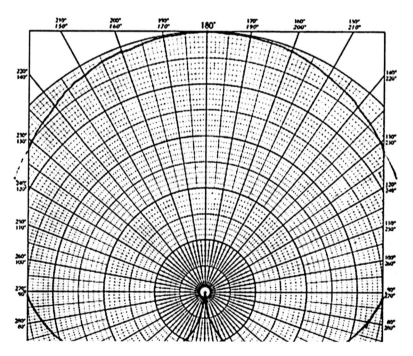

Figure 50. In a bipolar recording, the maximum amplitude can indicate a 180° phase delay (antiphase) while the minimum amplitude can indicate phase synchrony (0 °).

In conclusion, it should be noted that this new "bipolar" neurofeedback method is at a very experimental stage, and there are a number of uncertainties inherent in this method. In principle, it is always difficult to assess to what extent the absolute left and right amplitude and to what extent phase delays determine the amplitude of each EEG frequency in a bipolar EEG montage. On the other hand, Putman (2001) and Lubar (2001) noted that bipolar training facilitates precise measurement of the amplitude and phase delays between two locations; consequently, training can target these differences with precision. In his original research, Lubar used Sterman's bipolar training method with the two measuring points in close proximity to each other (for instance using a measuring point halfway between F3 and C3, another measuring point halfway between C3and P3 and eventually Fz-Cz or Cz-Pz). In contrast, in his recent protocols, Othmer employed homologous locations on the left and right, such as T3 and T4, lying far apart from each other. Because of this uncertainty, the use of two monopolar montages is in principle useful if coherence and phase measurements are desired between frequencies or frequency bands from two different scalp locations.

Summary

Othmer emphasized that it is not so much the case that static patterns are trained in neurofeedback, but that neurofeedback challenges dynamic mechanisms. Therefore, training does not necessarily lead to changes in the basic statistical measurements of QEEG but to changes in dynamic measurements such as ERD/ ERS.

6.19 40 Hz (35-45Hz) Neurofeedback

Chapter 4 discusses the role of the 40 Hz (35-45 Hz) rhythm in attention and motor stillness in more detail. Sheer (1976) found no increase in electrical activity in children with ADHD during problem solving tasks in comparison to that observed in typically developing children (who moreover demonstrated better task performance). He showed the 40 Hz rhythm to be an expression of focused arousal, a process of some importance in consolidating information from short-term memory into long-term memory. Technically, it is extremely difficult to detect these small fast waves in the EEG (5-15 µV) and to distinguish them from electrical muscle activity (EMG). That is why neurofeedback research has developed little at this end of the spectrum. The capability to reliably measure 40 Hz has become available only in recent years with advances in measuring equipment.

In 1976, Bauer investigated the effects of approximately 40 Hz neurofeedback training in cats (using cortically implanted electrodes), which he clearly demonstrated to be a form of operant conditioning similar to that employed by Sterman in his original research, also on cats. The cats received milk as a reward whenever the targeted 40 Hz activity occurred in the EEG. This research indicated it was possible to strengthen 40 Hz activity in different brain areas. It was also observed that the cats were immobile during the training. If the 40 Hz activity was trained at the visual cortex, the cats would also visually fixate. This research is in good agreement with the research of Rougeul-Buser (1994) who investigated the link between 40 Hz activity and unmoving fixation of attention in cats as described in chapter 4.4.

In 1975, Sheer demonstrated that 40 Hz activity in the human visual cortex (O1-P3) increased with neurofeedback (with electrodes at the scalp) over the course of 8 daily sessions of 30 minutes in a group of five human adults. He used ingenious methods to prevent the misreading of muscular electrical activity (EMG) as 40 Hz activity. At moments when 40 Hz activity was present in the EEG, the next slide in a series of slides was displayed and subsequently rewarded with money. The number of slides projected during the whole session (a form of operant conditioning) determined the exact monetary amount. During training, 40 Hz activity increased by 160% on average while EMG activity fell by 16% on average.

One to three weeks after the neurofeedback training, the experimental subjects were invited to voluntarily produce the 40 Hz activity (without feedback) and most succeeded. Eight weeks after training, the subjects were once again asked to produce the 40 Hz activity and to solve some problems while in this voluntary brain state. The quantity of 40 Hz EEG activity was then compared with the quantity generated solving similar problems but with the command to voluntarily suppress 40 Hz activity.

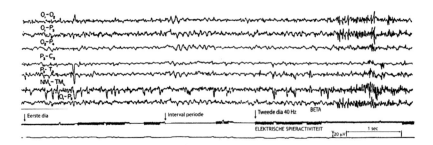

Figure 51. During administration of Sheer's test battery, EMG as well as EEG were measured. Slides were projected as feedback if a 40 Hz discharge occurred in the EEG (O1-P3). In this participant, following 40 Hz training, 40 Hz activity appeared at O1-P3 (Upper 2nd trace) during presentation of the first and second slides (indicated by small vertical arrows). At the end of the slide of the presentation, verbal answers were requested. They were associated with the EMG and most visible in the sixth trace NM-TM (neck muscles, temporal muscles). The 40 Hz activity is minuscule and can barely be discerned in the raw EEG, so that a computer analysis is best used to detect and quantify this activity. On the bottom right, the horizontal calibration line indicates a time unit of one second and the vertical line amplitude of 20 μV. Reprinted from Behavior and Brain Electrical Activity, Sheer, Copyright (1975), with permission from Plenum Press.

This command proved impossible to fulfill. During problem solution, 40 Hz activity was the same in both conditions. However, 40 Hz activity during both problem solution conditions was higher than prior to training. Moreover, these participants clearly showed better problem solving performance in psychological tests. To illustrate, thirty words were presented on slides in a word-learning test, one word each per slide per second with a pause of 15 seconds between slides. After training, subjects remembered on average 16.6 words compared to five words prior to training. Furthermore, it was demonstrated that prior to training, seventy-seven 40 Hz discharges occurred on average in the EEG during this task, after training, this increased to an average of one hundred twenty-one 40 Hz discharges in the EEG.

Another test consisted of a series of five problem assignments, each displayed for 30 seconds on a slide. After a 15 second break, five slides were shown with a multiple-choice question shown until the participant answered or until 60 seconds passed without an answer. Prior to training, the participants solved on average 1.6 out of the 5 problems. After training, and with a new series of problems, participants solved on average 4.4 problems. Prior to training, there were, on average, forty-one 40 Hz discharges during this task. After training, there were 158 discharges. We can conclude that the subject can voluntarily generate this rhythm, following indications of a successful 40 Hz training. Rather more to the point, 40 Hz activity at moments of task solution was involuntarily stronger than prior to training, and the tasks were also better performed.

Bird (1978) trained two groups of 8 adults each (18 to 27 years old) with 40 Hz neurofeedback in six daily sessions of thirty minutes One group was trained at O1-Cz (left) and the other at O2-Cz (right). This training appeared feasible and showed that training 40 Hz activity on one side also increased the 40 Hz effect on the other side. Most subjects were able to voluntarily increase 40 Hz activity for several weeks following training.

Later, Ford assessed six adults (20 to 24 years old) from Bird's original group of 16 adults and found that the effects of 40 Hz neurofeedback training were maintained three years later. The six participants who participated in the 1978 study retrained best at O1-Cz. In the first phase of the assessment, they were trained again at 40 Hz. For five of the six participants it was possible to obtain an increase within the first five minutes of the first session. One participant required four sessions to achieve the same result. Thus, for five of the six participants, the trained skills were maintained three years after the initial training. In the second phase on the day after, the participants had to demonstrate that they could voluntarily induce 40 Hz activity. These five participants were presented with four types of problem tasks on slides, each slide with 10 problems in multiple-choice format. While solving each of the first five tasks, the participants were asked to voluntarily increase 40 Hz activity. Subsequently the participants were asked to solve the remaining problems without generating 40 Hz activity. Both of these problem-solving conditions lasted five minutes. However, in five of the six participants, the task solution was associated with an increase in 40 Hz activities in both conditions. This confirms original research by Sheer (1975). The subjects' ability to voluntarily increase 40 Hz activity after training argues for a conscious self-regulating mechanism, despite the apparent impossibility of consciously suppressing 40 Hz activity during problem solving.

Summary

Forty hertz neurofeedback training leads to improvements in attention and learning abilities. In practice, this training is technically not easy to implement because these fast EEG waves are very low voltage and therefore difficult to distinguish from technical noise and electrical muscle activity. However, new and more advanced software and hardware makes it possible to detect this signal more accurately. The effects of this training are abrupt and appear to be maintained three years later.

7.

Tomographic (LORETA) 3D Neurofeedback

One of the limitations of modern neurofeedback methods is that it supplies limited information, originating from just one or two electrode readings placed on the scalp. In theory, targeting feedback brain activity from specific areas deep in the cerebral cortex can lead to significant improvements in efficiency and precision. Classically, the EEG is measured at 19 points on the scalp, forming a somewhat geometrical shape of a hemisphere. Commonly, the source of measured activity lies deep in the brain. By calculating an inverse mathematical solution involving the three dimensional distribution of each EEG activity measured at the scalp (such as certain EEG frequencies, epileptic discharges, or evoked potentials), it is possible to localize the source (or sources) and to measure its current density. These calculated three dimensional localizations can be linked to data from a brain atlas in order to obtain functional anatomic images similar to images obtained from other functional brain imaging research techniques such as PET scans (positron emission tomography) or fMRI (functional magnetic resonance imaging). The images are displayed in a cross section, hence the origin of the term tomography.

LORETA (low resolution brain electromagnetic tomography) developed in 1994 by Pascual-Marqui (Pascual-Marqui, Michel, & Lehmann, 1994; Pascual-Marqui, 2002) is one of the most well known and used methods of source localization. Many research groups have used it successfully in electrophysiological studies of trained activity. This mathematical reconstruction is only used for imaging the cerebral cortex, and thus not for imaging the white matter which consists of the neurons connecting different brain areas, for the grey nuclei deep in the brain (basal ganglia and thalamus) or for the cerebellum. This restriction should be kept in mind because all EEG activity that is measurable at the scalp originates in the cortex (Nunez, 1995).

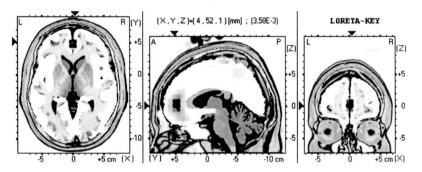

Figure 52. Three-dimensional cross sections of the brain from the Talairach Brain Atlas (Lancaster et al., 1997; Lancaster, et al., 2000) indicate areas of maximal distribution of certain electrical current densities; the reconstruction is based on the distribution of certain EEG activity over the surface of the scalp. In these images, current density is maximal in the anterior cingulate (colored black).

Furthermore, white matter and the grey nuclei have a different electrical resistance, which would complicate the mathematical model.

Naturally, this does not simply imply that no electrical activity is processed in the grey nucleus. On the contrary, an important part of EEG activity measured at the scalp is processed in the thalamus and the reticular formation in the brain stem, playing an important role in determination of states of consciousness and attention. These areas generate electrical activity in the cerebral cortex and this is the activity measured in EEG.

Chabot (1998, 2001) examined a group of 344 children diagnosed with ADHD. Using LORETA, he located the source of the most abnormal frequency band. Subsequently, these results were compared with values obtained from 130 typically developing children (6 to 16 years). This research identified two groups of children: 1) a group with an excess of alpha activity (11 Hz on average), and 2) a group with an excess of theta activity (on average 5.4 Hz) that was shown to originate in the temporal cortex and hippocampus. A positive response to Ritalin correlated with normalization of the LORETA abnormalities.

These results are somewhat surprising. In the majority of EEG studies, abnormal theta or alpha activity was linked to frontal areas with the assumed origin in either the thalamus or the caudate nucleus or both areas. Using LORETA, the increased theta/beta ratio in the EEG of most children with ADHD has been sourced to the anterior or mid cingulate (Lubar, personal communication). This is in line with this author's clinical experience. The anterior cingulate is known to be linked to the hippocampus. Another reason Chabot's findings were unexpected is because classical theta activity originating from the hippocampus has been associated with good cognitive functioning, in contrast to the theta activity associated with lowered consciousness or attentional problems. In these cases, theta activity is associated with altered activity in the thalamocortical circuit, demonstrating more burst activity that normally occurs only during sleep. A possible explanation for these patterns is that statistical comparisons between groups can produce unexpected results. In this complete group of 344 children with ADHD, a mixture of pattern subtypes would be expected to be present.

Neurofeedback is traditionally limited to EEG biofeedback. fMRI measures regional oxygen use in all brain areas, creating a picture of brain activity during certain tasks. In 2002, the first study was published on the training of brain activity associated with right hand motor skills (Yoo, 2002). Feedback was delivered with a 20-second delay. Although EEG spatial resolution is recognized to be inferior to other modern imaging techniques, EEG time resolution in milliseconds is certainly superior.

Weiskopf (2003) succeeded in training anterior cingulate activity in an experimental subject using fMRI neurofeedback, with a latency of less than two seconds. What is more, it appeared possible to train separately the ventral (affective) part and the dorsal (cognitive) part of the anterior cingulate.

Using research methods such as these, it seems in principle possible to target certain brain areas for neurofeedback to identify which mental functions neurofeedback alters. This is contrary to the most popular research paradigm that employs fMRI imaging to identify brain areas active during certain mental tasks.

DeCharms (2004) showed that during fMRI neurofeedback, subjects increased activity in sensorimotor cortex while imaging hand movements without performing the movements. After training, fMRI imaging identified more activity in the brain areas involved during imagined hand movements than prior to training.

Although these initial findings are encouraging, it is unlikely that fMRI neurofeedback shall have widespread clinical applications for a number of reasons, including the lack of real time resolution and the sheer expense and unwieldiness of the fMRI apparatus. Neither is it known if there are long-term adverse effects on the brain from repeated exposures to the strong magnetic fields used in fMRI. Another disadvantage is that measurement of oxygen consumption gives only an indirect measure of electrical brain activity. It is known that a (functionally important) high voltage EEG band arises from synchronization of small groups of neurons while unsynchronized activity of large groups of neurons causes low voltage EEG frequency bands. In the latter case, fMRI will image increased activity. As an example, all EEG frequency bands show an increased average voltage in people with higher IQ; however, they show a decreased global fMRI activity. Additionally, fMRI cannot distinguish between areas of strong inhibition and strong activation, since both consume oxygen. The advantages of the technique are excellent spatial resolution obtained and the ability to image subcortical structures (basal ganglia, thalamus).

Congedo published a dissertation under Lubar's supervision in 2003 in which he developed a method to train LORETA information about a designated EEG frequency of a particular deep brain area using real time neurofeedback. In theory, this method can designate the target with more precision than in classical methods of neurofeedback. EEG activity measured at a specific point at the scalp is composed of activity originating from multiple brain areas, both at the surface and deep in the brain. Consequently, classical neurofeedback offers little precision concerning the anatomic localization of the trained function such that it is almost impossible to target training of function in specific brain areas. In the treatment of ADHD, this is probably not a critical shortcoming of classical neurofeedback because the abnormal theta/beta-1 ratio (maximum at the scalp midline) is not directly linked to a particular brain area; rather, it is associated with the non-specific thalamocortical circuits that play a role in the organization of consciousness and attention.

Congedo's experimental research employed three subjects without a psychiatric history and with normal QEEG and LORETA, as determined by the distribution of population norms. The ratio between beta (16-20 Hz) and slow alpha (8-10 Hz) current density was trained in the cognitive (posterior) part of the anterior cingulate to increase this ratio. Early studies of the anterior cingulate showed that different component areas each have a distinctive function so that a rough distinction can be made between areas dealing with cognitive and emotional processes (Bush, 1999). The cognitive area of the anterior cingulate plays a role in the initiation of actions, including goal directed actions, motivation, attention, and response selection.

The common pattern of increased slow alpha and decreased slow beta activity in people with ADHD does not motivate the choice of specific EEG frequency band relationships for selecting LORETA neurofeedback training. In this experiment, the relationship between beta and alpha current density was targeted for improvement. Beta/alpha current density appeared to improve over six sessions. Further analysis of the data showed that this was a consequence of increased beta activity and not of increased muscle activity since this was taken into account. These results are encouraging but not wholly persuasive. It is not clear if more training sessions would contribute to a further increase and if these outcomes would last. Neither is it known yet if there are any clinical applications to ADHD.

Cannon together with Congedo, Lubar, and co-investigators (2006, 2007) recently published two studies on LORETA neurofeedback training of eight normal students. Over 33 sessions, each consisting of four four-minute periods (three times a week over eleven weeks), were conducted to train the current density in the cognitive part of the anterior cingulate, which was reconstructed in real time from 14-18 Hz frequency bands as measured on the 19 classic scalp measuring points. A sound feedback was given and received via a computer game. The EMG signal was suppressed during training at the temporal and occipital electrodes along with eye movement activity at the frontal electrodes. It was indeed possible to strengthen activity in the anterior cingulate. Subsequently, other brain areas in the LORETA 14-18 Hz band were investigated, which showed activity that correlated with activity in the anterior cingulate. These were identified as the left and right dorsolateral prefrontal cerebral cortex and the right post central gyrus. The anterior cingulate is known to monitor requirements for executive control and signal the prefrontal cerebral cortex to exercise that control (Markela-Lerenc, 2004). Executive functions are not only instrumental to cognitive processes, but also to effort and the maintenance of attention. Furthermore, these studies demonstrated improved working memory and increased speed of task processing as measured by neuropsychological tests.

In his second study, Cannon investigated the changes in EEG at the scalp surface following the same LORETA neurofeedback training administered to the eight students in the first study. 14-18 Hz activity decreased in more posterior areas but the faster beta activity increased. There was reorganization of all frequencies in multiple brain areas. The absolute power of several EEG frequency bands increased in many areas known to have anatomical links with the anterior cingulate. In frontal and parietal areas, 14-18 Hz activity increased; these areas are part of the executive function circuit. Coherence of delta, theta, alpha, and 14-18 Hz EEG bands increased while coherence of the slower beta activity decreased. These studies support the idea that the anterior cingulate plays an important role in the initiation of mechanisms in different brain areas of the circuit responsible for executive functions. These findings affirm Lubar's earlier findings that theta/SMR neurofeedback at Cz leads to changes in the EEG frequency spectrum at most other measuring points on the scalp, and that this training improves functioning of the anterior cingulate.

Summary

LORETA (low resolution brain electromagnetic tomography) allows three-dimensional localization of the source deep in the brain of specific EEG activity measured at the scalp. Therefore, with neurofeedback, it is possible, in principle, to train specific source activity deep in the brain. This is, however, very problematic (requiring at least 19 measuring points at the surface of the scalp, with the possibility of a great deal of technical disturbance via muscle activity and eye movements) and not a realistic method in clinical practice. Nevertheless, it has proved to be an extraordinarily useful method for investigating those brain circuits that play a role in attention and executive functions.

LORETA neurofeedback training of 14-18 Hz in the cognitive area of the anterior cingulate leads to an improvement in this activity, not just in the trained area, but also in multiple brain areas that form part of the cognitive circuits (especially frontal and right parietal areas). This new method of neurofeedback is currently in the experimental stages.

8.

Slow Cortical Potentials (SCP) Neurofeedback

8.1 Slow Negative Cortical Potentials

Slow cortical potentials (SCP) have a frequency of less than 1-2 cycles per second and therefore a minimum duration of 0.5 seconds; however, they can last for up to 6 seconds. The EEG can measure these slow potentials by adjusting the filter width of the EEG band. In order to obtain these measurements, it is necessary to adjust the low-pass filter to 1.6 Hz and the high-pass filter to 10 Hz. Slow potentials are sometimes also called DC (direct current) potentials because they can be measured reliably only with DC amplifiers. They are a direct current in the brain on which faster AC (alternating current) waves ride.

Negative slow potentials reflect the provision of certain ability to the brain that we can characterize as working memory in which attention also plays a major part. Negative potentials correspond with processing capacity in the brain areas that bring about these changes.

The EEG shows a negative shift of the direct current base line, for example, during wakefulness and motor arousal, indicating that it occurs at moments of increased cortical excitability. The occurrences of these slow cortical potentials are associated with better response organization, perception, and problem solving.

A well known way to excite slow brain potentials is using the so-called contingent negative variation (CNV) first described by the British neurologist Grey Walter. A second stimulus that requires a particular response (such as pushing a button), which triggers the appearance of a slow negative potential, follows a warning stimulus one to six seconds later. The first half of the SCP (occurring between 400 and 800 ms after the first stimulus) is an indicator of expectation of the second stimulus. The second half reflects preparation to execute the required action.

The majority of events in everyday life are not unexpected. The experiences gained earlier of the sequence of events in certain environments support anticipation and prediction of what will happen next. The event is described as contingent with the first warning stimulus.

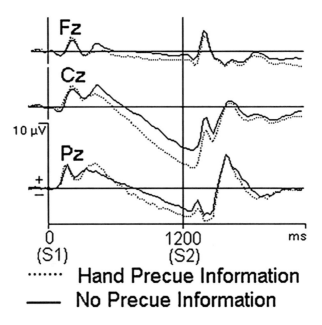

Figure 53. The CNV occurs between the warning stimulus S1 and the imperative stimulus S2 and is maximal at the crown of the scalp. If additional warning information (pre-cue) is given, the negative potential is more pronounced. Also notice the electrically positive P300 (following from S2) maximal at Pz.

The first component of the contingent negative variation is maximally measurable at the front and center of the vertex of the scalp, the second component over the central cerebral cortex, and the active component in response preparation prior to the second stimulus. Usually, a button push is the required response to the second stimulus and is associated with a component that is maximally measurable over the left cerebral cortex (if the button is pushed with the right hand). The normal CNV amplitude lies between -12 µV and -20 µV in 12 year olds with a maximum recorded over the posterior cerebral cortex, and in 12 to 15 years old, the maximum activity moves to the adult frontocentral position. In people with ADHD, the CNV amplitude is reduced. Aydin (1987) found that the average CNV is lower in children with ADHD than in other children. In 44% of the children with ADHD, no CNV was measurable, which was never the case for the other children. CNV intensity correlated with school performance and was inversely proportional to the degree of hyperactivity. The administration of Ritalin normalized CNV.

Three research approaches have built a better understanding of these potentials through the examination of: 1) self-regulation of SCP through neurofeedback, 2) weak external direct currents at the scalp, 3) fMRI research looking at the role of deeper brain structures in generating CNV, as well as the role that deeper brain structures play in the strengthening of SCP shifts during neurofeedback. The application of weak direct current (DC stimulation of 1 mA over 5 minutes) over the dorsolateral prefrontal cortex improves working memory (Lyer, 2005), but the effect is transient in nature. Ongoing studies are attempting to determine if there is a lasting effect following a series of such transcranial stimulations. An antidepressant effect was described following a course of five daily DC stimulations at the left frontal cerebral cortex (F3) of 2 mA each lasting 20 minutes (Fregni, 2005).

Negative slow potentials happen if action potentials of the underlying neurons transpire for a longer period at higher frequencies. A normal EEG shows a few waves with a low amplitude and high frequency (beta, gamma). Simultaneous depolarization of neurons in the outermost layer of the cerebral cortex creates slow negative potentials, which are suspected to be initiated by the thalamocortical neurons.

8.2 A New Biological Approach to Cognitive Evoked Brain Potentials

The current explicative model of the evoked cognitive brain potentials described in earlier chapters of this book suggests that evoked potentials reflect successive stages of stimulus processing mechanisms that occur between the perception of a stimulus and the execution of an action. Theoretical models from cognitive psychology were used in its development and founded in the view that the brain's main task is to build a representation of reality that we label knowledge or cognition. Kotchoubey (2006) has proposed an alternative model in which cortical behavioral control is considered as a repeating sensorimotor cycle that is built from two phases: a proactive anticipation phase, and a cortical performance feedback phase. It has been described as a dynamic and interactive model. Kotchoubey himself choose the term a "biological approach" in order to stress the contrast between the basic cognitive assumption and his basic assumption according to which behavior and linked brain processes are part of life and the chief function of the brain is to ensure survival of the organism by optimal adoption of behavior to the environment, rather than by processing information and gathering knowledge about the environment. Kotchoubey's approach is in harmony with that taken by Freeman who also described proactive anticipation as the primary drive behind behavior and contrasted it with the idea that mechanisms in the brain reflect reality (Freeman, 1999). These approaches are in line with Bente's (1964) description of the EEG as an expression of the degree of vigilance (in which vigilance is defined as the individual's ability to adapt to the environment) and with Van Orden's (2002) interaction dominant dynamic, which he contrasted with the component dominant dynamic when studying aspects of neuropsychological cognitions. Cosmides (1994) summarized succinctly, 'Cognitive psychology has been conducted as if Darwin had never lived.' Koboutchey's biological approach is very close to the new perspectives on ADHD described at the beginning of this book. Attention is not itself the problem in ADHD; it is a weakened ability to adapt to the environment alongside decreased proactive anticipation of what will happen next. From the biological approach, each perceptive task or cognitive task is a specific moment in the adaption of the organism to the environment. These moments may be the artificial requirements of an experimental laboratory task or a motivational state. This state facilitates the organism's ability to search for relevant stimuli in their environment. This state of preparation for perception can be expressed by a particular alignment of receptors or reactivation of specific sensory neurons. The manner in which the environment responds is the perceived event and plays a central role in cognitive brain potentials, such that they are better named as "event related potentials" (ERP). The different approaches to ERP components imply differing opinions about how the cerebral cortex controls behavior.

In the cognitive model, only the beginning and end states of processing stages interact with the environment while in the biological model, all processing steps are in contact with the environment.

Slow cortical potentials (such as the CNV) usually occur prior to an "event," but classical ERPs are normally fast positive or negative potentials that follow an event. This distinction is relative, inasmuch as the fast ERPs, which follow in the first couple of hundred seconds after an event, often appear against a background of overlapping slow potentials (frequently not measured because slow potentials are often filtered from an EEG channel). In recent years, it has appeared that the traditional explanation of consecutive ERPs as a sequence of cognitive processes during perception and reaction is inadequate. Kotchoubey's alternative biological model shows that perception and action are two aspects of the same entity simply described as control behavior or sensorimotor coordination. Both stimulus and response related ERP components (such as the P300 and the readiness potential, respectively) bring different aspects to the expression of the same entity, sensorimotor coordination.

With regard to the slow cortical potentials, we have very good insights into both the physiological cause and the functional significance. Whenever an area of the cerebral cortex prepares itself for a future activity, it is expressed neurophysiologically as an increase in thalamocortical excitatory input in the outermost layer (I) of the cerebral cortex, which triggers a negative electrical potential measurable at the scalp. This in turn facilitates processing in this area of the cerebral cortex - a "warming up" of neuronal groups to just under the firing threshold that is expressed in behavior. Such preparation of the cerebral cortex originates in the thalamus with the reticular nucleus of the thalamus playing a leading role. This nucleus has the most important corticothalamic pathways under inhibitory control, and is itself modified by the prefrontal cortex via a feedback ring that passes through the striatum. This cortico-subcortical ring allows the brain to preactivate both ascending and descending neurons.

Positive slow cortical potentials probably originate with a decrease in negativity (through inhibitory processes) or through excitation (depolarization) in deeper layers of the cerebral cortex (layers III and IV).

Negative slow cortical potentials reflect the provision of cortical energy for an expected activity and positive slow cortical potentials reflect the use of this energy in activity.

The same reasoning can be applied to the ERPs that occur following a stimulus. The same patterns of neuronal activation are seen whenever ascending pathways excite the cerebral cortex. This place of arrival of a specific excitation is always in cerebral cortex layer III or IV and associated with a positive potential measurable at the scalp. This reflects a negative potential or depolarization in the upper cerebral cortex layer I, both for the prestimulus and post stimulus potentials. In functional terms, both cases reflect a negative potential and preparation of energy resources to receive incoming information while the use of this energy reflects the positive wave that follows, created by increased activity in deeper cortical layers.

Kotchoubey (2006) proposed a cyclic biphasic process in place of this classical description of the successive ERP components of consecutive processing stages occurring between stimulus and response. In the first preparatory phase, anticipatory states build up in some cortical networks that controls specifically sensorimotor coordination. The corresponding ascending and descending pathways then open for excitation. In the subsequent consumption phase, information from the environment is processed in anticipation of the prepared activity. This information delivers feedback, which the cortical model of the immediate future either confirms or corrects, and in this way optimizes the difference between the model and the external world. This cyclic process can repeat itself many times, depending on the nature of the task and the complexity of the stimuli. The negative ERP waves reflect the activation of anticipation while positive ERP waves reflect the comparison with the expected input and updates.

From a cognitive perspective, the task of the brain after stimulus presentation is to build up a representation of the stimulus. In contrast, the biological approach assumes that following stimulus presentation, the brain must organize behavior interactively with the stimulus. From this standpoint, many things must be prepared or anticipated. In the first place, a response must be prepared. Second, another stimulus that would follow from the first must be prepared. Third, recognition of some relevant stimulus characteristics can evoke preparation for other behaviorally relevant event characteristics.

If we contrast the anticipatory model with the conventional cognitive processing model, we can interpret classical cognitive potentials or more aptly, event related potentials, in a different way.

1. Attention related negative potentials reflect feed forward anticipatory activity.

Termed "processing negativity" by Näätänen (1982) and "negativity difference" (ND) by Hansen (1980), a slow negative potential occurs in classical selective attention tasks with the first peak being recorded about a 100 ms after the stimulus. "Late frontal negativity" is a late component of this negative potential during which, according to Näätänen, a comparison is made between the actual input and an activated representation of a task relevant event. The biological model uses the same reasoning, but the interpretation thereafter is completely different. In the biological preparatory model, the organism creates the negative potentials, which reflect the feed forward anticipation of the next relevant stimulus characteristics following recognition of previous indications of stimulus relevance. In the cognitive processing model, the negative potentials reflect information processing rather than the preparation of cortical energy for this processing. The stimulus creates them in association with the processing of characteristics that are perceived to be common to both real world stimulus and a relevant event.

The anticipatory model can also better explain the attention related negative potentials measurable in the very early stages of perception (such as in the cochlea, the hearing neuron, and the lower brain stem). In this model, the stimulus itself does not determine the negative potential. It arises from top down preparation in which instruction related modulation of early cortical, or even peripheral sensory processes, can be understood as a construction of active information seeking hypotheses. The stimulus can certainly play a modulating or synchronizing role but not an instigating role.

2. Positive ERP components represent the uptake of information.

In this model, positive ERPs are associated with incoming feedback information from the environment, which can be used to confirm or actualize the preactivated sensorimotor networks. Thus, positivity marks the end of a specific cycle of information exchange between the organism and the environment. This is in agreement with the traditional view that the P300 reflects the comparison between the person's expectations and sensory input, and the final processes in the course of processing the results of this comparison. The prior P200 component always occurs after the first negative (N100) component and if there are no more associated cognitive tasks. The P200 can be described as the last ERP component of the brain's response after the N100, which uses the energy prepared for the task.

8.3 Operant Conditioning of SCP (SCP neurofeedback)

The research group surrounding Birbaumer at the German University of Tübingen has meticulously studied SCP neurofeedback from 1979 to the present day, especially in its applications to the treatment of epilepsy. However, since 1980, research has focused on the role of attention and especially the role of thalamocortical mechanisms in this area and finally, over the last several years, investigated the therapeutic applications of SCP neurofeedback to ADHD.

A warning stimulus evokes a slow negative potential, thereupon an experimental participant must try to fulfill instructions to increase the strength of this negativity. Then, the neurofeedback session experienced as a game rewards the participant. The German research group Birbaumer, Rockstroh, Lutzenberger, and Elbert showed that within two sessions, that is, within 80-160 feedback events, more than 200 participants (from eight different studies) succeeded in increasing or decreasing the negativity of the slow cortical potentials (Lutzenberger, 1984). The EEG baseline was measured for one second prior to the presentation of the warning stimulus with a 6-second interval between the two stimuli. Forty trials were administered within each session. The same stimulus was presented afterwards, accompanied by the same instructions but without feedback. The changes in potentials happened to the same extent as with feedback, creating the appearance of transfer.

Whenever self-regulation skills are acquired, they can be maintained over long periods even if no more feedback is given, just like a well learned skill such as riding a bike.

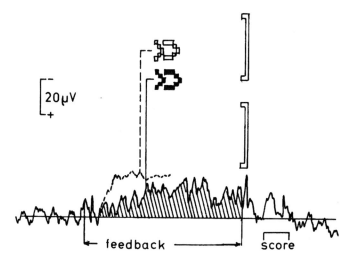

Figure 54. The slow electrical negative potentials with a 6-second interval for visual feedback are depicted. The bold line and rocket graphic indicate less negativity than the broken line, also with a rocket graphic at one end. During trials, the patient tried to dock the rocket in the uppermost port on the right, success being dependent on negativity strengthening (Rockstroh, 1984).

A pseudofeedback control group in which the trajectory of the rocket depended on the brain potentials of another participant was also examined. The group that received neurofeedback acquired control of the process, which was not the case for the pseudo-neurofeedback group.

Since only some brain areas are specifically prepared for an anticipated task during a CNV, this process reflects aspects of attention functions. Attention is responsible, among other things, for the selection of relevant stimuli from among the many other stimuli present. Inattentive behavior or a short attention span is frequently associated with a lowered CNV and a decreased ability to acquire self-regulation via feedback. The stimulus selection that is contingent with the second stimulus in the CNV task is indeed lessened in quality in people with attention disorders. Preactivation of the neuronal networks that is necessary for execution of the expected task is of lower quality.

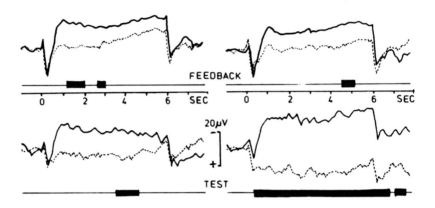

Figure 55. Slow cortical potentials measured at Cz in a normal adult during a second training session. The uppermost figure indicates the average values from the first series of feedback trials (1-40) on the left and the average values from the second series of feedback trials (51-90) on the right. The left graphic underneath shows the average values from the first course of transfer trials without feedback (41-50) that followed the first training trials and, on the right, the average values from the second series of transfer trials without feedback trials (trials 91-100) that followed the second training series. The bold line indicates those trials that targeted negativity for strengthening; the dotted lines those trials that targeted the negativity for weakening. The thick black band indicates the occurrence of significant differences between the two conditions (Rockstroh, 1984).

Lutzenberger (1980) found a lower early CNV component in patients with bilateral frontal brain injuries. Unlike healthy participants, while these patients succeeded in making this component stronger during neurofeedback, there was no transfer of skill to the situation where the same stimulus and instructions were offered without neurofeedback. Rockstroh (1990) replicated these findings in children with ADHD. A lower early CNV indicates decreased anticipation of a task in these children with ADHD. The late component that occurs prior to task execution is also lower. Furthermore, if there is no prior warning stimulus, the negative potential following an imperative stimulus prior to a motor reaction is also lower in ADHD. Such negative potentials are known as "Bereitschaftspotentials" or readiness potentials.

Two schools of thought may explain the slow negative brain potentials described in people with ADHD. The first explanation uses the state regulation deficit model (Sonuga-Barke, 2002), which is related to the self-regulation deficit model (Douglas, 1972). According to the state regulation deficit model, children with ADHD have difficulties regulating their activation level. The cognitive energetic model of Sergeant (2000) argues that the activation level is not adapted to cirucmstances in ADHD. Both models view the ability to regulate level of activation as essential.

A lowered CNV in ADHD indicates a diminished ability to regulate cortical activation using thalamocortical feedback loops. Neurofeedback training of the SCP aims to improve this cortical self-regulation.

Leins (2004) investigated ADHD in a group of 19 children by providing neurofeedback training of the slow potentials over 30 sessions (once every school day), each consisting of four blocks of 38 trials lasting about 6 seconds. A 6-12 second interval between trials was given to avoid habituation. Half of the trials aimed to increase the brain potentials, the other half to decrease them. Earlier research had demonstrated that 40 trials were sufficient to strengthen the negativity, to obtain a clear improvement in symptoms, and to maintain these improvements after six months. Improvements were found on social behavior at home and at school as measured by the DSM-IV criteria as well as on attention tests and IQ scales. The improvements were more marked after six months than at the end of training. The skills appeared to have been automatically acquired.

A recent study of a group of 23 children with ADHD (Strehl, Leins, Goth, Klinger, Hinterberger, & Birbaumer, 2006) confirmed these results. Furthermore, it appeared that only those children who were able to evoke slow negative potentials outside the context of the thirty training sessions showed lasting behavioral improvement. Six months later, in comparison with the findings immediately after treatment, additional significant improvements were demonstrated on all behavioral scales! Two years later, the improvements were still evident (Gani, 2008).

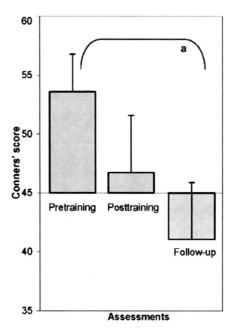

Figure 56. A clear improvement on the Connors parents rating scale following training and a more marked improvement six months after training are shown. The clinical cut off value bordering normal and abnormal is set at 45 (Strehl et al., 2000). Reproduced with permission from Pediatrics, Vol. 118(5), 1530-1540, Copyright (2006) by the AAP.

During Leins's study of SCP neurofeedback, a control group of 19 children with ADHD were treated with neurofeedback training of the theta/beta ratio. The children were not aware of the treatment protocol (thus a single blind study). Both groups of children showed the same degree of improvement on all the assessment scales. A recent follow up study also showed that the improvements were maintained and, moreover, increased six months, and even two years (Gani, 2008) after treatment (Leins, 2007).

Even two years after the end of neurofeedback training (for both a theta/beta group and a group of randomly assigned children in which the slow cortical potentials were trained) the results were maintained. Both the ability to self-regulate the EEG and the results from clinical scales improved, and in each group half of the children no longer met ADHD criteria (Gani, 2008).

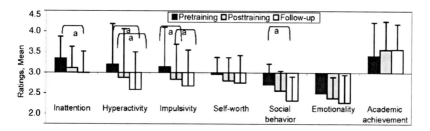

Figure 57. A clear improvement on teachers' assessment scales six months after treatment, with additional improvement at the six months follow up (Strehl et al., 2006). Reproduced with permission from Pediatrics, Vol. 118(5), 1530-1540, Copyright (2006) by the AAP.

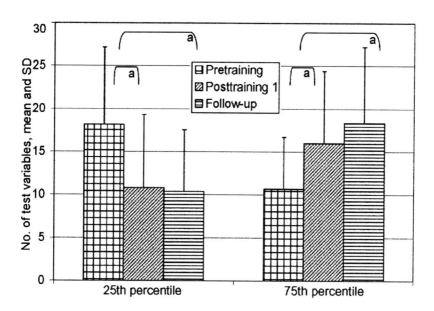

Figure 58. Prior to training, these values from an attention test lay below the 25th percentile for most of the children with ADHD. Only a minority were above the 25th percentile. This ratio was reversed after training and more so at six months follow up (Strehl et al., 2006). Reproduced with permission from Pediatrics, Vol. 118(5), 1530-1540, Copyright (2006) by the AAP.

Heinrich (2004) demonstrated that following a successful neurofeedback (25 sessions spread over three weeks), the CNV intensity increased in a group of 13 children (7 to 13 years) with ADHD. In this group, ADHD symptoms (assessed by behavioral scales) decreased about 25% on average, and the number of impulsive errors on attentional tasks declined. In seven children and in the control group of children with ADHD placed on a waiting list (no neurofeedback condition), there was no improvement in the CNV or in attention or behavior.

Drechsler (2007) compared the treatment outcome for slow cortical potential neurofeedback in 17 children with ADHD with that for cognitive behavioral therapy in 13 children with ADHD. There was significantly more improvement in the neurofeedback group.

8.4 The Origins of CNV and SCP in the Brain

During SCP negativity, fMRI research has shown increased activity in prefrontal and parietal cerebral cortex and in all areas of the thalamus that play a role in the activation of selective attention (Hinterberger, 2003).

During the early phase (one second after the warning stimulus) of the CNV, there is an increased activity in the thalamus, the cingulum, and the supplementary motor area (SMA) that borders the upper side of the cingulum, the insula, the dorsolateral prefrontal and cerebral cortex (Nagai, 2004). The activity in both the cingulum and SMA are determined during the early and late phase of the CNV and correlate most strongly with activity in the thalamus. Rostral areas of the anterior cingulate are most strongly activated during the first phase, reflecting an orienteering reaction, while the dorsal anterior cingulate is more active in later, motor preparation phases of the CNV. The anterior cingulate plays an important role in tasks that involve working memory, selective attention, and response conflict monitoring. The reticular nucleus of the thalamus is inhibited during attentional tasks, which increases the flow of information in thalamocortical circuits, giving rise to the CNV. In addition to the role of the thalamic reticular nucleus as a filter mechanism for sensory information, local inhibitory thalamic neurons in the mediodorsal nucleus play a critical role in thalamocortical information processing. Activity in the anterior cingulate is most pronounced in the first phase of the CNV, which gives ground for suspicion that the CNV originates there. The thalamus, possibly together with the basal ganglia, acts as a secondary regulator of anticipatory cerebral activity. It is interesting that LORETA research has demonstrated the source of the early CNV to be in the anterior cingulate and the supplementary motor area (SMA) (Gomez, 2005).

8.5 Can People Be Consciously Aware of their Brain State (SCP)?

While the brain enables us to perceive the interaction between the outside world and our body, it remains unclear if one can perceive brain processes in and of themselves. Subjects succeed better at estimating the strength of the SCP shifts during training if they receive additional feedback. The question posed is whether the acquirement of EEG control (SCP neurofeedback) leads to awareness of conscious control strategies or direct awareness of the controlled SCP state.

This question was examined in a study consisting of 20 daily sessions of 140 trials each lasting eight seconds and an additional ten sessions after an eight week break (Kotchoubey, 2002). Half of the 140 trials trained the SCP negativity and the other half the SCP positivity. Neurofeedback was given in the first 70 to 90 trials; however, no feedback was provided in the remaining 50 to 70 trials so that the researcher could assess if the participant could increase the positivity or negativity without feedback. In this last phase, following the 70 to 90 feedback trials, the study investigated if the participant could succeed in transferring the acquired ability without feedback. In the transfer condition, following each eight second trial, the subject was requested to give a digit between 1 and 3 as quickly as possible as an indication of how well he thought he had attained a good SCP negativity or SCP positivity. This request was repeated in the second, fifteenth, and thirtieth neurofeedback session. Only in the thirtieth session was there a reliable link between estimated perception of the SCP and the measured SCP, although by the fourteenth session, SCP control with neurofeedback was clearly demonstrable. Further, it was found that the same subjects who best succeeded in regulating SCP with neurofeedback also succeeded best in correctly estimating the SCP. This indicates that estimation and control are linked to each other in some way.

Earlier theories about neurofeedback control suggested that the ability to be consciously aware of the control process is a necessary condition for the acquirement of control. This is in agreement with general cognitive models, which argue that perception plays a critical role in facilitating action. However, this perspective cannot explain why subjects were able to control SCP shifts several weeks before they developed the ability to evaluate these shifts. It appears that the ability to accurately judge the degree of shift develops as a result of efficient control over these shifts rather than vice versa. This could have major implications in the study of consciousness. This would mean that whenever we begin active learning of a completely new subject (in this case our own brain waves), the process of behavioral control appears first, with conscious perception following in relatively late stages of learning. The question remains as to what physiological mechanism is responsible for the learned perception and the changes in brain activity. One explanation assumes that the strategies become effective sooner than self-perception. In contrast with previous models, participant learning in order to obtain the correct result is not the consequence of controlled actions but the action itself. Accordingly, a very simple interpretation would be that people monitor their level of alertness and estimate the SCP shifts successfully when they think they had been attentive enough. However, these simple explanations are not in agreement with the data. In his SCP neurofeedback study, Kotchoubey (2002) simultaneously measured visual potentials that gave an indication to the quality of attention and the EEG spectra. Neither the visual potentials nor EEG spectra differed nor depended on subjective estimation of the SCP shifts. The alertness level in itself (which is, however, a subjective value) was therefore not correlated with the strength of SCP shift.

This means that the most plausible explanation is that when participants estimate their control strategies, these strategies are specifically linked to the control parameter (the slow potential) rather than to some general state such as the of level alertness. This visualization of perception as a function of control is well recognized in control theory: "when one is watching an aircraft fly overhead, neither the visual direction of the aircraft nor the aircraft's motion is represented on the retina. Rather, they are represented in extraretinal oculomotor signals corresponding to the movements of the eyes. The position of the image on the retina is relatively fixed, reflecting simply the intent to watch the objects. The motion of the aircraft is registered in the aircraft a posteriori in terms of the oculomotor efference required to keep the aircraft's image on the fovea."

These similarities suggest that the experimental subjects (at least those who succeeded in estimating SCP shifts accurately) were able to control the result of their activity (for example, by holding it constant), consequently moving the slow brain potentials in the correct direction on the screen, just as the perceiver of the aircraft maintained its image centrally on the retina. The participant, who after 15 training sessions succeeded in moving the SCP in the desired direction with neurofeedback, appeared to be still able to evoke these shifts during the transfer sessions without neurofeedback. Nonconscious strategies are conditioned via neurofeedback. To achieve this, the experimental subjects employed individual cognitive strategies that were not articulated. From this perspective, the perception arose from the strategies used to gain control of the SCP shifts. This implies that physiological information is perceivable when it is meaningful, for example, when the neurofeedback signal promotes operant conditioning.

There remain two possibilities at this point in the argument. The subject assesses the controlling strategies directly yet cannot separate these strategies from those brain states, which provided the medium for creation of those strategies. However, one could argue that these strategies form through the agency of a "supervisory executive system" and consolidate into a perception. We are not yet able to distinguish between these two possibilities. A decisive experiment would record the actual and the estimated SCP shifts in a state that is different from SCP neurofeedback. The CNV is a state of expectation for a relevant imperative stimulus following a warning signal. If the skill acquired (via neurofeedback) to correctly estimate the SCP shifts can transfer to a situation where these shifts are not directly occurring, it is possible that the participant's strategies that were strengthened during neurofeedback training will ultimately lead to two identifiable states of cortical negativity and positivity, which intensities can be correctly estimated. Another informative experiment would be to evoke a direct current in the frontal cerebral cortex using a transcranial stimulator, which is either positive or negative depending on whether cathode or anode is used. It could then be investigated if the participant can estimate the intensity of the slow cortical potential following successful neurofeedback training.

8.6 Activation by Transcranial DC Stimulation (tDCS), Micropolarization, and Neuroplasticity

In the introduction of this chapter, we compared slow cortical potentials with the negative potentials that can be evoked by direct current stimulation. The stimulating positive electrode (the anode) is placed over the area intended for stimulation while the negative electrode (the cathode) is placed at another point on the scalp. Anodal stimulation has been shown to trigger activation of underlying brain areas and thus decrease theta and alpha waves in the EEG and increase beta and gamma waves. This technique uses 5x5 cm wet sponge electrodes with a direct current of 1 mA over 15 to 20 minutes.

Since the beginning of the 19th century, the literature has been describing direct current treatments. However, they fell into disuse with the development of electroconvulsive therapy in modern psychiatric treatment. Since 2000, researchers (Priori, 2003; Nitsche & Paulus, 2001; Nitsche, et al., 2003) have began utilizing this method again, primarily in order to study precisely the way stimulation activates the underlying brain areas in the form of membrane polarization of neurons.

It is common knowledge that neuronal activation leads to an increase in electrical negative discharges on the outside of the cell membrane and an increase in electrically positive discharges on the inside of the cell membrane. This means that the irritability of these areas increases, which also means that less triggering factors are necessary to bring about an action potential in the affected areas. The information transfer system between neuron systems in the brain is electrical-chemical-electrical. Thus, any sensory stimulation initiates electrical activity in the sensory neurons (i.e., an action potential), which will travel to the synapses that connect the neuron with the following circuit neurons. At the synapse, the electrical potential is converted in the form of release of a chemical into the synaptic cleft between the two neurons, which will shortly occupy receptors on the next neuron in the chain. Depolarization is triggered with the discharge of an action potential in this neighboring neuron. In recent years, research has shown that tDCS can activate underlying brain areas accompanied by improved functioning of the concerned brain areas. Stimulation of the dorsolateral prefrontal cortex has been shown to lead to improved executive functions such as working memory (Kincses, 2003; Iyer, 2005; Fregni, 2005) and to improved symptoms of depression. Stimulation with direct current of 1 mA for 15 minutes improves functioning for a period of 90 minutes. A few recent studies demonstrated that when a dozen such sessions are given (for example, three times a week), the outcomes are maintained for at least a couple of months. Fregni (2006) successfully applied this treatment to depression in a double blind study. This method has been successfully used to treat 57 children and adolescents with ADHD (Chutko, 2002) and a group of 12 children with ADHD (Saraev, 2002). The stimulating anode was placed over the right prefrontal cerebral cortex. Multiple researchers demonstrated that the obtained increase in the activation ability in the stimulated areas was best used in conjunction with revalidation techniques. Accordingly, it has been shown that moderate paralysis after stroke rehabilitation techniques led to better clinical outcomes in the field of fine motor skills, if cortical stimulation is given over the affected motor cortex (Hummel, 2005). Kropotov (personal communication, 2005) found that the best results were obtained for ADHD if tDCS was combined with a course of neurofeedback (strengthening of beta waves and weakening of alpha waves).

These studies indicated that the active principle is not the direct current itself but the micropolarization field. This research has also elucidated the mechanism by which electrical stimulation can promote neuroplasticity in the form of permanently improved neural connectivity. Stimulation causes depolarization of the neuronal membrane, which then leads to an increased presynaptic electrical discharge. Together, both phenomena lead to activation of the postsynaptic NMDA receptor. This triggers a greater influx of calcium ions into postsynaptic neurons. The calcium influx triggers chemical reactions that strengthen synaptic connections.

Short-lived excitation by the anode stimulator (which mimics natural sensory or internally invoked neuronal activation) leads to early long term potentiation (LTP). LTP enables internal or external activation to trigger a higher postsynaptic action potential for a period lasting around an hour. The action of certain enzymes (protein kinases) initiates early LTP in response to increased calcium presence in the cell. These enzymes activate certain proteins, including specialized protein receptors on the postsynaptic membrane, allowing these neurons to demonstrate a stronger response to stimulation.

Late LTP, which is more permanent in nature, occurs following a long lasting or repeated external or internal stimulus. A long lasting memory is formed if LTP occurs in neural memory circuits. If LTP occurs in the prefrontal cortex, permanent improvements in attention, depression, and working memory, among others, may be obtained. In these cases, calcium activates many types of kinases that enter the nucleus and activate CREB proteins, which in turn activate specific genes. These proteins are synthesized at the synapses to strengthen synaptic connections and to forge new ones.

These new treatment methods are very promising, and there is extensive scientific research over the mechanisms of neuroplasticity. These and other therapeutic techniques, such as transcranial magnetic stimulation, vagus nerve stimulation, and a form of electrostimulation that uses an electrode placed deep in the brain are gradually gaining acceptance in psychiatry. The growth of these techniques has contributed to the growing recognition that building an understanding of the brain should include its bioelectric functioning. Such insights will have major therapeutic consequences. These techniques reflect the continuing interventionist attitudes to medicine and a growing interest in bioelectric regulation of the brain. This is just one small step towards gaining insight into the functioning systems of self-regulation of the brain. Neurofeedback can be seen as a dynamic control procedure that leads to reorganization of neuronal functions. A neuroplasticity model can provide a better explanation for the evidence that, in a number of patients, short-lived improvements appear in the first session of neurofeedback and remain after sufficient number of additional sessions. In tDCS, a short-lived improvement in both electrical activity and behavior can be observed, however, the effects are only maintained after following a course of repeated sessions. This same pattern has been recognized for a long time in electric shock therapy, which classically applies six to ten sessions over a two to three week period.

Recognizing that anode tDCS stimulation increases beta and gamma activity in the EEG (Antal, 2004), Kropotov applied tDCS over the dorsolateral prefrontal cerebral cortex alongside neurofeedback therapy to the treatment of children with ADHD and obtained positive results. Anode tDCS also stimulates a negative DC potential and has been studied as a form of "priming "or "shaping" in order to facilitate training of the desired DC negativity during SCP neurofeedback.

8.7 Explanatory Models of SCP Neurofeedback

There are a number of models to explain the efficacy of SCP neurofeedback, which are not mutually exclusive:

1) Activation of the underlying brain areas

This is the simplest and the earliest explanation that assumes that the early CNV component occurred in the dorsolateral prefrontal cortex, which has a role in attention and working memory. This somewhat simplistic model is also found in neurofeedback literature in which quantitative EEG is used to detect which brain areas are the most statistically abnormal in certain EEG bands and, thereafter, to train that frequency using operant conditioning.

2) Activation of neuronal networks

If neurofeedback is applied at just one specific place on the skull, it does not follow that EEG changes only occur at that place on the skull. It is possible nowadays to identify functional correlations with other brain areas using quantitative EEG and LORETA.

In SCP neurofeedback, the thalamocortical attention circuits, including the anterior cingulate, are trained. They form part of a network and enhance the functions of different parts of the network. fMRI research has confirmed that a particular network is active in the CNV. This explanatory model is in opposition to Lubar's model with regard to theta/beta training. Recently, Cannon (2006, 2007) has further developed and documented this model in connection with LORETA neurofeedback. LORETA neurofeedback of the cognitive anterior cingulate has clearly demonstrated that EEG changes occur across extended circuits involved in attention and executive functions.

The trained children are, for the most part, not aware of the conscious strategies that they applied and therefore it is likely that nonconscious learning processes play an important role in the integration of cortical self-control skills.

3) Self-organizing complex systems

In a study of the application of SCP neurofeedback to epilepsy, Kirlangic (2005) found that the breathing pattern changed along with the trained SCP shift. The results indicated an interaction between the cognitive processes that accompany SCP changes during the neurofeedback process and vegetative functions, such as breathing and heart rhythm patterns, and electrical skin conductance. Although these complex interactions are crucial to the neurofeedback process, it cannot be said that feedback about breathing patterns is crucial to the control of SCP changes. The importance of these complex interactions implies we can no longer simply consider neurofeedback as just another feedback ring to the brain. The analyses of complex processes that can bring about changes in a complex system, such as neurofeedback, exceed the boundaries of conventional system approaches applied to closed systems. From a thermodynamic perspective, biological systems are open, complex energy systems that exchange material and information with their surroundings, while maintaining their structure and functions. Complex system approaches offer the possibility to model neural interactions of brain processes on a microscopic level, and to raise cognitive structure on a macroscopic level. In the model developed by Kirlangic, the EEG is a parameter on an intermediate level ('microscopic level') between the psychological macro and the neurobiological micro level. In open systems far from equilibrium, self-organization at the microscopic level has been demonstrated to be the fundamental mechanism of spontaneous pattern formation on a macroscopic level.

Self-regulation and self-organization are two strongly related phenomena that are both determined by nonlinear interactions at a microscopic level. The outcomes obtained from SCP neurofeedback in which the negativity and positivity are successfully acquired, indicate nonlinear phase transitions between these two states. The synergetic approach taken by Haken (1996) offers a descriptive theoretical framework for self-organization that leads to the emergence of new properties on a macroscopic level. The phase transitions that occur in unstable states can be analyzed with the concepts of control and order parameters, in Haken's phraseology "Versklavung" (literally: enslavement) and circular causality.

A *control parameter* is a parameter that controls the macroscopic behavior of a system. A control parameter arises at a critical value and a bifurcation (breakdown) in the macroscopic system behavior occurs.

An *order parameter* describes the system at a macroscopic level. Whenever one or more control parameters are changed, the system becomes unstable.

This leads to configurations set by the order parameters, which determine the behavior of the parts of the system via the slavery principle. The order parameters control the number of component systems by recruiting these component systems as slaves.

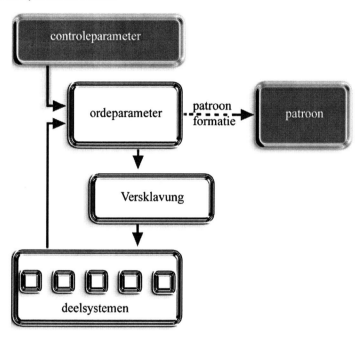

Figure 59. Changes in the control parameters cause changes in order parameter(s). As new patterns form, reconfiguration of the component systems takes place via the principle of enslavement while the order parameters self-generate from interactions between the component systems (Beek, 1998).

The principle of circular causality determines the causality between the order parameters and the behavior of part of the system. These parts of the system together determine the order parameters, which in turn determine the cooperation of individual parts of the system.

Synergetics offers a theoretical framework for analyzing neurofeedback as a complex learning process through examination of the effects of the learning process on the order parameters of a system.

Numerous mechanisms can play a part in the learning process that produces changes in the EEG pattern described by the order parameters:

1) The dynamic of the order parameters can change if the potential landscape undergoes a transition.

2) New order parameters can arise because of interaction with old order parameters.

3) New order parameters can arise from microscopic component parts because of changes in control parameters at a microscopic level.

The pedalo experiment, which analyzed movement patterns produced during the learning process of learning to drive a pedalo, provides an ingenious example of a synergetic analysis of operant conditioning. As learning progressed, the learning pattern demonstrated fewer and fewer degrees of freedom. Finally, a single complex order parameter controlled the movement.

Analogies exist between the neurofeedback learning process and the pedalo experiment. In the pedalo experiment, motor units, such as parts of the four limbs under voluntary control, formed the subsystems. In the neurofeedback learning process, the subsystems are units of the brain's higher functions, including the cognitive functions and the autonomous nervous system such as breathing, heart rate, and electrical skin conductance. The similarities can be summarized as: 1) the learning process results in attainment of a new specific coordination between subsystems; 2) this new coordination can be called upon and activated whenever a situation requires (for example, a situation which requires attention).

Different characteristics of changes in the DC level suggest that an order parameter can operate in the brain as a complex open system:

1) Switching the order parameters and the DC level

In the synergetic approach, the critical values of the control parameter can lead to a bifurcation (splitting) in which the order parameters have a conversion function between two of the multiple possible states. The results of SCP neurofeedback can be considered as a conversion from a more to a less responsive state and vice versa. The changes seen in the CNV potential can be interpreted in the same manner.

2) Order parameters are long lasting.

DC level is maintained until the next stimulus in the CNV potential occurs and during the neurofeedback session. This determination argues for the long lasting property of the order parameters.

3) Governing role of order parameters

The perception of breathing patterns and electrical skin conductance may change during negativity and positivity training. This, together with the fact that voluntary DC regulation is not reached using breathing biofeedback, suggests that the DC level has a governing role over other sub systems such as functions of the autonomic nervous system.

4) An order parameter describes the system on a macroscopic level

The DC shift is an indication of changes in the cerebral cortex's sensitivity to stimuli. The shifts in DC potential can be defined as a functional reflection of the brain on a macroscopic level.

It cannot be claimed whether the DC shifts observed in different states have the same source and mechanism of generation without investigating the correlations at the microscopic level (for example, the diverse control parameters: degree of acidity in the blood, CO_2 content in the blood, ions and hormones in the blood, but also external information such as the warning stimulus in the CNV potential). No consensus exists about the generator(s) of the DC potential shifts (such as neurons, glia cells, the blood brain barrier, and cerebral blood circulation). However, the concept of order parameters provides a medium for describing DC shifts in different states on the macroscopic level because of the circular causal relationship between the DC level and the microscopic level. The DC level originates at the microscopic level, which in turn determines the sensitivity at the macroscopic level, where sensitivity is a measure of firing speed at the neuronal level.

Summary

Slow cortical potentials express the sensitivity of the cerebral cortex to stimuli. In the frontal cerebral cortex, they originate in the prefrontal areas, the parietal cortex, and the thalamus. It is possible to strengthen these potentials with neurofeedback training. With enough training, the feeling arises in the trainee as to which strategies can strengthen these potentials. Strong negative slow cortical potentials are associated with improved attention and improved frontal executive functions.

9.

ADHD: A Clinical System Perspective

Earlier chapters have described how knowledge of neurobiology, EEG, and neurofeedback research can give us a better insight into the underlying nature of ADHD. In this chapter, we explore the utility of this knowledge in clinical practice and the utility of concrete behavioral treatment in ADHD. This section has been very much influenced by the book "Rethinking Attention Deficit Disorders" by Cherkes-Julkowski, Sharp, and Stolzenberg (1997). The term 'a system perspective' denotes that the problem is not simply considered as the sum of the symptoms but as a complex aggregate of the divergent elements that contribute to the creation of the system and are accompanied by interactions that often cannot be wholly reconstructed. As described previously, the EEG is also a mechanism in which changes in certain aspects lead to global changes, such as in the case of behavioral patterns.

We have described the attention system as arising from within a complex neural network that involves executive functions and interconnected motivational and emotional systems. Within this system, the anterior cingulate plays a key role in executive attention and task adaptive behavior is strongly linked to limbic structures where emotion and motivation originate.

The thrust of the argument is that this system of self-regulation arises mostly because of nonconscious processes. Remarkably, the system develops from these processes without the guidance of an "I" that starts all of this. The behavioral characteristics of ADHD are therefore from this perspective best considered as a constructive effort towards self-organization. The undesirable behavior exhibited in ADHD reflects the way individuals cope with their impairment in self-regulation and, therefore, it must be considered as such. If someone with ADHD appears, for example, unmotivated to carry out particular tasks or has emotional outbursts, this can be viewed as a manner of adaptive compensation for inadequate self-regulation. Weak motivation is too quickly considered as resulting from a weak personal "will." However, the weak will is actually a consequence. The so-called behavioral deficiencies express the way in which someone with ADHD handles inadequate self-regulation so that self-regulation can be optimized in his/her specific case.

Thus, it is possible that it is better for someone with ADHD not to try to make an effort in order to protect self-regard and mental equilibrium. If we want to understand this better, we should not fixate on superficial behavioral characteristics such as listed in the DSM- IV, but become additionally aware of the underlying cognitive, emotional, and motivational self-regulation. In other words, we must try to understand the functional meaning of behavioral characteristics, not just in order to attain insight, but also to find behavioral solutions. We can define adaptive behavior as an expression of vigilance, as Bente (1964) described (optimal adaptive ability), which originates from selection processes within the individual, not in response to external instructions (Edelman, 1992). The system creates itself. This implies that training in self-instruction or external directives will not attain the desired behaviors. In classical behavioral therapy, cognitive self-instruction training, and classical educational method, instruction takes the form of strategy training and repeated drills of particular rules. However, these techniques will frequently not produce a change or will be counterproductive if this does not connect with the self-regulation of an individual. Effective educational methods should be adapted precisely to offer appropriate opportunities that would progress actively and with personal engagement for the individual's level of functioning.

The ability to regulate a global state is present in the first months of life and is the primary source of attention responses. Young children, and especially more vulnerable premature children and children with ADHD, are dependent on their mother or caretakers to bring their own efforts of self-regulation of arousal level under control, adapted to their own rhythms and needs. In these vulnerable children, many functional processes in the brain assign priority to the regulation of basic functions of the autonomous nervous system (e.g., breathing, heart rhythm, temperature regulation, etc.). We can conclude that the fundamentals of self-regulation are weaker in these children and therefore functional attention and motivation processes are less well developed. If the interventions of a mother or a caretaker are not adaptive, disorganization in the child will increase and hinder the child's own efforts towards self-regulation (Cherkes-Julkowski, Sharp, & Stolzenberg, 1997). In an inspired study by Thoman (1987) called "Blue Bear," a teddy bear was placed in the corner of the cradle of premature babies. The teddy bear had the breathing pattern and heart rhythm of a child. In this manner, the rhythms of the child were exhorted to remain stable. The bear was placed in such a way that the child could choose to seek alignment, depending on child's need for support of self-regulation. Thoman found that these children developed a better self-regulation system in which their attentional system was more in line with the internal and external world.

The implications of this research for the treatment of schoolchildren is that parents, care givers, and teachers can do better by focusing on what the child is already doing to regulate behavior and attention, fostering further development in these areas rather than imposing directive rules. It is also better not to ask children "to try harder" to actively sustain their attention. These less directive but more responsive methods to support the child's own efforts at self-regulation appear to be the most effective in helping the child develop optimal state regulation. If we adapt ourselves to the child's own rhythm and support the child's own self-regulation, we can attain optimal stabilization within that rhythm.

Just as in earliest infancy, the mother has a role of a pacesetter, validating a certain balance and paving the way towards further development. Such an external source of regulation is even more important for children with weakened self-regulation and organization, such as children with ADHD. The child does not experience such regulation occurring within the context of the mother-child bond as external. The child makes his mother's actions his own. The typically developing child experiences his self as possessing a certain stability and flexibility from about three years of age. The course of this development is more troubled in children with ADHD and the need for external regulation from others is therefore much greater.

Considering these factors, it is easy to understand why cognitive therapy that is based on models and incentives fails to teach cognitive control. It does not take into account the biological processes of self-regulation that can support or hinder cognitive control. Moreover, cognitive behavioral therapy assumes the existence of an identifiable cognitive behavioral function; however, in reality, cognitive control arises from many system dynamic models. A focus on self-instruction overlooks the great value of fostering conscious experience of active self-generating processes within the context of the individual's frame of self-reference and expectations. A certain amount of self-generated experimentation should rise out of the individual's thought processes producing mistakes and the opportunities to learn from them.

1) *Activation level (arousal)* is determined in right parietal areas linked to limbic areas in which mood and emotions connect. Noradrenergic systems play a major role in this process. People with the form of ADHD without hyperactivity, ADD, show an apparent lack of motivation to orient themselves towards external goals determined by others. ADD is often associated with passivity, social isolation, anxiety, and depression. The global arousal level is involved in the global orientation reaction to new stimuli and the global activation level, among other things. Focused attention, working memory, and multiple executive functions are especially associated with frontal areas. If the first of these systems (right parietal) fails, the second system (left frontal) will dominate, leading to over focus, perseveration, and compulsive behavior.

2) *Rewards* have less effect on children with ADHD compared to other children. If taking Ritalin, these children are more likely to pay attention to rewards and to perform boring tasks more readily. Ritalin increases the availability of dopamine and this leads to closer and more lasting behavioral control. Dopamine facilitates the natural orientation reaction to new stimuli (thus decreasing distractibility) and compensates for the loss of intentionality. Conversely, noradrenalin helps overcome too narrow a focus, which otherwise may lead to over focusing, perseveration, and compulsive behavior.

3) *Effort*, driven by attention, is associated with the left cerebral cortex, contributes to sustained attention, and is a component of working memory. A feeling of effort soaks up energy that would otherwise be available for fluent thinking. This helps explain why so many children with ADD have no idea how they performed in their exams. The feeling of effort in someone with

ADHD is associated with an ongoing attentional insufficiency. We cannot say that these children have lower frustration tolerance; on the contrary, they have much more frustration to tolerate! These children have the feeling of making a tremendous effort, but onlookers who often get the impression that these children are very idle do not perceive this.

4) *Balance (homeostasis)* maintains well-modulated motivation that in turn supports the optimal attention system (neither too little nor too much). In a well-regulated system, the amount of effort does not appear to lie under voluntary control. It appears to be determined by the intrinsic requirements of the task, which in turn are determined by the internal memory capacity. If a task is overwhelming, or if arousal is too low, the system of homeostasis will try to arouse the emotions or other phenomena.

To not try anything can be a very motivated response in a situation where effort will probably lead to failure. All behavior of an individual must be described as the motivated best effort of that individual, regardless of how inappropriate that behavior seems to others. The process of socialization has the upper hand over other natural forms of motivation but requires well-developed executive functions. Second to the function of homeostasis, motivation also plays a role in the inherent incentives of open systems to promote the attainment of higher levels of organization and complexity (homeorhesis).

5) *Consistent reinforcement* can influence behavior, especially when the system can respond with high or low arousal. However, in general, internal motivational power and homeostasis are more important in the determination of attention and other responses to motivation.

6) *Novelty* also influences motivation to activate attention. It is remarkable that diagnostic criteria for ADHD stress that attentional disorder is present in all circumstances. Many arguments substantiate that situational effects are stronger in children and adults with ADHD because they have less internal control and are more dependent on external factors.

7) *Active involvement and participation* are important for sustaining attention and motivation. A self-generated thought, in which behavior occurs in a meaningful context, will lead to much better performance than situations un-

folding out of the context of the child's frame of reference, as is so often the case at school where teachers determine the centre of focus and motivation. If regulatory systems are imposed by directive, for example in school, they will seem arbitrary from the perspective of a child with ADHD. This has the consequence that these children do not succeed in internalizing these representations of how their feelings regulate behavior. Simply put, these children do not learn to understand how their feelings regulate behavior.

8) *The will* is an aspect of motivation that also arises from lower processes and not from a higher system of control. Teachers must therefore offer support to the lower levels of the system in a child with ADHD in order to aid the development of self-organization so that the higher levels of self-regulation and motivation can develop. We should abandon the consistent affirmation that everyone concerned should try to manipulate "the center of the will." Teachers must try to work alongside the child with ADHD to promote optimal results at the level of the child's internal struggle. Teachers cannot motivate the child without respecting the complexity of the attention system. Likewise, the child cannot self-motivate independently of the dynamic self-organizing properties of his or her own attention system.

In summary, we can state that it is of crucial importance to understand the function of behavioral characteristics in order to help someone with ADHD function better. We can then rally to the side of the functional level that is active at that moment. If we take no account of these factors, the person concerned will experience interventions as arbitrary, experiencing such interventions as irrelevant and ineffective. If we nurture whatever is functionally active and motivated in the individual, we will be in a position to identify the best way to proceed.

Afterword

Insights into neurological functioning in people with ADHD have increased greatly over the last few years, partly thanks to new functional imaging techniques such as fMRI, but also due to new electrophysiological research methods such as QEEG, event related synchronization and desynchronization, cognitive brain potentials, and LORETA. In 2004, American Academy of Pediatrics announced for the first time that, alongside the classical diagnoses, the QEEG provided a particularly interesting objective, biological, and noninvasive diagnostic tool for ADHD based on the rating scales of clinical characteristics. American Academy of Pediatrics came to this decision after considering 13 scientific publications from five independent research groups published since 1997 that involved 2,642 children. Recent research shows that parents of children with ADHD are better able to understand ADHD as a disorder of self-regulation with disturbance of frontal executive functions and, consequently, adhere better to treatment following this type of neurobiological assessment. This signifies that both psychoeducation and neuroeducation are significant for those affected with ADHD.

ADHD is a disorder of self-regulation with disordered frontal executive functions. Newer theoretical models emphasize that these executive functions cannot be understood separately from motivational and emotional processes. ADHD can therefore be conceptualized as an expression of slight mental disintegration, which at a behavioral as well as executive functions level demonstrates abnormalities similar to what is shown by sleep deprived subjects through the EEG.

Practitioners need to be familiar not just with the symptoms in behavioral terms, but also with the underlying system dynamic of inadequate behavioral regulation. In a similar way, it is best not to limit the investigation to EEG examination but also to use statistical QEEG measurements that analyze the

EEG as a stationary event. In recent years, dynamic methods for analyzing the disturbed dynamic systems in ADHD have become increasingly more available, including the vigilance-stabilizing role of central beta rhythms, dynamic self-organization of the EEG, and its various ongoing event related pattern changes in the EEG.

Although first applied in 1976 to treatment of ADHD in form of training designed to strengthen SMR rhythm (12-15 Hz) and weaken theta rhythm (4-7 Hz) at the crown of the scalp, neurofeedback was misapprehended for many years in the scientific world. A number of case studies were published in these early years, followed by some group studies. Single blind studies, using control groups treated by medication only, followed group studies. More recently, some double blind studies have also been published.

Over the years, insight has grown into the electrophysiological changes that result from neurofeedback. Localized training can trigger widespread changes in the EEG, which are carried over the entire cerebral cortex through neuronal circuits. Subsequently, the global EEG spectrum normalizes despite the fact that only two frequency bands are trained. Moreover, we have learned that the SMR rhythm has a stabilizing function that supports self-regulation. Frequently, no clear changes in the statistical QEEG are measurable after neurofeedback training; however, clear improvements that are more dynamic and associated with attentional tasks are frequently measurable in the EEG.

Research using imaging methods such as fMRI and LORETA (three-dimensional reconstructions of the sources of EEG activity) demonstrates that the anterior cingulate functions suboptimally in people with ADHD, leading to secondary difficulties with inadequate executive functions in the frontal cerebral cortex. The same imaging methods have revealed normalization in these brain areas following theta/SMR neurofeedback, which is rather dramatic because the scientific community commonly accepts these functional brain imaging research methods as a gold standard. Studies show that the experimental technique of LORETA neurofeedback therapy, which trains anterior cingulate activity, leads to favorable changes that are measurable in the EEG in untrained areas, such as the frontal cerebral cortex. The association of functional changes in the anterior cingulate with stabilization of the EEG can be understood in the light of research that has demonstrated that frontal areas and particularly the anterior cingulate play a role in higher, more complex adaptive regulation of mental processes.

German researcher Birbaumer, who studied slow cortical potentials for many decades, and his research team have demonstrated convincingly since 2003 onwards that neurofeedback training of the slow cortical potentials can also bring about improvements in people with ADHD and that these improvements are similar to those produced by theta/SMR neurofeedback. Imaging research has shown that these negative slow potentials have their origin in the anterior cingulate, the frontal cerebral cortex, right cerebral cortex, and the thalamus. These areas play a central role in attentional regulation and executive functions.

Neurofeedback therapy for people with ADHD causes a global reorganization of the neuronal circuits implicated in attention and executive functions and, among other things, improves measured IQ and decreases excessive elevated coherency between frontal hemispheres. We can interpret these changes as the outcome of operant conditioning. Reorganization of the EEG, because of neurofeedback can be better understood at the dynamic level of the EEG, explains why statistical measurements such as the theta/beta-1 ratio are not always altered following successful neurofeedback therapy. More dynamic neurofeedback measurements, however, frequently evidence clear changes. Therefore, it is useful to understand both the statistical and the dynamic approaches to EEG measurement. The information from each method is useful, but each has its own particular limitations, so the two approaches complement each other well.

The increased interest in bioelectrical regulation of brain functions (transcranial magnetic stimulation, brain stimulation using deep electrodes, and transcranial direct current stimulation), the associated neuroplasticity, and new experimental fMRI neurofeedback methods have begun to melt the skepticism of scientists towards neurofeedback therapy. Historically, neurofeedback researchers have followed a separate path from the majority of EEG researchers, but over recent years, neurofeedback has become more accepted in the mainstream for a number of reasons. This transformation has occurred partly because of new insights into the attentional regulating roles of the sleep spindles in ADHD. We gained a better understanding of how changes in people with ADHD occur following neurofeedback therapy in event related synchronizations and desynchronizations, in the measurements of cognitive evoked brain potentials, in EEG coherence values, and more recently in fMRI activity in the brain. Of course, new studies published over the last few years supporting the effectiveness of neurofeedback in ADHD are contributing to increased acceptance of this treatment (Arns, 2009).

Besides providing an efficient treatment method, neurofeedback opens the way to deep-seated effects on brain functioning in ADHD. Furthermore, it offers new perspectives on the true nature of ADHD and on a mechanism that would allow us to better understand the frontal executive functions. The influence of attention disorders on the understanding of ADHD dates back to the eighties, when cognitive psychology was dominant. The latest developments help us understand that ADHD is more a disorder of self-regulation, in which the ability to adapt to the environment while accounting for the long term consequences to the individual is inadequate. The attentional disorder is thus only part of a wider disorder such that it is misleading to give "attention" a central place in the definition of the disorder. There are good arguments for a new name, such as self-regulation disorder or "intention deficit disorder."

Published results from investigations on neurofeedback therapy and neurophysiology reveal to us that the true nature of some functional disorders, such as ADHD, is biological, both static and dynamic in nature. This could explain why purely cognitive behavioral therapies adopt too simple an approach. Newer models cross the borders between behavioral and cognitive psychological models by focusing on motivationally guided self-regulation. These models allow the acquisition of a deeper insight into the problems, thereby, lead to a better and more human interaction of ADHD individuals with everyday problems, allowing for the optimization of the adaptive ability of children and adults with ADHD.

Thank you to the pioneers of neurofeedback treatment for people with ADHD!

Barry Sterman, now professor emeritus at UCLA, is the founder of scientific neurofeedback since his pioneering basic scientific research, first, in the late sixties with cats and then in the seventies using human subjects. He first described the SMR rhythm and proposed that training could strengthen this rhythm, which can lead to a global normalization of the EEG. He has investigated event related  synchronization and desynchronization following attention tasks, and he has published in numerous prestigious scientific periodicals.

Joel Lubar, professor of psychology at the University of Tennessee in Knoxville. In the early years, he was influenced by Sterman's work. Initially, he investigated the effects of neurofeedback therapy in epilepsy. In 1976, he described a favorable outcome of neurofeedback in a child with ADHD for the first time. Since then, he has further adapted his protocol to deliver optimal results for the treatment of ADHD.

Linda Thompson, psychologist, director of the ADD centre in Toronto. She has published a number of scientific studies on neurofeedback applied to ADHD as well as thorough and detailed manuals on the subject. She has adhered closely to the methods of Joel Lubar. In 2005, she published research findings on QEEG applied to adults with ADHD.

Vincent Monastra, adjunct professor of psychology at the University of Birmingham (New York) and clinical director of the Attention Disorders Clinic in Endicott (New York). Together with Joel Lubar, he published pioneering theta/beta-1 normative data, which provided a method to diagnose ADHD with high sensitivity and specific ity objectively using QEEG data. In 2002, he published a crucial study, which demonstrated that neurofeedback training of people with ADHD normalized the theta/beta-1 ratio and led to outcomes that are comparable to those obtained from Ritalin treatment.

Siegfried Othmer, engineer and neuroscientist, has applied neurofeedback therapy to the treatment of ADHD since 1988. He developed the first training program for neurofeedback therapists in Encino, California. Additionally, he developed variants of Lubar's training protocols and developed new theoretical models that are more consistent with the scientific dynamic EEG research than with the static QEEG.

Niels Birbaumer, professor of clinical and physiological psychology at the University of Tubingen in Germany since 1975. He has performed fundamental research into neurofeedback of the slow brain potentials since the late seventies, publishing numerous studies in prestigious scientific journals. His coworkers included Brigitte Rockstroh, Werner Lutzenberger, and Ute Strehl.

Juri Kropotov, professor of psychophysiology at the Human Brain Institute in St Petersburg, Russia, has performed extensive research into neurofeedback and transcranial direct current stimulation of people with ADHD. He has also studied event related synchronization and desynchronization and go/no-go event related potentials in people with ADHD before and after neurofeedback treatment.

References

Achim, A., Michaud, K., & Robaey, P. EEG states before correct and incorrect trials in children with and without ADHD, 12th Annual Forum of the International Society for Neuronal Regulation, Fort Lauderdale, Florida, 2004.

Ahveninen, J., Kahkonen, S., Tiitinen, H., Pekkonen, E., Huttunen, J., Kaakkola, S., Ilmoniemi, RJ., & Jaaskelainen, IP. Suppression of transient 40-Hz auditory response by haloperidol suggests modulation of human selective attention by dopamine D2 receptors, in *Neuroscience Letters*, 292, 2000, p. 29-32.

Alper, K., Günther, W., Prichep, LS., John, ER., & Brodie, J. Correlation of qEEG with PET in schizophrenia, in *Neuropsychobiology*, 38, 1998, p. 50-56.

Amen, DG., *Change Your Brain, Change Your Life*, Times Books, New York, 1998.

American Academy of Pediatrics, *ADHD: A Complete and Authorative Guideline*, 2004.

American Psychiatric Association. *Diagnostic and Statistical Manual of Mental Disorders* (4th ed.). Washington, DC, 1994.

Antal, A., Varga, ET., Kincses, TZ., Nitsche, MA., & Paulus, W. Oscillatory brain activity and transcranial direct current stimulation in humans, in *Neuroreport*, 15, 2004, p. 1307-1310.

Arns, M., de Ridder, S., Strehl, U., Breteler, M., & Coenen, M. Efficacy of neurofeedback treatment in ADHD: the effects on inattention, impulsivity and hyperactivity: a meta-analysis, in *Clinical EEG and Neuroscience*, 40, 2009, p. 180-189.

Aydin, G., Idiman, F., & Idiman, E. Contingent negative variation in normal children and children with attention deficit disorder, in *Advances in Biological Psychiatry*, 16, 1987, p. 178-195.

Bakhshayesh, AR. *Die Wirksamkeit von Neurofeedback im Vergleich zum EMG-Biofeedback bei der Behandlung von ADHS-Kindern.* PhD Thesis, Universität Potsdam, Germany, 2007.

Banaschewski, T., Brandeis, D., Heinrich, H., Akbrecht, B., Brunner, E., & Rothenberger, A., Association of AD/HD and conduct disorder - brain electrical evidence for the existence of a distinct subtype, in *Journal of Child Psychology and Psychiatry*, 44, 2003, p. 356-376.

Bannatyne, A., Language, *Reading and Learning Disabilities*, Charles C. Thomas, Springfield, IL., 1971.

Bannatyne, A., Diagnosis: a note on recategorization of the WISC-R scaled scores, in *Journal of Learning Disabilities*, 7, 1974, p. 13-14.

Barkley, RA., *Attention Deficit Hyperactivity Disorder: A Handbook for Diagnosis and Treatment.* Guilford, New York, 2006.

Barkley, RA., *ADHD and the Nature of Self-Control,* Guilford, New York, 1997.

Barry, RJ., Clarke, AR., McCarthy, R., & Selikowitz, M. EEG coherence in attention deficit/hyperactivity disorder: a comparative study of two DSM-IV subtypes, in *Clinical Neurophysiology*, 113, 2002, p. 579-585.

Bartlett M, Makeig S, Bell AJ, Jung TP., & Sejnowski TJ. Independent Component Analysis of EEG Data, in *Society for Neuroscience Abstracts*, 21(437), 1995.

Basar, E., Basar-Eroglu,C., Rosen, B., & Schutt, A. A new approach to endogenous event related potentials in man: relation between EEG and P300 wave, in *International Journal of Neuroscience*, 26, 1984, p. 161-180.

Bates, JA., Electrical activity of the cortex accompanying movement, in *Journal of Physiology* (London), 113, 1951, p. 240-257.

Bauer, RH., & Jones, CN. Feedback training of 36-44 Hz EEG activity in the visual cortex and hippocampus of cats: evidence for sensory and motor involvement, in *Physiology of Behavior*, 17, 1976, p. 885-890.

Beauregard, M., Effect of neurofeedback training on the neural substrates of selective attention in children with attention-deficit/hyperactivity disorder: a functional magnetic resonance study, in *Neuroscience Letters*, 394, 2006, p. 216-221.

Beek, P., & Daffertshofer, A. Zelforganisatie in het brein, in *Neuropraxis*, 2, 1998, p. 37-41.

Bente, D. Vigilanz, dissoziative Vigilanzverschiebung und Insuffizienz des Vigilitätstonus, in Kranz H. en Heinrich, K. (Eds.), *Begleitwirkungen und Misserfolge der psychiatrischen Pharmakotherapie*, Thieme, Stuttgart, 1964, p. 13-28.

Berner, I., Schabus, M., Wienerroither, T., & Klimesch, W. The significance of sigma neurofeedback training on sleep spindles and aspects of declarative memory, in *Applied Psychophysiology and Biofeedback*, 31, 2006, p. 97-114.

Bird, BL., Newton, FA., Sheer, DE., & Ford, M. Behavioral and electroencephalographic correlates of 40-Hz EEG biofeedback training in humans, in *Biofeedback and Self-Regulation*, 3, 1978, p. 13-28.

Blanco, S., D'Attellis, CE., Isaacson, SI, Rosso, OA., & Sirne, RO. Time-frequency analysis of electroencephalogram series. II. Gabor and wavelet transforms, in *Phys. Rev. E.*, 54, 1996, p. 6661–6672.

Block, V. Facts and hypotheses concerning memory consolidation processes, in *Brain Research*, 24, 1970, p. 561.

Booth, JR., Burman, DD., Meyer, JR., Lei, Z., Trommer, BL., Davenport, ND., Li, W., Parrisch, TB., Gitelman, DR. & Mesulam, MM. Neural development of selective attention and response inhibition, in *NeuroImage*, 20, 2003, p. 737-751.

Bouyer, JJ., Montaron, MF., & Rougeul, A. Fast fronto-parietal rhythms during combined focused attentive behaviour and immobility in cat: cortical and thalamic oscillations, in *Electroencephalography and Clinical Neurophysiology*, 51, 1981, p. 244-252.

Bouyer, JJ., Tilquin, C. & Rougeul-Buser, A. Thalamic rhythms in cat during quiet wakefulness and immobility, in *Electroencephalography and Clinical Neurophysiology*, 55, 1983, p. 180-187.

Bresnahan, SM., & Barry, RJ. Specificity of quantitative EEG analysis in adults with attention deficit hyperactivity disorder, in *Psychiatry Research*, 112, 2002, p. 133-144.

Brunner, DP., Dijk, DJ., & Borbély, AA. Repeated partial sleep deprivation progressively changes the EEG during sleep and wakefulness, in *Sleep*, 16, 1993, p. 100-113.

Bush, G., Frazier, JA., Rauch SL., Seidman LJ., Whalen, PJ., Jenike, MA., Rosen, BR., & Biederman, J. Anterior cingulate cortex dysfunction in attention-deficit/hyperactivity disorder revealed by fMRI and the Counting Stroop, in *Biological Psychiatry*, 45, 1999, p. 1542-1552.

Buzsaki, G., *Rhythms of the Brain*, Oxford University Press, New York, 2006.

Buzsaki, G., & Draguhn, A. Neuronal oscillations in cortical networks, in Science, 304, 2004, p. 1926-1929.

Cannon, R., Lubar, J., Congedo, M., Thornton, K., Towler, K., & Hutchens, T. The effects of neurofeedback training in the cognitive division of the anterior cingulate gyrus, in *International Journal of Neuroscience*, 117, 2007, p. 337-357.

Cannon, R., Lubar, J., Gerke, A., Thornton, K., Hutchens, T., & McCammon, T. EEG spectral-power and coherence: LORETA neurofeedback training in the anterior cingulate gyrus, in *Journal of Neurotherapy*, 10, 2006, p. 5-31.

Cannu, MH., & Rougeul, A. Nucleus reticularis thalami participates in sleep spindles, not in beta rhythms concomitant with attention in cat, in *Comptes Rendus de l'Académie des Sciences, Série III*, 315, 1992, p. 513-520.

Canon, WB. *Bodily changes in pain, hunger, fear, and rage*. Appleton, New York, 1915.

Cartozzo, HA., Jacobs, D., & Gevirtz, RN. EEG biofeedback and the remediation of ADHD symptomatology: a controlled treatment outcome study, in *Proceedings of the Association of Applied Psychophysiology and Biofeedback*, 1995, p. 21-25.

Caspers, H. DC potentials of the brain, in Haschke, W., Speckman EJ., & Roitbak, AI. (Eds.), *Slow Potentials in the Brain, Chapter 1*. Birkhauser, Boston, 1993, p. 9-20.

Chabot RJ., & Serfontein,G. Quantitative electroencephalographic profiles of children with attention deficit disorder, in *Biological Psychiatry*, 40, 1996, p. 951-963.

Chabot, RJ, diMichele, F., John, ER., & Valdes, P. Quantitative EEG profiles and LORETA imaging of children with attention deficit and learning disorders. 4th International Conference on Functional Mapping of the Human Brain, Montreal, 1998.

Chabot, RJ., diMichele, F., Prichep, L., & John, ER. The clinical role of computerized EEG in the evaluation and treatment of learning and attention disorders in children and adolescents, in *The Journal of Neuropsychiatry and Clinical Neurosciences*, 13, 2001, p. 171-186.

Cherkes-Julkowski, M., Sharp, S., & Stolzenberg, J., *Rethinking Attention Deficit Disorders*, Brookline Books, Cambridge, MA, 1997.

Chutko, LDS., Kropotov, YD., Yakovenko, EA., & Surushkina, SY. Transcranial micropolarization in the treatment of children with attention deficit hyperactivity disorder in children and adolescents, in *Ros Vestn Perinatol Pediat*, 4, 2002, p. 35-38.

Cinciripini, PM. Discrimination of sensorimotor EEG (12-15 Hz) activity: a comparison of response, production, and no-feedback training sessions, in *Psychophysiology*, 21, 1984, p. 54-62.

Clarke, AR., Barry, RJ., McCarthy, R., & Selikowitz, M. Electroencephalogram differences in two subtypes of attention-deficit/hyperactivity disorder, in *Psychophysiology*, 38, 2001, p. 212-221.

Clarke, AR., Barry, RJ., McCarthy, R., & Selikowitz, M. Excess beta activity in children with attention-deficit/hyperactivity disorder: an atypical electrophysiological group, in *Psychiatry Research*, 103, 2001, p. 205-218.

Clarke, AR., Barry, RJ., McCarthy, R., & Selikowitz, M. EEG-defined subtypes of children with attention-deficit/hyperactivity disorder, in *Clinical Neurophysiology*, 112, 2001, p. 2098-2105.

Clarke, AE., Barry RJ., McCarthy, R., & Selikowitz, M. EEG differences between good and poor responders to methylphenidate and dexamphetamine in children with attention-deficit/hyperactivity disorder, in *Clinical Neurophysiology*, 113, 2002, p. 194-205.

Clarke, AR., Barry, RJ., McCarthy, R., Selikowitz, M., Clarke, D. & Croft, RJ. Effects of stimulant medications on children with attention-deficit/hyperactivity disorder and excessive beta activity in their EEG, in *Clinical Neurophysiology*, 114, 2003, p. 1729-1737.

Coben, R. Assessment-guided neurofeedback for autism spectrum disorder, 13th Annual Forum of the International Society for Neuronal Regulation, Denver, 2005.

Colditz, PB., Burke, CJ., & Celka P. Digital processing of EEG signals, in *IEEE Engineering in Medicine and Biology*, September/October 2001, p. 21-22.

Congedo, M., *Tomographic Neurofeedback: A New Technique for the Self-Regulation of Brain Activity*, Doctoral Dissertation, 2003, University of Tennessee, Knoxville.

Cosmides, L., & Tooby, J. Beyond intuition and instinct blindness: toward an evolutionary rigorous cognitive science, in Cognition, 50, 1994, p. 41-77.

Crick, F.,*The Astonishing Hypothesis*, Simon & Schuster, London, 1994.

Cumyn, L., French, L., & Hechtman, L. Comorbidity in adults with Attention-Deficit Hyperactivity Disorder, in *Canadian Journal of Psychiatry*, 54(10), October 2009, p. 673-680.

Dahl, RE., The regulation of sleep and arousal: development and psychopathology, in *Developmental Psychopathology*, 8, 1996, p. 3-27.

DeBeus, R., Ball, JD., & DeBeus, M.E. Attention training with ADHD children: preliminary findings in a double-blind placebo-controlled study, in *Journal of Neurotherapy*, 8, 2004, p.145-147.

deCharms, RC., Christoff, K., Glover, GH., Pauly, JM., Whitfield, S., & Gabrieli, JD. Learned regulation of spatially localized brain activation using real-time fMRI, in *NeuroImage*, 21, 2004, p.436-443.

Delignières, D., Fortes, M., & Ninot, G. The fractal dynamics of self-esteem and physical self, in *Nonlinear Dynamics in Psychology and Life Sciences*, 8, 2004, p. 479-510.

Delorme, A., & Makeig, S. EEG changes accompanying learned regulation of 12-Hz EEG activity. *IEEE Transactions on Neural Systems and Rehabilitation Engineering*, 11, 2002, p. 133-136.

Desmedt, JE, & Tomberg, C. Transient phase-locking of 40 Hz electrical oscillations in prefrontal and parietal human cortex reflects the process of conscious somatic perception, in *Neuroscience Letters*, 168, 1994, p. 126-129.

Dostrovsky, J., & Bergman, H. Oscillatory activity in the basal ganglia - relationship to normal physiology and pathophysiology, in *Brain*, 127, 2004, p. 721-722.

Douglas, VI. Stop, look, and listen: the problem of sustained attention and impulse control in hyperactive and normal children, in *Canadian Journal of Behavioural Science*, 4, 1972, p. 259-282.

Drechsler, R., Straub, M., Doehnert, M., Heinrich, H., Steinhausen, HC., & Brandeis, D. Controlled evaluation of neurofeedback training of slow cortical potentials in children with attention deficit/hyperactivity disorder (ADHD), in *Behavioral Brain Functions*, 3, 2007, p. 35-47.

Dumenko, VN. Changes in the electroencephalogram of the dog during formation of a motor conditioned reflex stereotype, in *Pavlov Journal of Higher Nervous Activity*, 11, 1961, p. 64.

Edelman, GM. *Bright Air, Brilliant Fire: on the Matter of the Mind*. Basic Books, New York, 1992.

Egner, T., & Gruzelier, JH. Learned self-regulation of EEG frequency components affects attention and event-related brain potentials in humans, in *Neuroreport*, 12, 2001, p. 4155-4159.

Evans, BM. Periodic activity in cerebral arousal mechanisms - the relationship to sleep and brain damage, in *Electroencephalography and Clinical Neurophysiology*, 83, 1992, p. 130-137.

Evans, BM. Cyclical activity in non-rapid eye movement sleep: a proposed arousal inhibitory mechanism, in *Electroencephalography and Clinical Neurophysiology*, 86, 1993, p. 123-131.

Falgätter, AJ., Ehlis, AC., Rösler, M., Strik, WK., Blocher, D., & Herrmann, MJ., Electrophysiological dysfunction in the anterior cingulate cortex in attention deficit hyperactivity disorder (ADHD), in *Brain Topography*, 16, 2003, p. 125.

Fassbender, C., Zhang, H., Buzy, WM., Cortes, CC., Mizuin, D., Becket, L., & Schweitzer, J. A lack of default network suppression is linked to increased distractibility in ADHD, in *Brain Research*, 1273, 2009, p. 114-128.

Fearing, F. (1970). Reflex action: A study in the history of physiological psychology, MIT Press, Massachusetts, (Original work published 1930).

Fernandez, T., Harmony, T., Rodriguez, M., Bernal, J., Silva, J., Reyes, A., & Marosi, E. EEG activation patterns during the performance of tasks involving different components of mental calculation, in *Electroencephalography and Clinical Neurophysiology*, 94, 1995, p. 175-182.

Fischer, S., Hallschmid, M., Elsner, AL. & Born, J. Sleep forms memory for finger skills, in *Proceedings of the National Academy of Sciences USA*, 99, 2002, p.11987-11991.

Fitzgerald, KD., Welsh, RC., Gehring, WJ., Abelson, JJ., Himle, JA., Liberzon, I., & Taylor, SF. Error-related hyperactivity of the anterior cingulate cortex in obsessive compulsive disorder, in *Biological Psychiatry*, 57, 2005, p. 287-294.

Fluck, E., File, SE., Springett, J., Kopelman, MD., Rees, J., & Orgill, J. Does the sedation resulting from sleep deprivation and Lorazepam cause similar cognitive deficits? *Pharmacology and Biochemistry of Behavior*, 59, 1998, p. 909-915.

Ford, M., Bird, BL., Newton, FA., & Sheer D. Maintenance and generalization of 40-Hz EEG biofeedback effects, in *Biofeedback and Self-Regulation*, 5, 1980, p. 193-205.

Fox, SS., & Rudell, AP. Operant controlled neural event: functional independence in behavioral coding by early and late components of visual cortical evoked response in cats, in *Journal of Neurophysiology*, 33, 1970, p. 548-561.

Freeman, WJ., *How Brains Make up their Minds*, Phoenix, London, 2000.

Freeman, WJ. A proposed name for aperiodic brain activity: stochastic chaos, in *Neural Networks*, 13, 2000, p. 11-13.

Freeman, WJ., Origin, structure, and role of the background EEG activity, Part 1. Analytic amplitude, in *Clinical Neurophysiology*, 115, 2004, p. 2077-2088.

Freeman, WJ. Origin, structure, and role of the background EEG activity, Part 2. Analytic phase, in *Clinical Neurophysiology*, 115, 2004, p. 2089-2107.

Fregni, F., Boggio, PS, Nitsche, M., Bermpohl, F., Antal, A., Feredoes, E., Rigonatti, SP., Silva, MT., Paulus, W., & Pascual-Leone, A. Anodal transcranial direct current stimulation of prefrontal cortex enhances working memory, in *Experimental Brain Research*, 166.1, 2005, p. 23-30.

Fregni, F., Boggio, PS., Nitsche, M., Marcolin, MA., Rigonatti, SP., & Pascual-Leone, A. Treatment of major depression with transcranial direct current stimulation, in *Bipolar Disorders*, 8, 2006, p. 203-204.

Friston, KJ., The labile brain.I. Neuronal transients and nonlinear coupling, in *Philosophical Trans Royal Society London*, 355, 2000, p. 215-236.

Fuchs, T., Birbaumer, N., Lutzenberger, W., Gruzelier, JH., & Kaiser, J. Neurofeedback treatment for attention-deficit/hyperactivity disorder in children: a comparison with methylphenidate, in *Applied Psychophysiology and Biofeedback*, 28, 2003, p. 1-12.

Galambos, R., Electrical correlates of conditioned learning, in Brazier, M. (Ed.), *The Central Nervous System and Behaviour*, Josiah Macy, Jr. Foundation, New York, 1958, p. 375.

Gallinat, J., & Hegerl, U. Elektroenzephalographie, in Hegerl, U. (Ed.), *Neurophysiologische Untersuchungen in der Psychiatrie*, Springer, Wenen, 1988, p. 7-94.

Gani, C., Birbaumer, N., & Strehl, U. Long term effects after feedback of slow cortical potentials and of theta-beta-amplitudes in children with attention-deficit/hyperactivity disorder (ADHD), in *International Journal of Bioelectromagnetism*, 10, 2008, p. 209-232.

Gehring, WJ., Himle, J., & Nisenson, LG. Action monitoring dysfunction in obsessive-compulsive disorder, in *Psychological Science*, 11, 2000, p. 1-6.

Gevensleben, H., Holl, B., Albrecht, B., Vogel C., Schlamp, D., Kratz O., Studer, P., Rothenberger, A., Moll, G., & Heinrich, H. Is neurofeedback an efficacious treatment for ADHD? A randomised controlled clinical trial, in *Journal of Child Psychology and Psychiatry*, 50(7), 2009, p. 767-780.

Gevensleben, H., Holl, B., Albrecht, B., Schlamp, D., Kratz O., Studer, P., Rothenberger, A., Moll, G., & Heinrich, H. Neurofeedback training in children with ADHD: 6-month follow-up of a randomised trial, in *European Child & Adolescent Psychiatry*, 2010, published online.

Giannitrapani, D. EEG average frequency and intelligence, in *Electroencephalography and Clinical Neurophysiology*, 27, 1969, p. 480.

Giannitrapani, D., The role of 13-Hz activity in mentation, in Giannitrapani, D., & Murri, L. (Eds.), *The EEG of Mental Activities*. Karger, Basel, 1988, p. 149-152.

Gilden, DL., Thornton, T., & Mallon, MW. 1/f noise in human cognition, in *Science*, 267, 1995, p. 1837-1839.

Gomez, C. Antizipatorische selektive Aktivierung der für die erwartete Aufgabe benötigten Hirnareale während der Contingenten Negativen Variation (CNV), CTW Congress, Berlin, 2005.

Grace, AA., The tonic/phasic model of dopamine system regulation: its relevance for understanding how stimulant abuse can alter basal ganglia function, in *Drug and Alcohol Dependence*, 37, 1995, p. 111-129.

Greco, D. A randomized, double-blind clinical trial of EEG neurofeedback treatment for attention deficit/hyperactivity disorder. 12th Annual Conference of the International Society for Neuronal Regulation, Fort Lauderdale, Florida, 2004.

Gruber, R., Sadeh, A., & Raviv, A. Instability of sleep patterns in children with attention deficit/hyperactivity disorder, in *Journal of American Child and Adolescent Psychiatry*, 39, 2000, p. 495-501.

Gurnee, RL. QEEG based subtypes of adult ADHD and implications for treatment. 8th Annual Conference of the International Society for Neuronal Regulation, St. Paul, Minnesota, 2000.

Hajcak, G., & Simons, RF. Error-related brain activity in obsessive-compulsive undergraduates, in *Psychiatry Research*, 110, 2002, p. 63-72.

Haken, H, *Principles of Brain Functioning. A Synergetic Approach to Brain Activity, Behavior and Cognition*, Springer, Berlijn, 1996.

Halpern, LE., MacLean, WE., & Baumeister, AA. Infant sleep-wake characteristics: relation to neurological status and the prediction of developmental outcome, in *Development Review*, 15, 1995, p. 255-291.

Hansen, JC., & Hillyard, SA. Endogenous brain potentials associated with selective auditory attention, in *Electroencephalography and Clinical Neurophysiology*, 49, 1980, p. 461-475.

Hauri, P., Treating psychophysiological insomnia with biofeedback, in Archives of *General Psychiatry*, 38, 1981, p. 752-758.

Hanslmayr, S., Sauseng, P., Doppelmayer, M., Schabus, M., & Klimesch, W. Increasing individual upper alpha power by neurofeedback improves cognitive performance in human subjects, in *Applied Psychophysiology and Biofeedback*, 30(1), 2005, p. 1-10.

Haschke, R., Tennigkeit, M., Lehmann, HJ., & Haschke, W. Changes of slow brain potential shifts following failure, in Haschke, W., Speckman, EJ., & Roitbak, AI. (Eds.), *Slow Potentials in the Brain*, Chapter 4, Birkhauser, Boston, 1993, p. 63-84.

Head, H. Vigilance: a physiological state of the nervous system, in *British Journal of Psychology*, 14, 1923, p. 126-147.

Heinrich, H., Gevensleben, H., Freisleder, FJ., Moll, GH., & Rothenberger A. Training of slow cortical potentials in attention-deficit/hyperactivity disorder: evidence for positive behavioral and neurophysiological effects, in *Biological Psychiatry*, 55, 2004, p. 772-775.

Hershberger, WA., Control systems with a priori intentions register environmental disturbances a posteriori, in Jordan JS. (Ed.), *Systems theories and a priori aspects of perception*, Elsevier, Amsterdam, 1998, p. 3-24.

Hess, WR., *Diencephalon: Autonomic and Extrapyramidal Functions*, Grune & Stratton, New York, 1954.

Hinterberger, T., Veit, R., Strehl, U., Trevorrow, T., Erb, M., Kotchoubey, B., & Birbaumer, N. Brain areas activated in fMRI during self-regulation of slow cortical potentials (SCP), in *Experimental Brain Research*, 152, 2003, p. 113-122.

Holtmann, M., Grasmann, D., Cionek-Szpak, E., Hager, V., Panzer, N., & Beyer, A. Spezifische Wirksamkeit von Neurofeedback auf die Impulsivität bei ADHS - Literaturüberblick und Ergebnisse einer prospective, kontrollierten Studie, in *Kindheit und Entwicklung*, 18, 2009, p. 95-104.

Howe, RC., & Sterman, MB. Cortical-subcortical EEG correlates of suppressed motor behavior during sleep and waking in the cat, in Electroencephalography and *Clinical Neurophysiology*, 32, 1972, p. 681-695.

Hummel, F., Celnik, P., Giraux, P., Floel, A., Wu, WH., Gerloff, C., & Cohen, LG. Effects of non-invasive cortical stimulation on skilled motor function in chronic stroke, in *Brain*, 128, 2005, p. 490-499.

Intriligator, J., & Polich, J. On the relationship between background EEG and the P300 event related potential, in *Biological Psychiatry*, 37, 1994, p. 207-218.

Iyer, MB., Mattu, U., Grafman, J., Lomarev, M., Sato, S., & Wassermann, EM. Safety and cognitive effect of frontal DC brain polarization in healthy individuals, in *Neurology*, 64, 2005, p. 872-875.

Johannes, S., Wieringa, BM., Nager, W., Rada, D., Dengler, R., & Emrich, HM. Discrepant target detection and action monitoring in obsessive-compulsive disorder, in *Psychiatry Research*, 108, 2001, p. 101-110.

John, ER. The neurophysics of consciousness, in *Brain Research Review*, 39(1), 2002, p. 1-28.

Kahn, A. & Rechtschaffen A. Sleep patterns and sleep spindles in hyperkinetic children, in *Sleep Research*, 7, 1978, p. 137.

Kaiser, DA., & Sterman, MB. Periodicity of standardized EEG spectral measures across the waking day. 7th Annual Summer Sleep Waking Multi-Site Training for Basic Sleep Research, September 16-21, 1994, Lake Arrowhead, California.

Kaiser, D. Efficacy of neurofeedback on adults with attentional deficit and related disorders. EEG Spectrum International Inc., Encino, California, 1997.

Kaiser, D. A little ditty about functional conformity, in *What's new in Neurofeedback* (web journal EEG Spectrum International, Inc.), 4, 2001.

Kamiya, J. Conscious control of brain waves, in *Psychology Today*, 1, 1968, p. 57-60.

Kaufman, AS., *Intelligent Testing with the WISC-R*, Wiley, New York, 1979.

Kelso, JAS. *Dynamic Patterns: The Self-Organization of Brain and Behavior*, MIT Press, Cambridge, Massachusetts, 1995.

Kencses, TZ., Antal, A., Nitsche, MA., Bartfai, O., & Paulus, W. Facilitation of probabilistic classification learning by transcranial direct current stimulation of the prefrontal cortex in the human, in *Neuropsychologia*, 42, 2003, p. 113-117.

Killam, KF., & Killam, EK. Rhinencephalic activity during acquisition and performance of conditional behavior and its modification by pharmacological agents, in Adey, WR., & Tokizane, T. (Eds.), Progress in Brain Research vol. 27, *Structure and Function of the Limbic System*, Elsevier, New York, 1967, p. 338.

Kingshott, RN., Cosway, RJ., Deary, IJ., & Douglas, NJ. The effect of sleep fragmentation on cognitive processing using computerized topographic brain mapping, in *Journal of Sleep Research*, 9, 2000, p. 353-357.

Kirlangic, ME., *EEG-biofeedback and epilepsy: concept, methodology and tools for (neuro)therapy planning and objective evaluation*, Dissertation, Il-lmenau, 2005.

Kiyatkin, EA. Functional significance of mesolimbic dopamine, in *Neuroscience Biobehavioral Reviews*, 19, 1995, p. 578-598.

Kleitman, D., *Sleep and Wakefulness* (2nd Ed.). University of Chicago Press, Chicago, 1963.

Kotchoubey, B., Kübler, A., Strehl, U., Flor, H., & Birbaumer N. Can humans perceive their brain states?, in Consciousness and Cognition, 11, 2002, p. 98-113.

Kotchoubey, B. Event-related potentials, cognition, behavior: a biological approach, in *Neuroscience and Behavioral Reviews*, 30, 2006, p. 42-65.

Kripke, DF., & Sonnenschein, D. A biologic rhythm in waking fantasy, in Pope, D., & Songer, JL. (Eds.), *The Stream of Consciousness*, Plenum Pub, New York, 1978, p. 321-332.

Kropotov, JD., Grin-Yatsenko, V., Ponomarev, AV., Chutko, SL., Yakovenko, AE., & Nikishena, SI. ERPs correlates of EEG relative beta training in ADHD children, in *International Journal of Psychophysiology*, 55, 2004, p. 1-12.

Kropotov, Y. QEEG/ERP/ERD based diagnosis and biofeedback treatment of executive dysfunction, in *Crossroads Institute Newsletter*, November, 2004b.

Lancaster, JL., Rainey, LH., Summerlin, JL., Freitas, CS., Fox, PT., Evans, AC., Toga, AW., & Mazziotta, JC. Automated labeling of the human brain: a preliminary report on the development and evaluation of a forward-transform method, in *Human Brain Mapping*, 5, 1997, p. 238-242.

Lancaster, JL., Woldorff, MG., Parsons, LM., Liotti, M., Freitas, CS., Rainey, L., Kochunov, PV., Nickerson, D., Mikiten, SA., & Fox, PT. Automated Talairach Atlas labels for functional brain mapping, in *Human Brain Mapping*, 10, 2000, pg. 120-131.

Lansing, RW., Schwartz, E. & Lindsley, DB. Reaction time and EEG activation under alerted and nonalerted conditions, in *Journal of Experimental Psychology*, 58, 1959, p. 1-7.

LaVaque, TJ., Hammond, DC., Trudeau, D., Monastra, VJ., Perry, J. & Lehrer, P. Template for developing guidelines for the evaluation of the clinical efficacy of psychophysiological interventions, in *Applied Psychophysiology and Biofeedback*, 27, 2002, p. 273-281.

Lavie, P. Ultradian rhythms in human sleep and wakefulness, in Webb, WB. (Ed.), *Biological Rhythms, Sleep, and Performance*, John Wiley & Sons, Chichester, 1982, p. 239-272.

Lavric, A., Pizzagali, DA., & Forstmeier, S. When 'go' and 'nogo' are equally frequent: ERP components and cortical tomography, in *European Journal of Neuroscience*, 20, 2004, p. 2483-2488.

Lehmann, D., Strik, WK., Henggeler, B., Koenig, T., & Koukkou, M. Brain electrical microstates and momentary conscious mind states as building blocks of spontaneous thinking: I. Visual imagery and abstract thoughts, in *International Journal of Psychophysiology*, 29, 1998, p. 1-11.

Lehmann, D., Faber, PL., Achermann, P., Jeanmonod, D., Gianotti, LRR., & Pizzagali, D. Brain sources of EEG gamma frequency during volitionally meditation-induced, altered states of consciousness, and experience of the self, in *Psychiatry Research*, 108, 2001, p. 111-121.

Leins, U., *Neurofeedback für Kinder mit einer Aufmerksamkeitsdefizit-/Hyperaktivitätsstörung*, Dissertatie, Tübingen, 2004.

Leins, U., Goth, G., Hinterberger, T., Klinger, C., Rumpf, N., & Strehl, U. Neurofeedback for children with ADHD: a comparison of SCP and theta/beta protocols, in *Applied Psychophysiology and Biofeedback*, 32, 2007, p. 33-88.

Leung, LS., & Yim, CY. Rythmic delta-frequency activities in the nucleus accumbens of anesthetized and freely moving rats, in *Canadian Journal of Physiology and Pharmacology*, 71, 1993, p. 311-320.

Liang,H., Bressler, SL., Ding, M. Truccolo, WA., & Nakamura, R. Synchronized activity in prefrontal cortex during anticipation of visuomotor processing, in *Neuroreport*, 13, 2002, p. 2011-2015.

Linden, M., Habib, T., & Radojevic, V. A controlled study of the effects of EEG biofeedback on cognition and behavior of children with attention deficit disorder and learning disabilities, in *Biofeedback and Self-Regulation*, 21, 1996, p. 35-49.

Linkenkaer-Hansen, K., Nikulin, V., Palva JM., Kaila, K., & Limoniemi, R. Stimulus-induced change in long-range temporal correlations and scaling behaviour of sensorimotor oscillations, *European Journal of Neuroscience*, 19, 2004, p. 203-211.

Liotti, M., Pliszka, SR., Perez, R., Kothmann, D., & Woldorff, MG. Abnormal brain activity related to performance monitoring and error detection in children with ADHD, in *Cortex*, 41, 2005, p. 377-388.

Lisman, JE., & Idiart, MA. Storage of 7 ± 2 short-term memories in oscillatory subcycles, in *Science*, 267, 1995, p. 1512-1515.

Llinas, RR., & Ribary, U. Temporal conjunction in thalamocortical transactions. Consciousness: at the frontiers of neuroscience, in *Advances in Neurology*, 77, 1998, p. 95-103.

Llinas, RR., Ribary, U., Jeanmonod, D., Kronberg, E., & Mitra, PP. Thalamocortical dysrhythmia: a neurological and neuropsychiatric syndrome characterized by magnetoencephalography, in *Proceedings of the National Academy of Sciences USA*, 96, 1999, p. 15222-15227.

Loo, SK., & Barkley, RA., Clinical utility of EEG in attention deficit hyperactivity disorder, *Applied Neuropsychology*, 12, 2005, p. 64-76.

Lubar, JF. Discourse on the development of EEG diagnostics and biofeedback for attention deficit/hyperactivity disorders, in *Biofeedback and Self-Regulation*, 16, 1991, p. 201-225.

Lubar, JF. Neocortical dynamics; implications for understanding the role of neurofeedback and related techniques for the enhancement of attention, in *Applied Psychophysiology and Biofeedback*, 22, 1997, p. 111-126.

Lubar, JF. Clinical corner, in *Journal of Neurotherapy*, 4, 2000, p. 83-93.

Lubar, JF. Rationale for choosing bipolar versus referential training, in *Journal of Neurotherapy*, 4, 2001, p. 94-97.

Lubar, JF. Neurofeedback for the management of attention deficit disorders, in Schwartz, MS., & Andrasik, F., (Eds.), *Biofeedback: A Practitioner's Guide*, Guilford Press, New York, 2003, p. 409-437.

Lubar, JF., & Lubar O. Neurofeedback assessment and treatment for attention deficit/hyperactivity disorders, in Evans, JR., & Abarbanel, A. (Eds.), *Introduction to Quantitative EEG and Neurofeedback*, Academic Press, San Diego, California, 1999, p. 103-143.

Lubar, JF., Shabsin, HS., Natelson, SE., Holder, GS., Whitsett, SF., Pamplin, WE., & Krulikowski, DI. EEG operant conditioning in intractable epileptics, in *Archives of Neurology*, 38, 1981, p. 700-704.

Lubar, JF., Swartwood, MO., Swartwood, JN., & O'Donnell, P. Evaluation of the effectiveness of EEG neurofeedback training for ADHD in a clinical setting as measured by changes in T.O.V.A. scores, behavioral ratings, and WISC-R performance, in *Biofeedback and Self-Regulation*, 20, 1995, p. 83-99.

Lutzenberger, W., Birbaumer, N., Elbert, T., Rockstroh, B., Bippus, W., & Breidt, R. Selfregulation of slow cortical potentials in normal subjects and patients with frontal lobe lesions, in Kornhuber, HH., & Deecke, L. (Eds.), *Motivation, motor and sensory processes of the brain. Electrical potentials, behavior and clinical use*, Elsevier, Amsterdam, 1980.

Lutzenberger, W., Pulvermüller, F., & Birbaumer, N. Words and pseudowords elicit distinct patterns of 30-Hz EEG responses in humans, in *Neuroscience Letters*, 176, 1994, p. 115-118.

Lutzenberger, W., Preissl, H., Birbaumer, N., & Pulvermüller, F. High-frequency cortical responses: do they not exist if they are small?, in *Electroencephalography and Clinical Neurophysiology*, 102, 1997, p. 64-66.

Luu, P., & Tucker, MD. Self-regulation by the medial frontal cortex: limbic representation of motive set-points, in Beauregard, M. (Ed.), *Consciousness, Emotional Self-Regulation and the Brain*, John Benjamin Publishing Company, Philadelphia, 2004, p. 123-161.

MacDonald, AW., Cohen, JD., & Stenger, VA. En Carter, CS. Dissociating the role of the dorsolateral prefrontal and anterior cingulate cortex in cognitive control, in *Science*, 288, 2000, p. 1835-1838.

Miano, S. NREM sleep instability is reduced in children with attention-deficit/hyperactivity disorder, in *Sleep*, 29, 2006, p. 797-803.

Makeig, S., Westerfield, M., Jung, TP., Enghoff, S., Townsend, J. Courchesne, E., & Sejnowski, TJ. Dynamic brain sources of visual evoked responses, in *Science*, 295, 2002, p. 690-694.

Makeig, S. Mining event-related brain dynamics, in TRENDS in *Cognitive Sciences*, 8, 2004, p. 204-210.

Malone, MA., Kershner, JR., & Swanson, JM. Hemispheric processing and methylphenidate effects in attention-deficit hyperactivity disorder, in *Journal of Child Neurology*, 9, 1994, p. 181-189.

Mandelbrot, B., *The Fractal Geometry of Nature*, Freeman, San Francisco, 1982.

Mann, CA., Sterman, MB., & Kaiser, DA. Suppression of EEG rhythmic frequencies during somato-motor and visuo-motor behavior, in *International Journal of Psychophysiology*, 23, 1996, p. 1-7.

Mantini, D., Perrucci, MG., Del Gratta, C., Romani, GL., & Corbetta, M. Electrophysiological signatures of resting state networks in the human brain, in *Proceedings of the National Academy of Sciences of the USA*, 104, 2007, p. 13170-13175.

Maquet, P., Schwartz, S., Passingham, R., & Frith C. Sleep-related consolidation of a visuomotor skill: brain mechanisms as assessed by functional magnetic resonance imaging, in *Journal of Neuroscience*, 23, 2003, p. 1432-1440.

Markela-Lerenc, J., Ille, N., Kaiser, S., Fiedler, P., Mundt, C., & Weisbrod, M. Prefrontalcingulate activation during executive control: which comes first, in *Cognitive Brain Research*, 18, 2004, p. 278-287.

Mattson, AJ., Sheer DE., & Fletcher, JM. 40 Hertz EEG activity in LD and normal children, in *Journal of Clinical and Experimental Neuropsychology*, 11, 1989, p. 32.

Mattson, AJ., Sheer DE., & Fletcher, JM. Electrophysiological evidence of lateralized disturbances in children with learning disabilities, in *Journal of Clinical and Experimental Neuropsychology*, 14, 1992, p. 707-716.

McEwen, BS. The neurobiology of stress: from serendipity to clinical relevance, in *Brain Research*, 886, 2000, p. 172-189.

Miano, S. NREM sleep instability is reduced in children with attention-deficit/hyperactivity disorder, in *Sleep*, 29, 2006, p. 797-803.

Michel, AM., Lehmann, D., Henggeler, B., & Brandeis, D. Localization of the sources of EEG delta, theta, alpha and beta frequency bands using the FFT dipole approximation, in *EEG and Clinical Neurophysiology*, 82, 1992, p. 38-44.

Michel, AM., Henggeler, B., Brandeis, D., & Lehmann, D. Localization of sources of brain alpha/theta/delta activity and the influence of the mode of spontaneous mentation, in *Physiology Measures*, 14, 1993, p. 21-26.

Monastra, VJ., Linden, M., Green, G., Phillips, A., Lubar, JF., VanDeusen, P., Wing, W., & Fenger, TN. Assessing attention deficit hyperactivity disorder via quantitative electroencephalography: an initial validation study, in *Neuropsychology*, 13, 1999, p. 424-433.

Monastra, VJ., Lubar, JF., & Linden, M. The development of a quantitative electroencephalographic scanning process for attention deficit-hyperactivity disorder: reliability and validity studies, in *Neuropsychology*, 15, 2001, p. 136-144.

Monastra, VJ., Monastra, DM., & George, S. The effects of stimulant therapy, EEG biofeedback, and parenting style on the primary symptoms of attention-deficit/hyperactivity disorder, in *Applied Psychophysiology and Biofeedback*, 27, 2002, p. 231-249.

Monastra, VJ. Overcoming the barriers to effective treatment for attention-deficit/hyperactivity disorder: a neuro-educational approach, in *International Journal of Psychophysiology*, 58, 2005, p. 71-80.

Morrell, F., & Jasper, HH. Electrographic studies of the formation of temporary connections in the brain, in *Electroencephalography and Clinical Neurophysiology*, 8, 1956, p. 201.

Nagai, Y., Critchley, HD., Featherstone, E., Fenwick, PBC, Trimble, MR., & Dolan, RJ. Brain activity relating to the contingent negative variation: an fMRI investigation, in *NeuroImage*, 21, 2004, p. 1232-1241.

Näätänen, R. Processing negativity, in *Psychology Bulletin*, 92, 1982, p. 605-640.

Nauta, WJH. The problem of the frontal lobe: a reinterpretation, in *Journal of Psychiatric Research*, 8, 1971, p. 167-187.

Naylor, E., Penev, PD., Orbeta, L., Janssen, I., Ortiz, R., Colecchia, EF., Keng, M., Finkel, S., & Zee, PC. Daily social and physical activity increases slow-wave sleep and daytime neuropsychological performance in the elderly, in *Sleep*, 23, 2000, p. 87-95.

Nikulin, VV., & Brismar, T. Long-range temporal correlations in alpha and beta oscillations: effect of arousal level and test-retest reliability, in *Clinical Neurophysiology*, 115, 2004, p. 1896-1908.

Nitsche, MA., & Paulus, W. Sustained excitability elevations induced by transcranial DC motor cortexstimulation in humans, in *Neurology*, 57, 2001, p. 1899-1901.

Nitsche, MA., Fricke, K., Henschke, U., Schlitterlau, D., Liebetanz, D., Lang, N., Henning, S., Tergau, F., & Paulus, W. Pharmacological modulation of cortical excitability shifts induced by transcranial direct current stimulation in humans, in *The Journal of Physiology*, 533.1, 2003, p. 293-301.

Norman, DA., & Shallice, T. Attention to action: willed and automatic control of behavior, in Davidson, RJ., Schwartz, GE., & Shapiro, D. (Eds.), *Consciousness and Self-Regulation*, Plenum, New York, 1986, p. 1-18.

Nowak, A., Vallacher, RR., Tesser, A., & Borkowski, W. Society of self: the emergence of collective properties in self-structure, in *Psychological Review*, 107, 2000, p. 39-61.

Nunez, P. *Neocortical Dynamics and Human EEG Rhythms*. Oxford University Press, Oxford, 1995.

Othmer, S., & Othmer, SF. EEG biofeedback training for attention deficit disorder, specific learning disabilities, and associated conduct problems, in *EEG Biofeedback Training for Attention Deficit Disorder and Specific Learning Disabilities*, EEG Spectrum, Encino, California, 1991.

Othmer, S., Othmer, SF., & Kaiser, DA. EEG biofeedback: an emerging model for its global efficacy, in Evans, JR., & Abarbanel, A. (Eds.), *Introduction to Quantitative EEG and Neurofeedback*, Academic Press, San Diego, California, 1999, p. 244-310.

Ozisik, HI., Karlidag, R., Hazneci, E., Kizkin, S., & Ozcan, C. Cognitive event-related potential and neuropsychological findings in Behçet's disease without neurological manifestations, in *Tohoku Journal of Experimental Medicine*, 206, 2005, p. 15-22.

Palva, JM., Palva, S., & Kaila, K. Phase synchrony among neuronal oscillations in the human cortex, in *Journal of Neuroscience*, 25, 2005, p. 3962-3972.

Parmelee, AH. Jr., & Stern, E. Developments of states in infants, in Clemente, C., Purpura, D., & Mayers, FE. (Eds.), *Sleep and the Maturing Nervous System*, Academic Press, New York, 1972, p. 199-228.

Pascual-Marqui., RD., Michel, CM., & Lehmann, D. Low resolution electromagnetic tomography: a new method for localizing electrical activity in the brain, in *International Journal of Psychophysiology*, 18, 1994, p. 49-65.

Pascual-Marqui, RD. Standardized low-resolution brain electromagnetic tomography (sLORETA): technical details, in *Methods Find Exp Clin Pharmacol*, 24(Suppl D), 2002, p. 5-12.

Patterson, MB., Gluck, H., & Mack, JL. EEG activity in the 13-15 Hz band correlates with intelligence in healthy elderly women, in *International Journal of Neuroscience*, 20, 1983, p. 161-172.

Paus, T. Primate anterior cingulate cortex where motor control, drive and cognition interface, in *Nature Reviews of Neuroscience*, 2, 2001, p. 417-424.

Pfurtscheller, G., & Aranibar, A. Voluntary movement ERD: normative studies, in Pfurtscheller, G., Buser, P., Lopes da Silva FH., & Petsche, H. (Eds.), *Rhythmic EEG Activities and Cortical Functioning*, Elsevier, Amsterdam, 1980, p. 151-177.

Picard, C. Double blind sham study of neurofeedback treatment in children with ADHD, 14th Annual Conference of the International Society for Neuronal Regulation, Atlanta, 2006.

Pliszka, SR., Liotti, M., & Woldorff, MG. Inhibitory control in children with attention deficit/hyperactivity disorder: event-related potentials identify the processing component and timing of an impaired right-frontal response-inhibition mechanism, in *Biological Psychiatry*, 48, 2000, p. 238-246.

Posner, MI., & Dehaene, S. Attentional networks, in *Trends in Neuroscience*, 17, 1994, p. 75-79.

Pribram, KH. A review of theory in physiological psychology, in *Annual Review of Psychology*, 11, 1960, p. 1-40.

Pribram, KH., Spinelli, DN., & Kamback, MC. Electrocortical correlates of stimulus response and reinforcement, in *Science*, 157, 1967, p. 94.

Prigogine, I., & Stengers I., *Order out of Chaos*, Bantam Books, New York, 1984.

Priori, A. Brain polarization in humans: a reappraisal of an old tool for prolonged noninvasive modulation of brain excitability, in *Clinical Neurophysiology*, 114, 2003, p. 589-595.

Putman, JA. Technical issues involving bipolar EEG training protocols, in *Journal of Neurotherapy*, 5, 2001, p. 51-58.

Putman, JA., Othmer, SF., Othmer, S., & Pollock, VE. TOVA results following interhemispheric bipolar EEG training, in *Journal of Neurotherapy*, 9, 2005, p. 37-52.

Quadens, O. Order and disorder in the brain function, in *Neuroendocrinology Letters*, 24, 2003, p. 151-160.

Rappelsberger, P., Pfurtscheller, G., & Filz O. Calculation of event-related coherence - a new method to study short-lasting coupling between brain areas, in *Brain Topography*, 7, 1994, p. 121-127.

Rizzuto, DS., Madsen, JR., Bromfield, EB., Schulze-Bonhage, A., Seelig, D., Aschenbrenner-Scheibe, R., & Kahana, MJ. Reset of human neocortical oscillations during a working memory task, in *Proceedings of National Academy of Sciences USA*, 100, 2003, p. 7931-7936.

Robinson, DL. The neurophysiological bases of high IQ, in *International Journal of Neuroscience*, 46, 1989, p. 209-234.

Rockstroh, B., Elbert, T., Lutzenberger, W., & Birbaumer, N. Operant control of slow brain potentials: a tool in the investigation of the potential's meaning and its relation to attentional dysfunction, in Elbert, T., Rockstroh, B., Lutzenberger, W., & Birbaumer, N. (Eds.), *Self-Regulation of the Brain and Behavior*, Springer, Berlin, 1984, p. 227-239.

Rockstroh, B., Elbert , T., Lutzenberger, W. & Birbaumer, N. Biofeedback: evaluation and therapy in children with attentional dysfunctions, in Rothenberger, A. (Ed.), Brain and Behavior in *Child Psychiatry*, Springer, Berlin, 1990, p. 345-357.

Rosenfeld, JP., Cha, G., Blair, T., & Gotlib, IH. Operant (biofeedback) control of left-right frontal alpha power differences: potential neurotherapy for affective disorders, in *Biofeedback and Self-Regulation*, 20, 1995, p. 241-258.

Rosenfeld, JP. EEG biofeedback of frontal alpha asymmetry in affective disorders, in *Biofeedback*, 25, 1997, p. 8-9; p. 25-26.

Rosenfeld, JP., & Baehr, E. EEG biofeedback ("neurofeedback") and affective disorders, in Beauregard, M. (Ed.), Consciousness, *Emotional Self-Regulation and the Brain*, John Benjamin Publishing Company, Philadelphia, 2004, p. 239-252.

Rossiter, TR., & La Vaque, TJ. A comparison of EEG biofeedback and psychostimulants in treating attention deficit/hyperactivity disorder, *Journal of Neurotherapy*, 1, 1995, p. 48-59.

Rossiter, TR. Neurofeedback for AD/HD: a ratio feedback case study and tutorial, in *Journal of Neurotherapy*, 6, 2002, p. 9-35.

Rossiter, TR. The effectiveness of neurofeedback and stimulant drugs in treating AD/HD: part II. Replication, in *Applied Psychophysiology and Biofeedback*, 29, 2004, p. 233-243.

Rougeul-Buser, A., Bouyer, JJ., Montaron, MF. & Buser, P. Patterns of activities in the ventrobasal thalamus and somatic cortex SI during behavioral immobility in the awake cat: focal waking rhythms, in *Experimental Brain Research*, suppl. 7, 1983, p. 69-87.

Rougeul-Buser, A. Electrocortical rhythms in the 40 Hz band in cat: in search of their behavioural correlates, in Buzsaki, G., Llinas, R., Singer, W., Berthoz, A., & Christen, Y. (Eds.), *Temporal Coding in the Brain*, Springer, Berlin, 1994, p. 103-114.

Rowland, V. Discussion under electroencephalographic studies of conditioned learning, in Brazier, M. (Ed.), *The Central Nervous System and Behavior*, Josiah Macy, Jr Foundation, New York, 1958, p. 347.

Sakhiulina, GT. EEG manifestations of tonic cortical activity accompanying conditioned reflexes, in *Pavlov Journal of Higher Nervous Activity*, 11, 1961, p. 48.

Saraev, SY., Kropotov, YD., & Ponomarev, VA. The possibilities of using direct transcranial polarization for treatment of children with attention deficit disorder, in *Russisch tijdschrift*, 2002.

Sartory, G., Heine, A., Müller, BX., & Elvermann-Hallner, A. Event- and motor-related potentials during the CPT in AD/HD, in *Journal of Psychophysiology*, 16, 2002, p. 97-106.

Schabus, M., Gruber, G., Parapatics, S., Sauter, C., Klösch, G., Anderer, P., Klimesch, W., Saletu, B., & Zeitlhofer, J. Sleep spindles and their significance for declarative memory consolidation, in *Sleep*, 27, 2004, p. 1479-1485.

Scheibel, AB. Anatomical and physiological substrates of arousal; a view from the bridge, in Hobson, JA., & Brazier, MAB. (Eds.), *The Reticular Formation Revisited*, Raven Press, New York, 1980, p. 55-66.

Scheinbaum, S., Zecker, S., Newton, CJ., & Rosenfeld, P. A controlled study of EEG biofeedback as a treatment for attention-deficit disorders, in *Proceedings of the Association of Applied Psychophysiology and Biofeedback*, 1995, p. 131-134.

Sergeant, JA. The cognitive-energetic model: an empirical approach to attention-deficit hyperactivity disorder, in *Neuroscience and Behavioral Review*, 24, 2000, p. 7-12.

Sheer, DE. Electrophysiological correlates of memory consolidation, in Ingar, G. (Ed.), *Molecular Mechanisms in Memory and Learning*, Plenum, New York, 1970.

Sheer, DE. Biofeedback training of 40 Hz EEG and behavior, in Burch, N., & Altschuler, HL. (Eds.), *Behavior and Brain Electrical Activity*, Plenum Press, New York, 1975, p. 325-362.

Sheer, DE. Focused arousal and 40 Hz EEG, in Knights, RM., & Bakker, DJ. (Eds.), *The Neurophysiology of Learning Disorders*, University Park Press, Baltimore, 1976, p. 71-87.

Sheer, DE. Biofeedback training of 40 Hz EEG and behavior, in Kamiya, J. (Ed.), *Biofeedback and self control*, 1976/77, Aldine, Chicago, 1977.

Sheer, DE. Focused arousal and the cognitive 40 Hz event-related potentials: differential diagnosis of Alzheimer's disease, in *Progress in Clinical and Biological Research*, 317, 1989, p. 79-94.

Shibagaki, M., Kiyono, S., & Watanabe, K. Nocturnal sleep in severe mentally retarded children: abnormal EEG patterns in sleep cycle, in *Electroencephalography and Clinical Electroencephalography*, 49, 1980, p. 337-344.

Simon, H., Scatton, B., & Le Moal, M. Dopaminergic A10 neurons are involved in cognitive function, in *Nature*, 286, 1980, p. 150-151.

Siniatchkin, M., Kropp, P., & Gerber, WD. Neurofeedback - the significance of reinforcement and the search for an appropriate strategy for the success of self-regulation, in *Applied Psychophysiology and Biofeedback*, 25, 2000, p. 167-175.

Skinner, JE., & Yingling, CD. Central gating mechanisms that regulate event-related potentials and behavior, in Desmedt, JE (Ed.), Attention, Voluntary Contraction and Event-Related Cerebral Potentials: Progress in *Clinical Neurophysiology*. Vol. 1, Karger, Basel, 1977, p. 30-69.

Sonuga-Barke, EJS. Interval length and time-use by children with AD/HD: a comparison of four models, in *Journal of Abnormal Child Psychology*, 30, 2002, p. 257-264.

Spydell, JD., & Sheer, DE. Effect of problem solving on right and left hemisphere 40 Hz EEG activity, in *Psychophysiology*, 19, 1982, p. 420-425.

Steriade, M., Nunez, A., & Amzica, F. A novel slow (<1Hz) oscillation of neocortical neurons in vivo: depolarizing and hyperpolarizing components, in *Journal of Neuroscience*, 13, 1993, p. 3252-3265.

Steriade, M., & Amzica, F. Intracortical and corticothalamic coherency of fast spontaneous oscillations, in *Proceedings of the National Academy of Sciences USA*, 93, 1996, p. 2533-2538.

Sterman, MB. Ontogeny of sleep: implications for function, in Drucker-Colin, R., Shkurovich, M., & Sterman, MB. (Eds.), *The Functions of Sleep*, Academic Press, New York, 1979, p. 207-232.

Sterman, MB. Physiological origins and functional correlates of EEG rhythmic activities: implications for self-regulation, in *Biofeedback and Self-Regulation*, 21, 1996, p. 3-26.

Sterman, MB., Kaiser, DA., & Veigel, B. Spectral analysis of event-related EEG responses during short-term memory performance, in *Brain Topography*, 9, 1996, p. 21-30.

Sterman, MB., & Bowersox, SS. Sensorimotor EEG rhythmic activity: a functional gate mechanism, in *Sleep*, 4, 1981, p. 408-422.

Sterman, MB., & Shouse, MN. Quantitative analysis of training, sleep EEG and clinical response to EEG operant conditioning in epileptics, in *Electroencephalography and Clinical Neurophysiology*, 49, 1980, p. 558-576.

Strehl, U., Leins, U., Goth, G., Klinger, C., Hinterberger, T., & Birbaumer, N. Self-regulation of slow cortical potentials: a new treatment for children with attention-deficit/hyperactivity disorder, in *Pediatrics*, 118(5), 2006, p. 1530-1540.

Suffin, SC., & Emory, WH. Neurometric subgroups in attentional and affective disorders and their association with pharmacotherapeutic outcome, in *Clinical Electroencephalography*, 25, 1995, p. 1-8.

Tallon, C., Bertrand, O., Bouchet, P., & Pernier, J. Gamma-range activity evoked by coherent visual stimuli in humans, in *European Journal of Neuroscience*, 7, 1995, p. 1285-1291.

Tallon-Baudry, C., Bertrand, O., Delpuech, C., & Pernier, J. Stimulus specificity of phase-locked and non-phase-locked 40 Hz visual responses in humans, in *Journal of Neuroscience*, 16, 1996, p. 4240-4249.

Tansey, MA. Righting the rhythms of reason: EEG biofeedback training as a therapeutic modality in a clinical office setting, in *Medical Psychotherapy*, 3, 1991, p. 57-68.

Tansey, MA. Wechsler (WISC-R) changes following treatment of learning disabilities via EEG biofeedback training in a private practice setting, in *Australian Journal of Psychology*, 43, 1991, p. 147-153.

Terzano, MG., Parrino, L., & Spaggiari, MC. The cyclic alternating pattern sequences in the dynamic organization of sleep, in *Electroencephalography and Clinical Neurophysiology*, 69, 1988, p.437-447.

Terzano, MG., Parrino, L., Smerieri, A., Chervin, R., Chokrovertry, S., Guilleminault, C., Hishkowitz, M., Mahowald, M., Moldofsky, H., Rosa, A., Thomas, R., & Walters, A. Atlas, rules and recording techniques for the scoring of cyclic alternating patterns (CAP) in human sleep, in *Sleep Medicine*, 2, 2001, p. 537-553.

Tesche, CD., & Karhu, J. Theta oscillations index human hippocampal activation during a working memory task, in *Proceedings of the National Academy of Sciences USA*, 97, 2000, p. 919-924.

Thatcher, RW. A predator-prey model of human cerebral development, in Newell, K., & Molenaar, P. (Eds.), *Applications of Nonlinear Dynamics to Developmental Process Modeling*, Lawrence Erlbaum Associates, Mahway, New Jersey, 1998, p. 87-128.

Thatcher, RW., North, D., & Biver, C. EEG and intelligence: relations between EEG coherence, EEG phase delay and power, in *Clinical Neurophysiology*, 116, 2005, p. 2129-2141.

Thelen, E. Self-organization in developmental processes: can systems approaches work?, in Johnson, MH. (Ed.), *Brain Development and Cognition*, Blackwell, Oxford, 1993, p. 555-592.

Thoman, E. Regulation of stimulation by prematures with a breathing blue bear, in *The Malleability of Children*, Gallagher, JJ., & Ramey, CT. (Eds.), Brooks Publishing, Baltimore, 1987, p. 51-70.

Thomas, M, Sing, H., Belenky, G., Holcomb, H., Mayberg, H., Dannals, R., Wagner; H., Thorne, D., Popp, K., Rowland, L., Welsh, A., Balwinski, S., & Redmond, D. Neural basis of alertness and cognitive performance impairments during sleepiness. I. Effects of 24 h of sleep deprivation on waking human regional brain activity, in *Journal of Sleep Research*, 9, 2000, p. 335-352.

Thompson, L., & Thompson, M. Neurofeedback combined with training in metacognitive strategies: effectiveness in students with ADD, in *Applied Psychophysiology and Biofeedback*, 23, 1998, p. 243-263.

Thompson, L., & Thompson, M. *The Neurofeedback Book: an Introduction to Basic Concepts in Applied Psychophysiology*. Association for Applied Psychophysiology and Biofeedback, Wheat Ridge, Colorado, 2003.

Thompson, L., & Thompson, M. Neurofeedback intervention for adults with ADHD, in *Journal of Adult Development*, 12, 2005, p. 123-130.

Tinius, T., & Tinius, KA. Changes after EEG biofeedback and cognitive retraining in adults with mild traumatic brain injury and attention deficit hyperactivity disorder, in Journal of Neurotherapy, 4, 2000, p. 27-44.

Tirsch, WS., Keidel, M., & Sommer, G. Time order in brain chaos, in Croon, MA., & van de Vijver, FJR. (Eds.), *Viability of Mathematical Models in the Social and Behavioral Sciences*, Swets & Zeitlinger, Lisse, 1995, p. 55-77.

Tirsch, WS., Keidel, M., Perz, S., Scherb, H., & Sommer, G. Inverse covariation of spectral density and correlation dimension in cyclic EEG dynamics of the human brain, in *Biological Cybernetics*, 82, 2000, p. 1-14.

Tirsch, WS., Stude, P., Scherb, H., & Keidel, M. Temporal order of nonlinear dynamics in human brain, in *Brain Research Reviews*, 45, 2004, p. 79-95.

Townsend, RE., & Johnson, LC. Relation of frequency-analyzed EEG to monitoring behavior, in *Electroencephalography and Clinical Neurophysiology*, 47, 1979, p. 272-279.

Tucker, DM., & Williamson, PA. Asymmetric neural control system in human self-regulation, in *Psychological Review*, 91, 1984, p. 185-215.

Ulrich, G. *Psychiatrische Elektro-Enzephalographie*. Fischer, Jena, 1994.

Vaidya, CJ., Austin, G., Krikorian G., Ridlehuber HW., Desmond GE., Glover GH., & Gabrieli, JD. Selective effects of methylphenidate in attention deficit hyperactivity disorder: a functional magnetic resonance study, in *Proceedings of the National Academy of Sciences USA*, 95, 1998, p. 14494-14499.

Van der Meere, J. ADHD en toestandregulatie, in *Neuropraxis*, 5, 2001, p. 185-190.

Vanhatalo, S., Palva, JM., Holmes, MD., Miller, JW., Voipio, J., & Kaila, K. Infraslow oscillations modulate excitability and interictal epileptic activity in the human cortex during sleep, in *Proceedings of the National Academy of Sciences USA*, 101, 2004, p. 5053-5057.

Vanhatalo, S., Voipio, J., & Kaila, K. Full-band EEG (FbEEG): a new standard for clinical electroencephalography, in *Clinical EEG and Neuroscience*, 36, 2005, p. 311-317.

Van Orden, G., & Holden, JG., Intentional contents and self-control, in *Ecological Psychology*, 14, 2002, p. 87–109.

Varela, FJ., Thompson, E., & Rosch, E. *The Embodied Mind*. MIT Press, Cambridge, MA, 1991.

Verstraeten, E., & Cluydts, R. Attentional switching-related human EEG alpha oscillations, in *Neuroreport,* 13, 2002, p. 681-684.

Wauquier, A. La microstructure du sommeil au cours du vieillissement. Founding Congress of the World Federation of Sleep Research Societies. Cannes, 1991.

Weiskopf, N., Veit, R., Erb, M., Mathiak, K., Grodd, W., Goebel, R., & Birbaumer, N. Physiological self-regulation of regional brain activity using real-time functional magnetic resonance imaging (fMRI): methodology and exemplary data, in *NeuroImage*, 19, 2003, p. 577-586.

Weiss, V. The relationship between short-term memory capacity and EEG power spectral density, in *Biological Cybernetics*, 68, 1992, p. 165-172.

Wiener, N. *Cybernetics, or control and communication in the animal and the machine*. MIT Press, New York, 1948.

Winson, J. Brain and Psyche: *the Biology of the Unconscious*. Vintage Books, New York, 1986.

Yoo, SS., & Jolesz, FA. Functional MRI for neurofeedback: feasibility study on a hand motor task, in *Neuroreport*, 13, 2002, p. 1377-1381.

LaVergne, TN USA
05 December 2010

207399LV00001B/5/P